MIDDLE SCHOOL MATH GRADE 6

STUDENT EDITION
VOLUME 1

Carnegie Learning

Carnegie Learning >

437 Grant St., Suite 2000
Pittsburgh, PA 15219
Phone 412.690.2442
Customer Service Phone 877.401.2527
Fax 412.690.2444

www.carnegielearning.com

ISBN: 978-1-60972-173-2
Student Edition, Volume 1

Printed in the United States of America
3-08/2013 B&B

Dear Student,

You are about to begin an exciting journey! These mathematical materials were written specifically for *you*, a middle school student. The book you are holding is *your* book. There is lots of space for writing, sketching, drawing, cutting, pasting, and constructing new mathematical ideas. You may want to highlight key terms, take notes in the margins, or even doodle on the cover.

Connections are important in life. The popularity of social networks shows the importance of connections. In much the same way, mathematics connects with so many activities in our lives. Throughout the lessons, you will build new knowledge based upon your prior knowledge. You will apply math to real-world situations so that you can see why it's meaningful. You will encounter models that portray mathematical concepts. Models will be presented in all sorts of ways—from lesson openers, to pictures, to different student methods and approaches to problem solving. You will also use manipulatives, which are objects that you can use to model or reinforce key mathematical concepts.

Of course, if you need additional practice, you can find it in your Assignments and Skills Practice book. Keep in mind, no professional athlete practices by just playing an entire game—ballet dancers repeat some basic steps, moves, and dances; basketball players practice dribbling, shooting, and defending; even writers jot ideas for novels in their spare time—all to improve their skills. Mathematics is no different and these materials enable and encourage you to practice.

I bet the folks at home would like to know what we're going to do this year!

Don't worry—you will not be working alone. We encourage students to work together in pairs or in groups because it gets you talking about your insights. Everyone will share his or her ideas and thoughts in class. Sometimes you will help your classmates, and other times they will help you.

Today's workplace demands teamwork and self-confidence. At Carnegie Learning, we have designed a Math Series to help you to make the most of your math course. Enjoy the journey and share your thoughts with others. Have fun while Learning by Doing!

The Carnegie Learning® Curriculum Development Team

ACKNOWLEDGMENTS

A Note from the Authors...

You are about to begin a journey as a "powerful problem solver." Mathematics is the key to many future opportunities, and this book will teach you a range of mathematical ideas—from number to algebra, and from geometry to statistics—that are useful in many professions and careers. Math is more than memorizing "how to do something," it is solving problems in unique ways and explaining your solutions to others in verbal and written ways—just like successful career professionals!

Have fun and learn a lot!

Core Authors

- William S. Hadley, Algebra and Proportional Reasoning
- Mary Lou Metz, Data Analysis and Probability
- Mary Lynn Raith, Number and Operations
- Janet Sinopoli, Algebra
- Jaclyn Snyder, Geometry and Measurement

Contributing Authors

- Janet Falkowski
- Marianne O'Connor
- Agnes Pavolovich
- Ken Labuskes
- Jennifer Panasko

Carnegie Learning Curriculum Development Team

- Sandy Bartle
  Senior Academic Officer
- Joshua Fisher
  Math Editor
- David "Augie" Rivera
  Math Editor
- David Dengler
  Director, Curriculum Development
- Jen Gansberger
  Editorial Assistant
- Lezlee Ross
  Curriculum Developer

Advisory Board

- Shelly Allen, Richmond County Schools
- Ryan Baker, Worcester Polytechnic Institute
- Bill Bush, University of Louisville
- John McCook, McCook and Associates
- Roxana Moreno, University of New Mexico
- Doug Rohrer, University of South Florida
- Bob Siegler, Carnegie Mellon University
- Mary Ann Stine, Private Consultant

Vendors

- Bookmasters, Inc.
- Mathematical Expressions
- Hess Print Solutions
- ESI Design
- Nesbitt Graphics, Inc.

Special Thanks

- Peter Arkle for the design and rendering of "The Crew."
- Richmond County School District, Georgia, for piloting lessons and providing implementation feedback.
- Carnegie Learning Managers of School Partnership for content and design review.
- The Children of Carnegie Learning employees for providing a "middle-schooler's" perspective, with special recognition to:
  - Matthew B.
  - Dawson D.
  - Allison M.
  - Adam, Nic, and Shane R.
  - Aaron and Melinda R.

TABLE OF CONTENTS

Table of Contents

FRACTIONS_____93

Table of Contents

DECIMALS —————————————— 225

5 RATIOS 305

Table of Contents

8 ALGEBRAIC EXPRESSIONS_____529

Table of Contents

THE CREW

The Crew is here to help you on your journey. Sometimes they will remind you about things you already learned. Sometimes they will ask you questions to help you think about different strategies. Sometimes they will share fun facts. They are members of your group—someone you can rely on!

Teacher aides will guide you along your journey. They will help you make connections and remind you to think about the details.

MATHEMATICAL REPRESENTATIONS

Introduction

During this course, you will solve problems and work with many different representations of mathematical concepts, ideas, and processes to better understand the world. Each lesson will provide you with opportunities to discuss your ideas, work within groups, and share your solutions and methods with your class. These process icons are placed throughout the text.

Discuss to Understand

- Read the problem carefully.
- What is the context of the problem? Do we understand it?
- What is the question that we are being asked? Does it make sense?
- Is this problem similar to some other problem we know?

Think for Yourself

- Do I need any additional information to answer the question?
- Is this problem similar to some other problem that I know?
- How can I represent the problem using a picture, a diagram, symbols, or some other representation?

Work with Your Partner

- How did you do the problem?
- Show me your representation.
- This is the way I thought about the problem—how did you think about it?
- What else do we need to solve the problem?
- Does our reasoning and our answer make sense to each other?
- How will we explain our solution to the class?

Share with the Class

- Here is our solution and the methods we used.
- Are we communicating our strategies clearly?
- We could only get this far with our solution. How can we finish?
- Could we have used a different strategy to solve the problem?

ACADEMIC GLOSSARY

Key Terms of the Course

There are important terms you will encounter throughout this book. It is important that you have an understanding of these words as you get started on your journey through the mathematical concepts. Knowing what is meant by these terms and using these terms will help you think, reason, and communicate your ideas. The Graphic Organizers shown display a definition for a key term, related words, sample questions, and examples.

You will create graphic organizers like these as your own references of key math ideas.

My folks are always trying to get me to be organized!

DEFINITION

To study or look closely for patterns. Analyzing can involve examining or breaking a concept down into smaller parts to gain a better understanding of it.

RELATED WORDS

- examine
- evaluate
- determine
- observe
- consider
- investigate
- what do you notice?
- what do you think?
- sort and match

ASK YOURSELF

- Do I see any patterns?
- Have I seen something like this before?
- What happens if the shape, representation, or numbers change?

ANALYZE

EXAMPLES

5. Look at these division problems.

   $7\overline{)56}$ $70\overline{)560}$ $700\overline{)5600}$ $7000\overline{)56,000}$

   a. How are the divisors and dividends in the last three problems related to the first problem?

   The divisor and dividends have each been multiplied by 10, 100, and 1000.

   b. Calculate all four quotients. What do you notice about them?

   All the quotients are 8. They are all the same.

   c. What happens to the quotient when the dividend and divisor are multiplied by the same number?

   The quotient remains unchanged.

1. The graph shown represents the number of gallons of water used for the number of times a toilet is flushed.

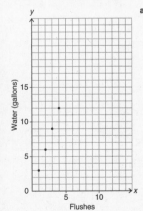

   a. Write each point on the graph as the ratio of *gallons of water used : number of flushes.*

   3 gallons of water : 1 flush
   6 gallons of water : 2 flushes
   9 gallons of water : 3 flushes
   12 gallons of water : 4 flushes

   b. What do you notice about each ratio?

   Each ratio is equivalent, 3 gallons of water : 1 flush.

DEFINITION

To give details or describe how to determine an answer or solution.
Explaining your reasoning helps justify conclusions.

RELATED WORDS

- show your work
- explain your calculation
- justify
- why or why not?

ASK YOURSELF

- How should I organize my thoughts?
- Is my explanation logical?
- Does my reasoning make sense?
- How can I justify my answer to others?

Don't forget to check your answers!

EXPLAIN YOUR REASONING

EXAMPLES

10. The Newspaper Club at Marshall Middle School meets every 6 school days. The Math Club meets every 8 school days. Luis is a member of both clubs. He needs to make a plan when both clubs meet on the same school day. Both clubs will meet today after school.

a. After today, when will both clubs meet on the same day again? Explain your reasoning.

Both clubs will both meet 24 school days from today.

$6 = 2 \times 3$

$8 = 2^3$

The LCM is $2^3 \times 3 = 24$.

h. 12.27 $>$ 7.75

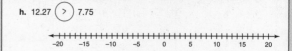

3. Explain how you knew which rational number was greater in Question 2.

The number to the right was the greater rational number.

DEFINITION

To display information in various ways. Representing mathematics can be done using words, tables, graphs, or symbols.

RELATED WORDS

- show
- sketch
- draw
- create

- plot
- graph
- write an equation
- complete the table

ASK YOURSELF

- How should I organize my thoughts?
- How do I use this model to show a concept or idea?
- What does this representation tell me?
- Is my representation accurate?

REPRESENT

EXAMPLES

2. Represent each product using an area model. Then, state the product.

a. $\frac{3}{4} \times \frac{1}{2}$

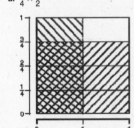

$\frac{3}{4} \times \frac{1}{2} = \frac{3}{8}$

1. Write a sentence to describe what the division expression is asking. Then, draw a diagram to represent the division problem. Finally, calculate the quotient, and write a sentence to describe your answer. Use your fraction strips to help you draw the model.

a. $\frac{3}{4} \div \frac{1}{4}$

How many fourths are in $\frac{3}{4}$?

$\frac{3}{4} \div \frac{1}{4} = 3$

There are three $\frac{1}{4}$ parts in $\frac{3}{4}$.

DEFINITION

To make an educated guess based on the analysis of given data.
Estimating first helps inform reasoning.

RELATED WORDS

- predict
- approximate
- expect
- about how much?

ASK YOURSELF

- Does my reasoning make sense?
- Is my solution close to my estimation?

Estimating gets you in the neighborhood, calculating gets you the address.

ESTIMATE

EXAMPLES

5. Rewrite each expression using benchmark fractions. Then, estimate the sum. Explain your reasoning.

a. $\frac{8}{9} + \frac{6}{7}$

$1 + 1 = 2$
I know that both fractions are close to 1. So, when I estimate the sum, it is close to, but less than 2.

2. Paul always estimates the total of his purchases at the supermarket. He estimates to ensure he has enough money to pay for his purchases. He also estimates to check that the cashier hasn't made a mistake when ringing up his total.

Today, Paul has these items in his grocery cart.

Bread	$3.25
Peanut Butter	$5.16
Jelly	$2.97
Hot Dogs	$4.86
Hot Dog Buns	$2.42
Mustard	$1.25
Soda	$4.99
Chips	$1.50

a. About how much money does Paul need to pay for his purchases? Explain your reasoning.

Paul needs about $26.
By rounding each item's cost to the nearest dollar, I was able to calculate that
$3 + 5 + 3 + 5 + 2 + 1 + 5 + 2 = 26$.

DEFINITION

To represent or give an account of in words. Describing communicates mathematical ideas to others.

RELATED WORDS

- demonstrate
- label
- display
- compare
- define
- determine
- what are the advantages?
- what are the disadvantages?
- what is similar?
- what is different?

ASK YOURSELF

- How should I organize my thoughts?
- Is my explanation logical?
- Did I consider the context of the situation?
- Does my reasoning make sense?

DESCRIBE

EXAMPLES

3. Look at the percents and the decimals you wrote for Question 2 to determine a pattern. Use this pattern to describe how you can write any percent as a decimal.

I can move the decimal point in a percent two places to the left to write the percent as a decimal.

1. The figure shown is composed of a rectangle and triangles.

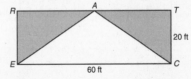

20 ft

60 ft

a. Describe a strategy that can be used to compute the area of the shaded region.

To compute the area of the shaded region, first compute the area of the rectangle. Next, compute the area of triangle AEC. Then, subtract the area of triangle AEC from the area of rectangle RECT.

Problem Types You Will See

Worked Example

When you see a Worked Example:

▶ Take your time to read through it,

▶ Question your own understanding, and

▶ Think about the connections between steps.

Ask yourself:

▶ What is the main idea?

▶ How would this work if I changed the numbers?

▶ Have I used these strategies before?

Remember, the ratio has to be maintained when labeling each number line.

The ratio $2.50 : 3 corn muffins is shown on the double number line.

Cost ($): 0   2.50

Number of corn muffins: 0   3

You can see other equivalent ratios of *cost : number of corn muffins* by continuing to label each interval.

Cost ($): 0   2.50   5.00   7.50

Number of corn muffins: 0   3   6   9

1. State the two new ratios of cost : number of corn muffins shown on the second double number line.

   $5.00 : 6 corn muffins made
   $7.50 : 9 corn muffins made

2. Describe the interval represented on each number line.

   The interval for the cost number line is $2.50.
   The interval for the number of corn muffins made number line is 3.

Problem Types

Let's consider an area model for $\frac{1}{4} \times \frac{1}{2}$ and what it represents.

To represent $\frac{1}{4}$ along one side of the square, divide the square into four equal parts along the vertical line. Then shade $\frac{1}{4}$.

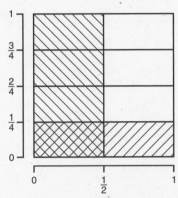

To represent $\frac{1}{2}$ along the other side, divide the square along the horizontal line into two equal parts. Then, shade $\frac{1}{2}$.

$$\frac{1}{4} \times \frac{1}{2} = \frac{1}{8}$$

The area of the overlapping region is the product of the fractions.

Can you set up the model to show $\frac{1}{4}$ along the horizontal line and the $\frac{1}{2}$ along the vertical line?

Thumbs Up

When you see a Thumbs Up icon:

▶ Take your time to read through the *correct* solution.

▶ Think about the connections between steps.

Ask yourself:

▶ Why is this method correct?

▶ Have I used this method before?

Problem Types

Kaye

I used the weights for a 30-lb person and a 90-lb person to obtain the weight of a 120-lb person.

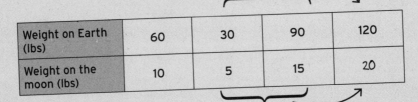

Weight on Earth (lbs)	60	30	90	120
Weight on the moon (lbs)	10	5	15	20

So that means 120 lbs on Earth : 20 lbs on the moon.

a. Explain Kaye's reasoning.

Kaye knew that 30 lbs on Earth plus 90 lbs on Earth gave her 120 lbs on Earth. So, she also added the corresponding weights on the moon—5 lbs plus 15 lbs to get 20 lbs.

Thumbs Down

8. Alexa wrote the reciprocal of the mixed number incorrectly. Explain why she is incorrect and provide the correct reciprocal.

Alexa did not take the reciprocal of the entire mixed number. She must first convert $3\frac{5}{8}$ to the improper fraction $\frac{29}{8}$, and then take the reciprocal, which is $\frac{8}{29}$.

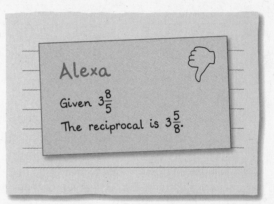

Alexa

Given $3\frac{8}{5}$

The reciprocal is $3\frac{5}{8}$.

Problem Types

Who's Correct?

4. Kaye said, "I see another equivalent ratio when I look at the way Carla showed her work."

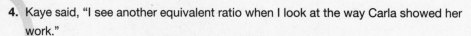

30 lbs on Earth : 5 lbs on the moon
120 lbs on Earth : 20 lbs on the moon
150 lbs on Earth : 25 lbs on the moon

Is Kaye correct? Explain her reasoning.

Kaye is correct. She added the corresponding parts of each equivalent ratio.

FACTORS, MULTIPLES, PRIMES, AND COMPOSITES

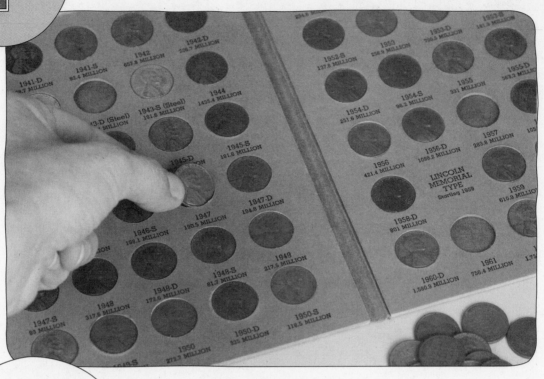

For almost as long as there have been coins, there have been coin collectors, also known as numismatists. Most numismatists collect coins for fun, but others do it for profit. The value of a coin is based on many factors, including its rarity and condition.

1.1 COLLECTION CONNECTIONS
Factors and Multiples

Learning Goals

In this lesson, you will:

▶ List factor pairs of numbers.

▶ Relate factors, multiples, and divisibility.

Key Terms

▶ array
▶ factor pair
▶ factor
▶ Commutative Property of Multiplication

▶ distinct factors
▶ perfect square
▶ multiple
▶ divisible

Many people are collectors. They often collect items like stamps, dolls, coins—well, almost anything you can think of! As their collections grow, people often want ways to display their cherished collections. Collectors might also want to group their prized possessions for a variety of reasons and in many different ways.

Do you collect anything? Can you think of some reasons why collectors might want to group their collectables?

Problem 1   Kenya's Rings

Kenya has a collection of 18 rings, and she wants to store them in a box. She uses an *array* that groups her collection into two rows, with each row having nine rings. An **array** is a rectangular arrangement that has an equal number of objects in each row and an equal number of objects in each column.

1. Use tiles to represent Kenya's 18 rings. Arrange the tiles to create other arrays.

    a. Describe the arrays you created.

    b. What mathematical operation(s) did you think about as you created your arrays?

    c. Is there more than one way to make an array with 2 rings in a row or column? Is there more than one way to make an array with 3 rings in a row or column? Explain your reasoning.

    d. How do you know when you have determined all of the arrays for a number?

Kenya notices that the number of rings she used in her rows and columns are the same as the *factor pairs* of 18. A **factor pair** is two natural numbers other than zero that are multiplied together to produce another number. Each number in a factor pair is a **factor** of the product.

2. Think about all the factor pairs that could be used to group Kenya's 18 rings.

   a. List all the factor pairs.

   b. How are the arrays you created in Question 1 related to the factor pairs you just listed?

   c. What mathematical operations can you use to determine factor pairs?

   d. How will these operations help you determine the factor pairs?

Kenya notices that the array of 2 rows of 9 rings is different from the array of 9 rows of 2 rings. However, when she multiplies the factor pairs for these groupings, the product is the same. In a multiplication sentence, this means $2 \times 9 = 9 \times 2$. The factor pair of 9 and 2 is equal to the factor pair of 2 and 9. This is an example of a very important property called the *Commutative Property of Multiplication.*

The **Commutative Property of Multiplication** states that changing the order of two or more factors does not change the product. For any numbers a and b, $a \times b = b \times a$.

> So, I can multiply the numbers in a factor pair in either order and get the same product, right?

3. Write another example of the Commutative Property of Multiplication using the arrays you created.

4. Will every factor pair in your arrays have an equal pair? Why or why not?

Mr. Rubenstein asked the class to write all of the *distinct factors* that appear in Kenya's arrays for the number 18. **Distinct factors** are factors that appear only once in a list.

5. What are the distinct factors of 18 from Kenya's arrays?

6. How are factors different from factor pairs?

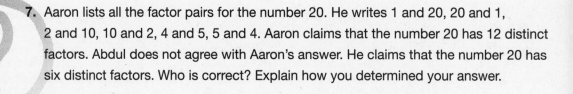

7. Aaron lists all the factor pairs for the number 20. He writes 1 and 20, 20 and 1, 2 and 10, 10 and 2, 4 and 5, 5 and 4. Aaron claims that the number 20 has 12 distinct factors. Abdul does not agree with Aaron's answer. He claims that the number 20 has six distinct factors. Who is correct? Explain how you determined your answer.

8. Marcus noticed that when he listed the distinct factors of a number in order from least to greatest and connected the factor pairs, he could create a rainbow. Marcus drew this picture.

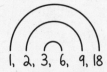

1, 2, 3, 6, 9, 18

a. List all of the distinct factors of 20 using Marcus' method.

b. List all of the distinct factors of 24. Create a rainbow diagram with the factor pairs.

c. Does every distinct factor of 24 have a partner? Why or why not?

9. Brynn wrote all the distinct factors for 36 in order from least to greatest. She connected the factor pairs and drew this picture.

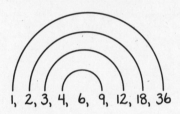

1, 2, 3, 4, 6, 9, 12, 18, 36

She noticed that 6 did not have a partner.

a. Why do you think 6 does not have a partner?

b. How is this list different from the lists for 20 and 24?

A number that is the product of a distinct factor multiplied by itself is called a **perfect square**. The number 36 is a perfect square because 6 is a distinct factor of 36, and $6 \times 6 = 36$.

That means that if a distinct factor of a number doesn't have a partner, then the number is a perfect square!

10. Choose another perfect square number.

   a. Write the number you chose.

   b. Order the factors for your perfect square from least to greatest. Then, create a rainbow diagram to show the factor pairs.

   c. Which factor multiplies by itself to get the perfect square?

11. Does a perfect square number have an even or odd number of distinct factors? Show how you determined your answer.

12. Show other examples to support your answer.

Problem 2   David's Baseball Cards

1. David has a collection of 48 baseball cards. He wants to put his cards into different groups.

a. How can David organize his collection of baseball cards?

By putting them in 8 groups.

David decides to organize his cards so that each group contains the same number of cards. He can use factors and factor pairs to complete this task.

b. List all the ways in which David can group his 48 cards into equal groups.

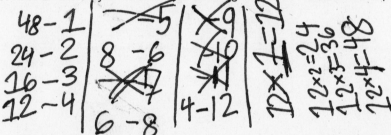

48 − 1

24 − 2

16 − 3

12 − 4

8 − 6

6 − 8

4 − 12

$12 \times 2 = 24$
$12 \times 3 = 36$
$12 \times 4 = 48$

c. What mathematical operations did you use to determine the groups?

Addition and multiplication and division

d. How are David's groups related to the factors of 48?

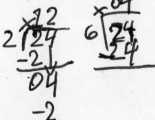

e. How can David arrange his cards into equal groups if he has ? cards?

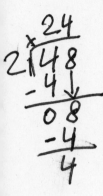

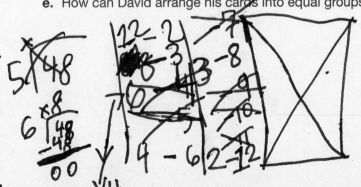

2. You previously determined the distinct factors for Kenya's 18 rings and David's 48 baseball cards.

   a. Explain how you determined the distinct factors for each of these numbers.

   b. Exchange the steps of your method for determining distinct factors with your partner. If your partner follows your method, can your partner determine the distinct factors of 28? If you follow your partner's method, will you be able to determine the distinct factors of 28?

   c. Were your methods similar? Did you and your partner determine the same list of distinct factors?

3. Determine the distinct factors of each.

   a. 11   b. 16

   c. 63   d. 72

   e. Explain how you determined the distinct factors of 72.

4. Look back at each list of distinct factors in Question 3. What factor is common to all the lists?

5. What did the number 1 represent when you were creating arrays for Kenya's ring collection and the different groupings for David's baseball collection?

6. Do you think 1 is a factor of every number? Explain why or why not.

7. Describe the numbers that will always have 2 as a factor. Explain your reasoning.

8. Describe the numbers that will never have 2 as a factor. Explain your reasoning.

Because 2 is an even number, and we need an odd number.

Problem 3   Exploring Multiples

1. Buy Rite Produce and Vitamins Store sells juice cartons. Each carton contains 12 cans of orange juice.

   a. If you buy 1 carton, how many cans of juice will you have?

   b. If you buy 2 cartons, how many cans of juice will you have?

   c. If you buy 7 cartons, how many cans of juice will you have?

2. How did you determine how many cans of juice you would have if you bought one carton of juice? Two cartons of juice? Seven cartons of juice?

3. How does the number 12 relate to the total number of cans of juice? Explain your reasoning.

When you multiply 12 by any other number, you get a *multiple* of 12. A **multiple** is the product of a given whole number and another whole number.

4. List three multiples of 12.

6, 3, 4

5. If you buy full juice cartons at Buy Rite, can you buy exactly 54 cans? Explain why or why not.

6. If you need to purchase 192 juice cans, how many cartons must you buy? Explain your reasoning.

Talk the Talk

1

In mathematics, there are many ways to show the relationship between a number and one of its factors. For instance, you can say that 5 is a factor of 35, or you can say that 35 is a multiple of 5. You can also say that 35 is *divisible* by 5. One number is **divisible** by a second number when the second number divides "evenly" into the first number.

1. Explain why 35 is a multiple of 5.

2. Explain why 35 is divisible by 5.

3. How are multiplication and division related? Give examples to explain your answer.

 Be prepared to share your solutions and methods.

1.2

MODELS AND MORE
Physical Models of Factors and Multiples

1

Learning Goals

In this lesson, you will:

▶ Determine factor pairs using arrays and area models.

▶ Classify numbers using Venn diagrams.

Key Terms

▶ area model

▶ set

▶ Venn diagram

Do you ever wonder how the new cars you see on the road or in car dealership windows are designed and made? Artist sketches and models play a huge part in the process of taking a designer's idea to the cars you see today. Can you think of other items that require artist sketches and models during the creation process?

Problem 1   Using Arrays to Plan Displays

Speedy Builders specializes in creating shelves, desks, and cases for collectible items. Speedy Builders wants to make rectangular cases with individual sections to display model cars. They want to design different-sized cases to display various numbers of cars. Before they build the cases, designers draw arrays on grid paper to make sure mistakes are not made.

Think about a case that holds exactly 12 model cars, with one car in each slot.

1. What arrays could be drawn?

2. What is the relationship between the arrays drawn and the factor pairs of 12?

You can draw rectangles on grid paper to learn more about factors. Think of factor pairs as the dimensions of any rectangle using an *area model*. An **area model** for multiplication is a pictorial way of representing multiplication. In the area model, the rectangle's length and width represent factors, while the rectangle's area represents the product.

> Remember, to write distinct factors means to list each factor once. The same is true for distinct area models. List the values of the width and length of an area model once.

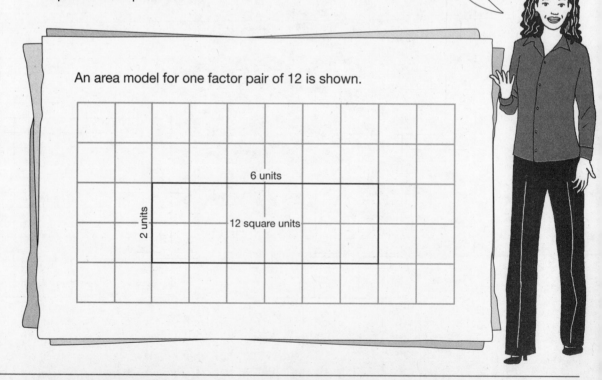

An area model for one factor pair of 12 is shown.

6 units

2 units

12 square units

3. Draw all of the possible distinct area models for each number from 1 through 30. You may want to use tiles before you draw your models on grid paper. Label all of the dimensions of your models.

Distinct Models for Numbers 1 through 5

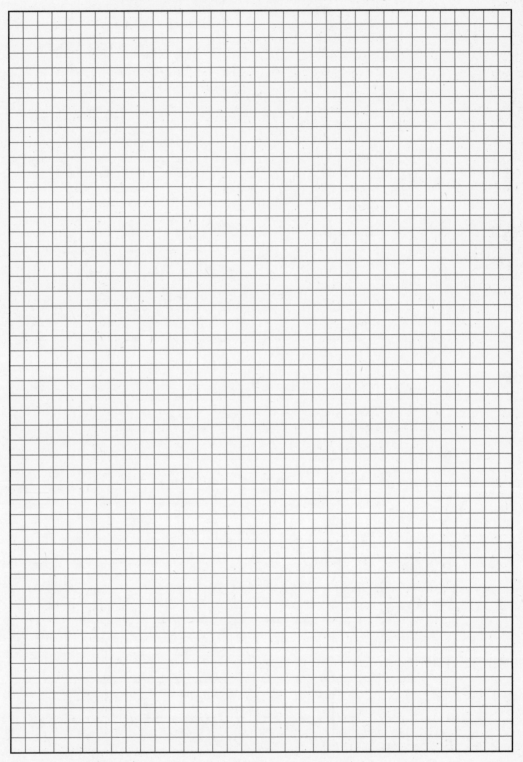

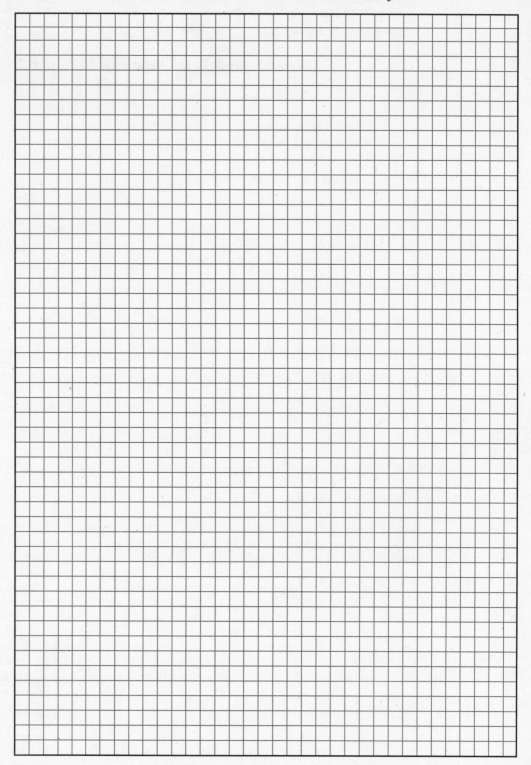

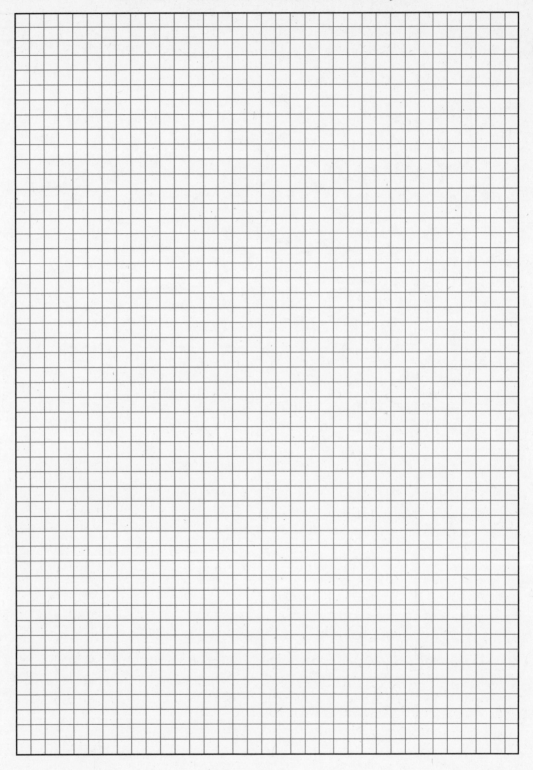

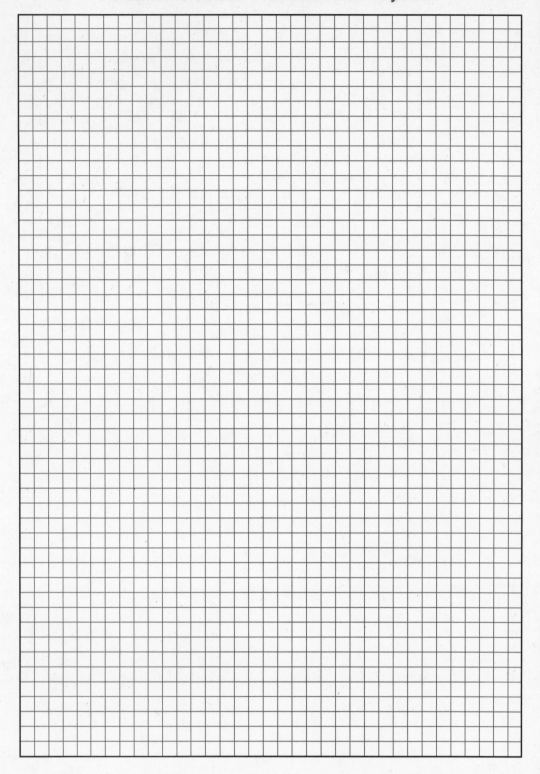

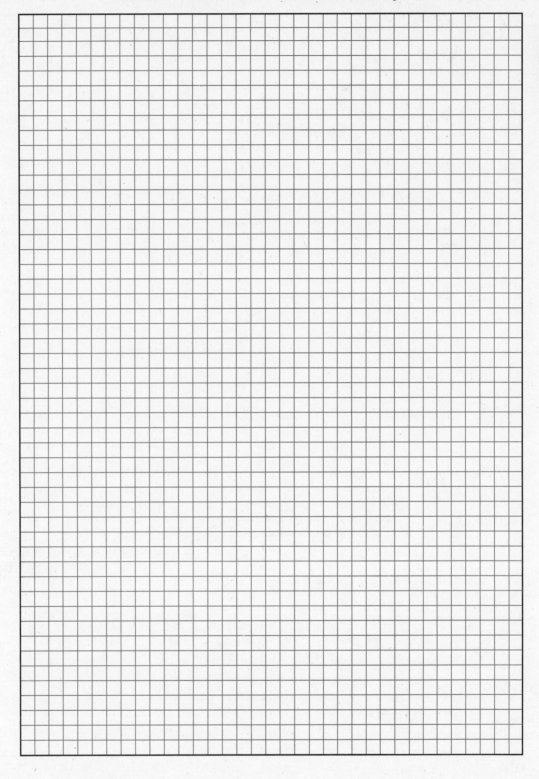

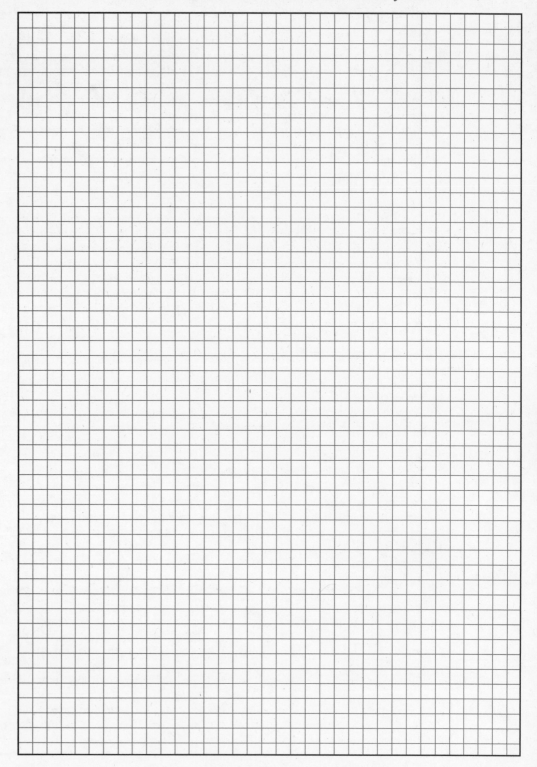

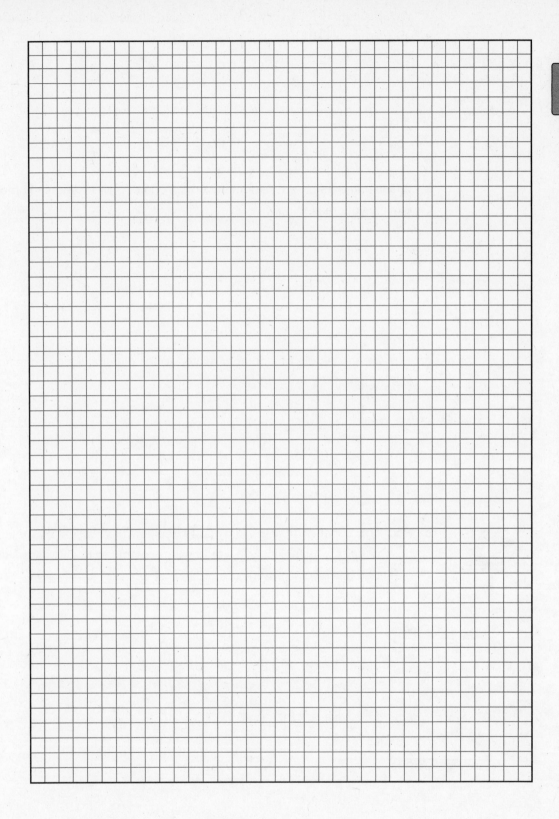

a. Which numbers have only one distinct area model? What do you know about these numbers?

b. Which numbers have a perfect square as one of their distinct area models? Explain your reasoning.

c. How are the factors of a number related to the dimensions of a distinct area model?

d. Recall that Speedy Builders is trying to decide which case they should design to hold 12 cars. Which display(s) would you recommend that Speedy Builders create? Explain your reasoning.

Problem 2   Arranging More than Music Notes

Mr. Jeffries, the music teacher at Harrison Middle School, has 36 students in his chorus. He wants to place the desks in his room in equal rows. He has a very large room, but he can't decide which arrangement he should use.

1. What are all the possible ways in which Mr. Jeffries can arrange the chairs in equal rows?

2. List all of the distinct factors for 36. Then, state the number of distinct factors of 36.

3. What do you know about a number that has an odd amount of distinct factors? Explain your reasoning.

So, that's another way to determine a perfect square. That makes two ways!

4. What recommendation would you make to Mr. Jeffries about his room arrangement? Explain why you selected this arrangement.

You have created models to show relationships between numbers. Sometimes when numbers are related in some way to each other, the numbers are called a *set*. A **set** is a collection of numbers, geometric figures, letters, or other objects that have some characteristic in common. Another model you can use to show relationships among numbers is a *Venn diagram*, named after British logician and philosopher John Venn. A **Venn diagram** is a picture that illustrates the relationships between two or more sets. Venn diagrams use circles to help you put numbers into common groups.

The example shown represents the natural numbers between 1 and 20 and the relationship between those numbers that are factors of 12, factors of 20, or factors of neither 12 nor 20.

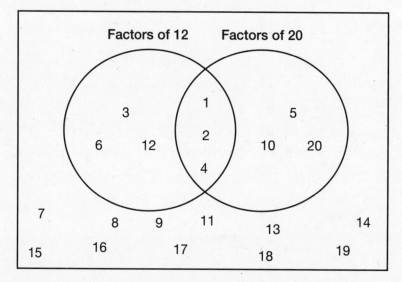

The numbers that are factors of 12 are in the region labeled "Factors of 12." The numbers that are factors of 20 are in the region labeled "Factors of 20." The numbers that are factors of both 12 and 20 are in the center where the circles overlap, or intersect.

Notice that there is no label for those numbers that are factors of neither 12 nor 20. If numbers do not fit into either category, they are outside of the circles but within the rectangle.

Natural numbers, or counting numbers, are the set of numbers starting at 1, 2, 3, 4, . . .

1. Complete the Venn diagram to show the factors of 15 and 18. Use the natural numbers between 1 and 20.

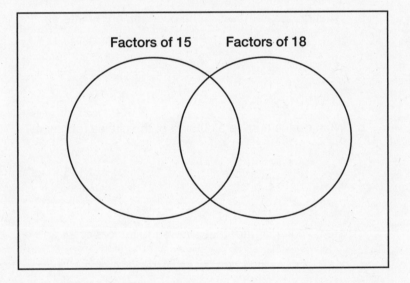

Factors of 15   Factors of 18

a. What do the numbers in the overlapping, or intersecting, region represent?

b. What do the numbers outside of the circles represent?

2. Complete the Venn diagram to show the multiples of 4 and 6. Use the natural numbers between 1 and 30.

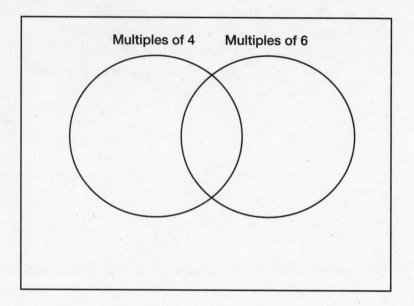

Multiples of 4   Multiples of 6

a. What do the numbers in the overlapping, or intersecting, region represent?

b. What do the numbers outside of the circles represent?

3. Create a Venn diagram that shows the factors of 24 and 40.

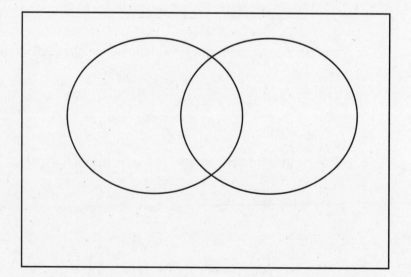

4. Answer each question using the Venn diagram you created.

   a. List all the distinct factors of 24.

   b. List all the distinct factors of 40.

   c. List the common factors of 24 and 40, if possible.

5. How can Venn diagrams help you organize information?

Be prepared to share your solutions and methods.

SIFTING FOR PRIME NUMBERS

1.3

Investigating Prime and Composite Numbers

Learning Goals

In this lesson, you will:

▶ Distinguish between prime and composite numbers.

▶ Identify and use the multiplicative identity.

Key Terms

▶ prime numbers

▶ composite numbers

▶ multiplicative identity

You may have heard that during the time of Columbus, many people believed that the Earth was flat. However, some historians think that this is a misconception.

These historians do make a good point. Greek mathematician, geographer, and astronomer Eratosthenes (pronounced Er-uh-TOSS-thuh-neez) has been credited as the first person to calculate the circumference of the Earth. He made this calculation roughly around 240 BCE — thousands of years before Columbus' time! If you remember, circumference is the distance around a circle. Therefore, even back then, people assumed that the Earth was round.

So, where do you think this misconception that many people in the 1400s believed in a flat Earth came from?

Problem 1 The Game

A sieve is an old tool that is used to separate small particles from larger particles and is usually a box with a screen for a bottom that allows the smaller pieces to fall through.

The Sieve of Eratosthenes screens out all of the *composite* numbers and leaves only the *prime numbers*. **Prime numbers** are numbers greater than 1 with exactly two distinct factors, 1 and the number itself. **Composite numbers** are numbers that have more than two distinct factors. You and your partner will use the Sieve of Eratosthenes to determine all of the prime numbers up to 100.

The figure shows the first 100 numbers written in numerical order in an array.

1	2	3	4	5	6	7	8	9	10
11	12	13	14	15	16	17	18	19	20
21	22	23	24	25	26	27	28	29	30
31	32	33	34	35	36	37	38	39	40
41	42	43	44	45	46	47	48	49	50
51	52	53	54	55	56	57	58	59	60
61	62	63	64	65	66	67	68	69	70
71	72	73	74	75	76	77	78	79	80
81	82	83	84	85	86	87	88	89	90
91	92	93	94	95	96	97	98	99	100

1. Start by putting a square around the number 1 because it is not a prime or composite number.
2. Circle the number 2 and cross out all of the multiples of 2.
3. Circle the next number after 2 that is not crossed out. Then cross out all the multiples of that number that are not already crossed out.
4. Continue in this fashion until you come to the first number greater than 10 that is not crossed out. All of the remaining numbers have "fallen through the sieve" and are prime numbers.
5. List all of the prime numbers up to 100.

6. How many of the prime numbers are even?

7. Is it possible that there are even prime numbers greater than 100? Explain your reasoning.

8. Why did you stop at 10? How do you know that any remaining number less than 100 must be a prime number?

9. Are all odd numbers prime? Explain your reasoning.

10. Recall the distinct area models you created for Speedy Builders in the previous lesson. Identify the prime numbers. How are all the area models of prime numbers similar?

Talk the Talk

- The number 1 is neither prime nor composite.
- The number 1 is a factor of every number.

The number 1 is called the *multiplicative identity*. The **multiplicative identity** is the number 1. When it is multiplied by a second number, the product is the second number. An example is $1 \times 5 = 5$.

1. Explain why the number 1 is neither prime nor composite.

2. State the characteristics prime numbers share.

3. State the characteristics composite numbers share.

Be prepared to share your solutions and methods.

1.4 DIVISIBILITY RULES!
Investigating Divisibility Rules

Learning Goals

In this lesson, you will:

▶ Formulate divisibility rules based on patterns seen in factors.

▶ Use factors to help you develop divisibility rules.

Key Term

▶ divisibility rules

Understanding relationships between numbers can save you time when making calculations. Previously, you worked with factors and multiples of various numbers, and you determined which numbers are prime and composite by using the Sieve of Eratosthenes. By doing so, you determined what natural numbers are divisible by other natural numbers.

In this lesson, you will consider patterns for numbers that are divisible by 2, 3, 4, 5, 6, 9, and 10. What type of patterns do you think exist between these numbers? Why do you think 1 is not a part of this list?

Problem 1   Exploring Two, Five, and Ten

1. List 10 multiples for each number.

   Multiples of 2:

   Multiples of 5:

   Multiples of 10:

2. What do you notice?

Divisibility rules are tests for determining whether one whole number is divisible by another. A divisibility rule must work for every number.

3. Write a divisibility rule for 2, 5, and 10. Then, show an example that follows your rule.

A natural number is divisible by	...if	Example
2		
5		
10		

Problem 2   Exploring Three and Six

Each number shown in the table is divisible by 3.

Number	Divisible by 2	Divisible by 3	Divisible by 5	Divisible by 10
300		✓		
1071		✓		
882		✓		
1230		✓		
285		✓		
3762		✓		
42		✓		
2784		✓		
3582		✓		
111		✓		

1. Place a check in the appropriate column for each number that is divisible by 2, 5, or 10.

2. Analyze each number that is divisible by 3. Then, write a rule in the table shown to indicate when a number is divisible by 3. (Hint: Consider the sum of the digits of the number.)

A number is divisible by	...if	Example
3		

3. Circle numbers you think are divisible by 6 in the table you completed in Question 1. Explain your reasoning.

4. Analyze each number you circled that you think is divisible by 6. Write a rule to indicate when a number is divisible by 6 in the table shown.

A number is divisible by	...if	Example
6		

5. Test the divisibility rules you wrote to indicate if a number is divisible by 3 or 6 by writing several three- or four-digit numbers that you think are divisible by 3 or 6. Then, use your calculator to determine if the numbers you wrote are divisible by 3 or 6.

Problem 3 · Exploring Nine

1. Place a check in the appropriate column for each number that is divisible by 2, 3, 5, 6, or 10. The column for Divisible by 9 is completed for you.

Number	Divisible by 2	Divisible by 3	Divisible by 5	Divisible by 6	Divisible by 9	Divisible by 10
3240					✓	
1458					✓	
18,225					✓	
2025					✓	
33						
7878						
3477						
2565					✓	
285						
600						

2. Analyze the numbers shown in the list. Write a rule to indicate when a number is divisible by 9. (Hint: Use the same clue you were given when exploring the divisibility rule for 3.)

A number is divisible by	...if	Example
9		

3. Test the divisibility rule you wrote to indicate if a number is divisible by 9 by writing several four- or five-digit numbers that you think are divisible by 9. Then, use your calculator to determine if the numbers you wrote are divisible by 9.

Problem 4   Exploring Four

Each number listed in the table is divisible by 4.

Numbers Divisible by 4	
116	35,660
1436	18,356
228	300,412
2524	59,140
41,032	79,424

1. What pattern do you notice about each number? (Hint: Look at the number formed by the last two digits in each number.)

2. Write a rule to tell when a number is divisible by 4.

A number is divisible by	...if	Example
4		

3. Test the divisibility rule you wrote to indicate if a number is divisible by 4 by writing several five-digit numbers that you think are divisible by 4. Then, use your calculator to determine if the numbers you wrote are divisible by 4.

Problem 5   It's a Mystery

1. Determine if each number is divisible by 3 using your divisibility rule. Explain your reasoning.

    a. 597

    b. 2109

    c. 83,594

2. Determine if each number is divisible by 9 using your divisibility rule. Explain your reasoning.

    a. 748

    b. 5814

    c. 43,695

3. Fill in the missing digit for each number to make the sentence true.

   a. The number 10,5__2 is divisible by 6.

   b. The number 505__ is divisible by 4.

   c. The number 133,0__5 is divisible by 9.

4. Rasheed is thinking of a mystery number. Use the following clues to determine his number. Explain how you used each clue to determine Rasheed's number.

   Clue 1: My number is a two-digit number.

   Clue 2: My number is a multiple of 5, but does not end in a 5.

   Clue 3: My number is less than 60.

   Clue 4: My number is divisible by 3.

5. Think of your own mystery number, and create clues using what you know about factors, multiples, and the divisibility rules. Give your clues to your partner. See if your partner can determine your mystery number!

Talk the Talk

Divisibility rules are tests for determining whether one number is divisible by another number.

A number is divisible by:

- 2 if the number is even.
- 3 if the sum of the digits is divisible by 3.
- 4 if the number formed by the last two digits is divisible by 4.
- 5 if the number ends in a 0 or a 5.
- 6 if the number is divisible by both 2 and 3.
- 9 if the sum of the digits is divisible by 9.
- 10 if the last digit is 0.

1. Determine if each number is divisible by 8 using the divisibility rule.

   a. 75,024

There is another divisibility rule that we didn't mention. A number is divisible by 8 if the number formed by the last three digits is divisible by 8.

   b. 1466

   c. 19,729

   d. 1968

Be prepared to share your solutions and methods.

1

• **Chapter 1**   Factors, Multiples, Primes, and Composites

Chapter 1 Summary

Key Terms

- array (1.1)
- factor pairs (1.1)
- factor (1.1)
- distinct factors (1.1)
- perfect square (1.1)
- multiple (1.1)
- divisible (1.1)
- area model (1.2)
- Venn diagram (1.2)
- set (1.2)
- prime number (1.3)
- composite number (1.3)
- multiplicative identity (1.3)
- divisibility rules (1.4)

Property

- Commutative Property of Multiplication (1.1)

1.1 Listing Factors and Multiples

A factor pair is two natural numbers other than zero that are multiplied together to produce another number. Each number in a factor pair is a factor of the product.

A factor of a number divides evenly into the number. A multiple of a number is the product of the number and any other number.

Example

The factors of 12 and the first five multiples of 12 are shown.

Factors: 1, 2, 3, 4, 6, and 12

Multiples: 12, 24, 36, 48, and 60

Why do I do well in math? Well, trying hard is a big *factor*!

1.2 Determining Factors Using Models

Rectangular arrays and area models can be used to illustrate multiplication and determine factors.

Example

The distinct area models for 16 are shown.

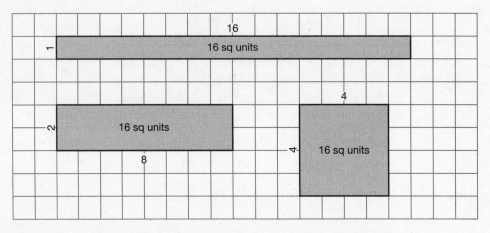

Using the area models, the distinct factors of 16 are 1, 2, 4, 8, and 16.

1.2 Classifying Numbers Using Venn Diagrams

A Venn diagram uses circles to represent the relationship between two or more sets.

Example

The Venn diagram shows the first 10 multiples of 5 and 6.

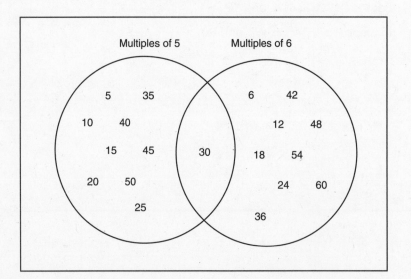

1.3 Distinguishing between Prime and Composite Numbers

Prime numbers have exactly two distinct factors, 1 and the number itself. Composite numbers have more than two distinct factors.

Example

Circled numbers are prime numbers. Numbers with a square are composite numbers. The number 1 is neither prime nor composite.

68 (73) (29) 1 81 95 (5) 54 27 42 36 (61)

1.3 Identifying the Multiplicative Identity

The multiplicative identity is the number 1. When it is multiplied by a second number, the product is the second number.

Example

In the number sentence $10 \times \underline{?} = 10$, 1 makes the equation true.

The number 1 makes that statement true because the product of 10 and 1 is 10.

1.4 Applying Divisibility Rules

A number is divisible by:

- 2 if the number is even.
- 3 if the sum of the digits is divisible by 3.
- 4 if the number formed by the last two digits is divisible by 4.
- 5 if the number ends in a 0 or 5.
- 6 if the number is divisible by both 2 and 3.
- 8 if the number formed by the last three digits is divisible by 8.
- 9 if the sum of the digits is divisible by 9.
- 10 if the last digit is 0.

Example

A four-digit number that is divisible by 2, 3, 4, 5, 6, 8, 9, and 10 must have these properties:

- The number must end in 0 to be divisible by 2, 5, and 10.
- The last two digits of the number must be divisible by 4.
- The last three digits must be divisible by 8.
- The sum of all of the digits must be divisible by both 3 and 9.
- The number will automatically be divisible by 6 because it is divisible by both 2 and 3.

The number 6120 is divisible by 2, 3, 4, 5, 6, 8, 9, and 10 using the divisibility rules.

2 PRIME FACTORIZATION AND THE FUNDAMENTAL THEOREM OF ARITHMETIC

Major aquariums are popular tourist attractions. According to the Association of Zoos and Aquariums, there are almost 270,000 marine fish and 171,000 aquatic invertebrates in commercial aquariums nationwide.

THE THINK TANK

2.1

Prime Factorization and Factor Trees

Learning Goals

In this lesson, you will:

▶ Determine the prime factorization of a number.

▶ Understand the usefulness of prime factors.

▶ Recognize that each whole number has exactly one prime factorization.

Key Terms

▶ prime factorization

▶ Associative Property of Multiplication

▶ factor tree

▶ power

▶ base

▶ exponent

▶ Fundamental Theorem of Arithmetic

2

Did you know that some scientists devote their study to one species of animal? In fact, some teams of oceanographers in Texas and California have dedicated their study to octopi, squid, nautiluses, and cuttlefish. Collectively, these animals are members of the class Cephalopoda, or commonly known as cephalopods (pronounced sef-e-le-pods). To study cephalopods, oceanographers use huge tanks to house the creatures in order to mimic the ocean environment.

Does your school have a fish tank? Do you or any of your classmates have a fish tank at home?

Problem 1   Dimensions of a Tank

Previously, you determined equal-sized groups to organize baseball cards. You also determined dimensions for display cases using factor pairs. Let's consider other ways to represent the factors of a number.

The Think Tank designs and creates customized tanks and aquariums for oceanographers. A team of oceanographers who study the characteristics of plankton requested a tank that has a volume of 240 cubic feet, but they didn't give the dimensions of the tank. You have been asked to help The Think Tank list possible tank dimensions using the information about the tank's volume.

Recall that volume is the amount of space occupied by an object. The only rule you need to follow is that none of the dimensions can be 1 foot. To calculate the volume of a tank, multiply the tank's length by its width and by its height.

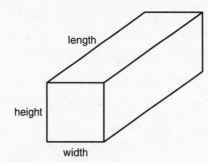

Let l = length

Let w = width

Let h = height

$V = lwh$

1. Complete the table by listing three possible tank dimensions for the volume given.

Length (ft)	Width (ft)	Height (ft)	Volume (ft³)
			240
			240
			240

2. How did you determine the possible dimensions of the tank? How did you verify you were correct?

3. Compare your possible tank dimensions to your classmates' dimensions. What do you notice?

4. Write the volume as the product of prime numbers for each row in your table. What do you notice?

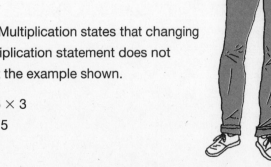

I can write any whole number—except for 1—as a product of prime numbers. So, 4 as a product of prime numbers would be 2 × 2.

A natural number written as the product of primes is the *prime factorization* of that number. **Prime factorization** is the long string of factors that is made up of all prime numbers.

5. Does the order of factors make a difference? Explain your reasoning.

Recall that the Commutative Property of Multiplication states that changing the order of two or more factors in a multiplication statement does not change the product. For instance, look at the example shown.

$$3 \times 5 = 5 \times 3$$
$$15 = 15$$

The **Associative Property of Multiplication** states that changing the grouping of the factors in a multiplication statement does not change the product. For any numbers a, b, and c, $(a \times b) \times c = a \times (b \times c)$.

For instance, look at the example of the Associative Property of Multiplication.

$$(2 \times 3) \times 3 = 2 \times (3 \times 3)$$
$$6 \times 3 = 2 \times 9$$
$$18 = 18$$

6. What is the difference between the Commutative Property of Multiplication and the Associative Property of Multiplication?

7. Rewrite each set of factors using the Associative Property of Multiplication.

    a. $(3 \times 4) \times 5 =$ _____

    b. $6 \times (5 \times 3) =$ _____

    c. $(2 \times 3) \times 5 =$ _____

8. Determine the product for each set of factors in Question 7. Which set of factors did you use, the set given or the set you rewrote using the Associative Property? Explain your choice.

> The Properties can help you add and multiply numbers more efficiently because you can reorder and regroup.

9. Write the prime factorization of 240. List the factors in order from least to greatest.

Problem 2 Factor Trees

A **factor tree** is a way to organize and help you determine the prime factorization of a number. Factor trees use branches to show how a number is broken down into prime numbers.

You can use the X or · symbols to represent multiplication. Make sure you use one symbol throughout each multiplication sentence.

An example of a factor tree for 240 is shown.

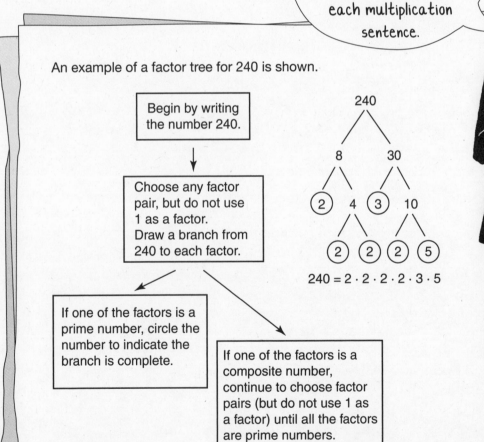

Begin by writing the number 240.

Choose any factor pair, but do not use 1 as a factor. Draw a branch from 240 to each factor.

If one of the factors is a prime number, circle the number to indicate the branch is complete.

If one of the factors is a composite number, continue to choose factor pairs (but do not use 1 as a factor) until all the factors are prime numbers.

$$240 = 2 \cdot 2 \cdot 2 \cdot 2 \cdot 3 \cdot 5$$

1. Complete each factor tree. Then, write the prime factorization as a mathematical statement.

a. 240

240
／＼
    120

b. 240

240
／＼
60   4

c. 720

720
／
9

d. 720

720
＼
360

e. 360

360
／
6

f. 360

360
＼
30

Did you notice that 2 and 3 were repeated factors of the prime factorizations in the factor trees you created? The prime factorizations were long, and you had to write a lot of numbers. Because 2 and 3 are repeated factors, you can write their repeated multiplication using a shorthand method. This method is called a *power*. A **power** has two elements: the base and the exponent, as shown.

$$2 \times 2 \times 2 \times 2 = 2^4$$

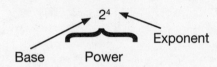

The **base** of a power is the factor that is multiplied repeatedly in the power, and the **exponent** of the power is the number of times the base is used as a factor of repeated multiplication.

You can read a power in the following ways:

"2 to the fourth power"
"2 raised to the fourth power"
"the fourth power of 2"

2. Identify the base and exponent in each power. Then, write each power in words.

   a. 7^2 b. 4^3

3. Write the prime factorizations using powers for the factor trees you completed in Question 1.

The **Fundamental Theorem of Arithmetic** states that every natural number is either prime or can be written as a unique product of primes.

4. Determine the prime factorization of each number using factor trees. Then, write the prime factorization using powers.

a. 180 =

b. 81 =

c. 48 =

5. Circle the prime factorization for the number 36. How do you know?

- $2 \times 2 \times 3 \times 3$
- 2×18
- 3×12

6. How do you know that the answer you selected is the only prime factorization for 36?

7. Use exponents to make each prime factorization true.

a. $24 \stackrel{?}{=} 2 \times 3$

b. $45 \stackrel{?}{=} 3 \times 5$

c. $54 \stackrel{?}{=} 2 \times 3$

d. $72 \stackrel{?}{=} 2 \times 3$

8. Khalil and Reyna are comparing their favorite numbers. Khalil says that the prime factorization of his number has three factors. Reyna says that the prime factorization of her number has four factors. Khalil says that his number must be less than Reyna's number since it has fewer factors in its prime factorization. Reyna thinks that Khalil is incorrect. Who do you think is correct? Use an example to support your answer.

Be prepared to share your solutions and methods.

2

2.2 TOGETHER AGAIN

Investigating Multiples and Least Common Multiples

Learning Goal

In this lesson, you will:

▶ Determine the least common multiple of two numbers.

Key Terms

▶ common multiple
▶ least common multiple (LCM)

Tick Tock, Tick Tock!

You've heard clocks or watches tick, and cuckoo clocks "cuckoo." You know that every one of those ticks represents one second, and every chime indicates the beginning of an hour. But have you ever wondered why there are 60 seconds in a minute? Or 60 minutes in an hour? Who came up with the concept of "time?"

To begin to answer these questions, you have to go all the way back to the Sumerian civilization—starting in 5300 BC! The Sumerians used a base 60 number system. Similar to the base 10 number system, 60 and multiples of 60 were the basis of this system. This may be why we measure the repeated cycle of 60 seconds in a minute and 60 minutes in the hour. What are some things you can name that repeat in cycles?

Problem 1   Times Tables

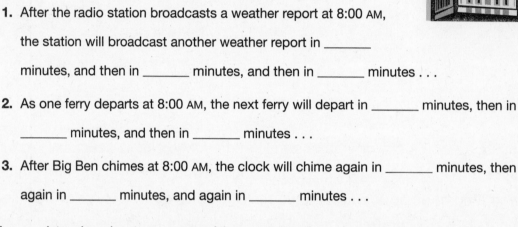

Many things in life repeat over and over again in a regular cycle.

- A news radio station in Atlanta broadcasts a weather report every 12 minutes.
- A ferry crosses Lake Champlain from Vermont to New York every 36 minutes.
- Big Ben in London, England, chimes every 15 minutes.

Determine when each event will repeat using multiples.

1. After the radio station broadcasts a weather report at 8:00 AM,

   the station will broadcast another weather report in _____

   minutes, and then in _____ minutes, and then in _____ minutes . . .

2. As one ferry departs at 8:00 AM, the next ferry will depart in _____ minutes, then in

   _____ minutes, and then in _____ minutes . . .

3. After Big Ben chimes at 8:00 AM, the clock will chime again in _____ minutes, then

   again in _____ minutes, and again in _____ minutes . . .

You can determine when two or more of these events will occur at the same time using
common multiples. A **common multiple** is a number that is a multiple of two or more numbers.

4. At 8:00 AM, the radio station broadcasted a weather report at the same time that
   Big Ben chimed.

   a. In how many minutes will the radio station broadcast a weather report and Big
      Ben chime at the same time again?
      List multiples of each and explain your reasoning.

   b. How can you continue to determine the next time both the radio station will
      broadcast a weather report and Big Ben will chime at the same time?
      Explain your reasoning.

The **least common multiple**, abbreviated as LCM, is the smallest multiple (other than zero) that two or more numbers have in common.

5. If a ferry departs for New York and Big Ben chimes at the same time at 12:30 PM, how can you determine when both events will occur again at the same time? Explain your reasoning.

A more efficient method to determine the least common multiple of two numbers is to use prime factors. Let's consider using prime factorization to determine the LCM of 36 and 15.

To calculate the LCM of 36 and 15, first write the prime factors of each, and identify the unique prime factors.

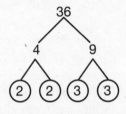

The unique prime factors are 2, 3 and 5.

Next, determine the greatest power of each prime factor.

$36 = 2^2 \times 3^2$
$15 = 3 \times 5$

Finally, multiply those factors.

$LCM = 2^2 \times 3^2 \times 5$
$\quad\quad = 4 \times 9 \times 5$ The LCM of 36 and 15 is 180.
$\quad\quad = 180$

6. What does LCM = 180 mean in terms of the ferry departing for New York and Big Ben chiming?

7. Calculate the product of all the prime factors of both 15 and 36.

8. How does the product of all the prime factors of both 15 and 36 compare to the LCM for the ferry departing for New York and Big Ben chiming? Explain your reasoning.

9. What is the greatest common multiple of 15 and 36? Explain your reasoning.

10. The Newspaper Club at Marshall Middle School meets every 6 school days. The Math Club meets every 8 school days. Luis is a member of both clubs. He needs to make a plan when both clubs meet on the same school day. Both clubs will meet today after school.

   a. After today, when will both clubs meet on the same day again? Explain your reasoning.

   b. How often will Luis have both club meetings on the same school day?

11. The school cafeteria serves pizza every 6 school days, chicken tenders every 8 school days, and salad every 10 school days.

a. If pizza and salad are served together today, in how many more school days will they be served together again? Show how you calculated your answer.

b. How could you mark your calendar to know when pizza and salad would be served together on the same school day?

c. Kevin likes chicken tenders with salad. If chicken tenders and salad are served together today, when will they be served together on the same school day again? Explain your reasoning.

d. If pizza, chicken tenders, and salad are all served today, when will they all be served together on the same school day again? Explain your reasoning.

12. The students at Independence Middle School have different schedules for sixth, seventh, and eighth grades. The sixth grade students have gym every 3 school days. The seventh grade students have art every 4 school days, and the eighth grade students have music every 6 school days. The middle school teachers are planning a special workshop, and they have to determine when students have these subjects on the same day.

a. If today the sixth grade has gym, the seventh grade has art, and the eighth grade has music, in how many school days will all three classes occur on the same day again?

b. If today the sixth grade has gym, the seventh grade has art, and the eighth grade has music, will these classes occur together 30 school days from today? Why or why not?

c. On the first day of school, the sixth grade has gym, the seventh grade has art, and the eighth grade has music. If the school year is 180 school days, how many times during the school year will the three classes be held on the same day?

Hmmm . . . so it IS possible to calculate the LCM of more than 2 numbers.

13. Determine the least common multiple for each pair of numbers using prime factorization. Create factor trees if you need help determining the prime factorization of each number.

a. 8 and 12

b. 126 and 45

c. 165 and 22

d. 6, 7, and 45

Talk the Talk

1. Why do you think the least common multiple is not always the product of the two numbers?

2. Explain how you can determine the least common multiple of any two numbers.

Be prepared to share your solutions and methods.

2

2.3 HAPPENINGS AT HARVEST DAY

Investigating Factors and Greatest Common Factors

Learning Goal

In this lesson, you will:

▶ Determine the greatest common factor
of two or more numbers.

Key Terms

▶ common factor
▶ greatest common factor (GCF)
▶ relatively prime numbers

2

State fairs, county fairs, and harvest days have been taking place for over a century. It is believed that the first state fair took place in 1841. State fairs are not only fun, but they are about big competition too! Farmers display their prized pigs, cows, chickens—well almost any farm animal you can think of—in hopes of attaining the blue ribbon! And the competition isn't limited to just animals; competition for largest vegetables, bake offs, and feats of strength have also been part of state fairs. Have you ever been to a state fair?

Problem 1 Harvest Day

1. Pat is creating thank-you fruit baskets for the adults who will volunteer at Saturday's Harvest Day event. She wants to make sure each basket contains an equal quantity of each type of fruit. She has 24 bananas, 12 apples, and 18 oranges.

   a. How many different fruit baskets can she make so that each one has an equal number of each type of fruit?

   b. What is the greatest number of fruit baskets she could assemble so that each basket has an equal quantity of each type fruit?

   c. How many bananas, apples, and oranges will be in each fruit basket if Pat decides to make the greatest number of fruit baskets? Explain your reasoning.

2. Michelle is organizing student teams for the scavenger hunt at the Harvest Day event. She wants to make sure that each team has an equal number of boys and an equal number of girls. There are 42 boys and 12 girls who signed up to participate in the scavenger hunt.

a. How many different teams can Michelle organize?

b. What is the greatest number of teams that Michelle can organize?

c. How many boys and how many girls can be on each team if Michelle decides to organize the greatest number of teams? Explain your reasoning.

You helped determine the greatest number of fruit baskets that can be created, and the greatest number of teams that can be organized. A **common factor** is a factor of two or more numbers. The **greatest common factor (GCF)** is the greatest factor two or more numbers have in common.

3. Determine the greatest common factor using prime factorization.

   a. Write the prime factorizations of 24 and 36 as mathematical statements.

   b. What factors are common to both 24 and 36?

   c. What is the greatest common factor of 24 and 36?

4. Write a rule for determining the greatest common factor of a set of numbers once you have completed the prime factorization for each number.

5. What is the least common factor of 24 and 36? Explain your reasoning.

6. What is the least common factor for any two numbers?

7. Determine the greatest common factor of each pair.

a. 20 and 40

b. 12 and 30

c. 36 and 48

d. 37 and 81

I wonder, can the greatest common factor be one of the two numbers I am trying to calculate the GCF of? I think that is possible— what do you think?

8. If the greatest common factor of two numbers is 1, what can you say about their factors?

Two numbers that do not have any common factors other than 1 are called **relatively prime numbers**.

9. Name two other pairs of numbers that are relatively prime. At least one of the numbers must be a composite number. Explain how you know they are relatively prime.

10. The students in Mr. Michael's art class are decorating a booth for Harvest Day. They have blue cloth that is 60 inches long, gold cloth that is 48 inches long, and white cloth that is 72 inches long.

   a. What is the greatest length of cloth they can cut if they want each piece of each color cloth to be the same length?
   Explain your reasoning.

   b. How many pieces of each color cloth will they have?

11. The students in Mrs. Howard's cooking class want to decorate their booth for Harvest Day. They have 12 feet of red streamer and 19 feet of blue streamer.

   a. What is the greatest length of streamer they can cut if they want each piece of each color to be the same length?

   b. How many pieces of each color streamer will they have?

12. Leon is creating the board for the dart game at the Harvest Day. The entire board is 32 inches by 48 inches. Within the board, he wants to create square targets. How can he mark off the board so that he has the largest square targets possible? Explain how you determined your answer.

 Be prepared to share your solutions and methods.

2

COMMON FACTORS OR COMMON MULTIPLES?
Using GCF and LCM to Solve Problems

2.4

Learning Goal

In this lesson, you will:

▶ Recognize how to use common factors and common multiples to solve problems.

2

You have learned how to determine common factors, common multiples, greatest common factors, and least common multiples. Sometimes it is necessary to decide whether you need to use common factors or common multiples. How can you determine when to use common factors or common multiples to solve problems? Can you think of any real-world examples of when you would use common factors or common multiples?

Problem 1 Solve Problems

Remember that common factors help you think about how to divide, or share things equally. Common multiples help you think about how things with different cycles can occur at the same time.

1. Sabrina is watching one of her favorite television shows. She notices that there is a commercial every nine minutes. Her brother, Michael, is watching one of his favorite shows on another television station at the same time. He notices that there is a commercial every 12 minutes. Sabrina and Michael wonder if there will ever be a commercial on both channels at the same time.

> Oh! I don't like commercials very much. When my television show is getting exciting, it seems there's another commercial break—ugh!

   a. If Sabrina's show begins at 8:00 PM and lasts for two hours, list all the times commercials will air during the show.

   b. Michael's show starts at the same time and also lasts for two hours. List all the times commercials will air during the show.

   c. Will Sabrina's and Michael's shows have commercials air at the same time? If yes, how many times will Sabrina's and Michael's television shows air commercials at the same time, and at what times will this occur?

   d. How many minutes will it take for commercials to air on both stations at the same time? Why?

2. Ramon and Justine are watching different broadcasts of the Rose Parade on television. The broadcast Ramon is watching airs commercials every 17 minutes. The broadcast Justine is watching airs commercials every 14 minutes. Both broadcasts started at 7:00 AM and are scheduled to end at 9:00 AM. When will commercials air on both broadcasts at the same time? Explain your reasoning.

3. Two bikers ride on the same circular path. The first rider completes a lap in 12 minutes. The second rider completes a lap in 18 minutes. Both riders start at the starting line at the same time and go in the same direction. If the riders maintain their speed, after how many minutes will they meet again at the starting line? Explain your reasoning.

4. Melissa has 72 carrot sticks, 56 pieces of cauliflower, and 64 pieces of broccoli. She wants to evenly divide each type of vegetable into veggie trays for a club reception.

   a. How many trays can Melissa make? Explain your reasoning.

   b. What is the greatest number of veggie trays that Melissa can make?

   c. Melissa's younger sister sees all of the veggies laid out on the table and takes 8 carrot sticks, 14 pieces of cauliflower, and 4 pieces of broccoli for her friends. Seeing this, Melissa knows she must recalculate the number of trays she can have if she wants each tray to have an equal amount of each type of vegetable. Now how many veggie trays can Melissa make?

   d. What is the greatest number of trays that Melissa can now make? Explain how you determined how many trays Melissa can make.

5. Dr. Abramson is a scientist. She and her assistants are working on three different experiments using water. For the first experiment, the water level must be checked every 12 seconds. For the second experiment, the temperature of the water must be checked every 30 seconds. For the third experiment, the color of the water must be checked every 36 seconds.

a. If all the experiments start at the same time, when is the first time all three experiments will need to be checked at the same time? Explain your reasoning.

b. What are some additional times that all three experiments will need to be checked at the same time?

c. In minutes, list the first four times all three experiments will be checked at the same time.

6. Brian and some friends are counselors at a summer camp. They like to have healthy snacks throughout the day as they work. They want to make snack bags consisting of raisin boxes and granola bars. Brian has 72 boxes of raisins and 64 granola bars.

a. What is the greatest number of snack bags Brian can make so that everyone gets the same amount of raisin boxes and the same amount of granola bars? Brian must use all of the raisin boxes and granola bars, so none can be left over. Explain how you calculated the amounts of each.

b. If Brian makes the greatest number of possible snack bags, how many raisin boxes will be in each bag? How many granola bars will be in each bag?

c. Are there different amounts of snack bags Brian can make?

7. Dulcina has 45 pencils and 36 markers. She wants to make back-to-school packs that contain the same amount of pencils and the same amount of markers to give to her friends. Dulcina does not want any leftover pencils or markers. She knows that she needs to determine the greatest common factor. Explain to Dulcina how to determine the greatest common factor in three different ways.

a. Determine the greatest common factor by listing the factors.

b. Determine the greatest common factor by using a Venn diagram.

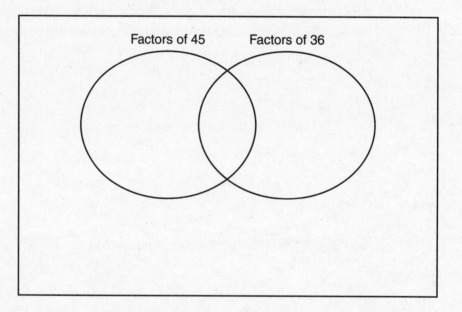

c. Demonstrate the greatest common factor using prime factorization. If you need help, create a factor tree.

d. Which method do you prefer? Why?

Talk the Talk

1. Use the terms factor, multiple, product, divisor, and divisible to write as many statements as you can about:

$$8 \times 7 = 56$$

2. Complete each graphic organizer for least common multiple and greatest common factor.

   For each graphic organizer:

   - Define LCM and GCF in your own words.

   - Choose a pair of numbers and use that pair of numbers consistently for each graphic organizer.

   - Provide an example and describe how to determine either the LCM or the GCF using a list, prime factors, and a Venn diagram.

   - Explain how you know when to determine the LCM or the GCF when solving a word problem. Create a word problem and show your solution using any method you choose.

DEFINITION IN YOUR OWN WORDS

DETERMINE AN LCM USING A LIST OF MULTIPLES

LEAST COMMON MULTIPLE (LCM)

DETERMINE THE LCM USING PRIME FACTORIZATION

DETERMINE THE LCM USING A VENN DIAGRAM

APPLYING YOUR KNOWLEDGE OF LCM

How can you tell when to determine the LCM when solving problems?
Create a word problem and show the solution.

2

DEFINITION IN YOUR OWN WORDS

DETERMINE A GCF USING A LIST OF FACTORS

GREATEST COMMON FACTOR (GCF)

DETERMINE THE GCF USING PRIME FACTORIZATION

DETERMINE THE GCF USING A VENN DIAGRAM

APPLYING YOUR KNOWLEDGE OF GCF

How can you tell when to determine a GCF when solving problems?
Create a word problem and show the solution.

3. Can you always determine the greatest common factor of any two numbers? Why or why not?

4. If the greatest common factor of two numbers is 1, what can you say about the numbers?

5. Can you always determine the least common multiple of any two numbers? Why or why not?

6. If the least common multiple of two numbers is the product of those numbers, what can you say about the two numbers?

7. Using prime factorization, how can you determine whether the least common multiple of two numbers is the product of the two numbers, or is less than the product of the two numbers?

 Be prepared to share your solutions and methods.

Chapter 2 Summary

Key Terms

▶ prime factorization (2.1)

▶ factor tree (2.1)

▶ power (2.1)

▶ base (2.1)

▶ exponent (2.1)

▶ common multiple (2.2)

▶ least common multiple (LCM) (2.2)

▶ common factor (2.3)

▶ greatest common factor (GCF) (2.3)

▶ relatively prime numbers (2.3)

Property

▶ Associative Property of Multiplication (2.1)

Theorem

▶ Fundamental Theorem of Arithmetic (2.1)

2

2.1 Determining the Prime Factorization of a Number

The Fundamental Theorem of Arithmetic states that every natural number is either prime or can be uniquely written as a product of primes. This product of primes is the prime factorization of the number. A factor tree is a useful tool for organizing the factors of a number. Powers are often used to express repeated factors.

Example

The prime factorization of 96 using a factor tree is shown. Below the factor tree, the prime factorization of 96 using powers is shown.

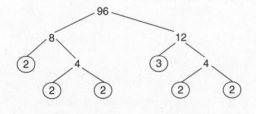

$$96 = 2 \times 2 \times 2 \times 2 \times 2 \times 3$$
$$= 2^5 \cdot 3$$

Your brain is composed of approximately 100 billion neurons which process and transmit information. How much is 100 billion? It's 1×10^{11} – that's a lot of zeros!

2.2 Determining the Least Common Multiple

The least common multiple, or LCM, is the least multiple (other than zero) that two or more numbers have in common.

Example

The least common multiple of 20 and 45 using prime factorization is shown.

$20 = 2 \times 2 \times 5 = 2^2 \cdot 5$

$45 = 3 \times 3 \times 5 = 3^2 \cdot 5$

$\text{LCM} = 2^2 \cdot 3^2 \cdot 5 = 180$

The LCM of 20 and 45 is 180.

2.3 Determining the Greatest Common Factor

The greatest common factor, or GCF, is the greatest factor that two or more numbers have in common.

Example

The greatest common factor of 64 and 120 using prime factorization is shown.

$64 = 2^6$

$120 = 2^3 \cdot 3 \cdot 5$

$\text{GCF} = 2^3$

$\quad\;\; = 8$

The GCF of 64 and 120 is 8.

2.4 Using GCF and LCM to Solve Problems

Common factors help determine how to divide or share things equally. Common multiples help determine how things with different cycles can occur at the same time.

Example

a. A florist has 24 daisies, 40 zinnias, and 32 snapdragons. She wants to divide the flowers evenly to make bouquets for her display case. The florist can determine the greatest common factor to calculate how many bouquets he can create.

Factors of 24: 1, 2, 3, 4, 6, 8, 12, 24

Factors of 40: 1, 2, 4, 5, 8, 10, 20, 40

Factors of 32: 1, 2, 4, 8, 16, 32

The GCF is 8.

The florist can make eight bouquets because the greatest common factor of 24, 40, and 32 is 8.

b. Carl has gym class every 4 school days and music class every 3 school days. If Carl has both gym class and music class today, in how many school days will he have both classes on the same day again?

Multiples of 4: 4, 8, 12, . . .

Multiples of 3: 3, 6, 9, 12, . . .

The LCM is 12.

Carl will have both classes on the same day in 12 school days.

2

3 FRACTIONS

Almost everyone likes pizza. There are approximately 39,000 pizzerias in the United States, serving about 3 billion pizzas every year. This amounts to about 46 slices per person per year.

3

3.1 FLAGS AND FRACTIONS

Modeling Parts of a Whole

Learning Goals

In this lesson, you will:

▶ Determine equal parts of a whole.

▶ Draw different representations of equal parts.

Key Terms

▶ fraction

▶ numerator

▶ denominator

D id you know that the first United States flag had 13 stars on it? You might have seen some historic flags with the 13 stars in a circle within a field of blue, or maybe you saw the 13 stars in rows. Because there were no government guidelines about how the flag's stars were to be organized in the blue field in the early days of the United States, the placement of stars varied. Since 1776, the United States has grown to include 50 states, so, the current flag has 50 stars. Do you remember what the 13 red and white stripes represent?

Problem 1 Part-Whole

In this chapter you will be adding to your knowledge of *fractions*. As you learned in elementary school, a **fraction** represents a part of a whole object, set, or unit. A fraction is written using two whole numbers separated by a bar. The number above the bar is the **numerator**, and the number below the bar is the **denominator**. The denominator (bottom number) indicates how many parts make up the whole, while the numerator (top number) indicates how many parts are counted.

There are 10 total bowling pins and 3 of the pins are knocked down.

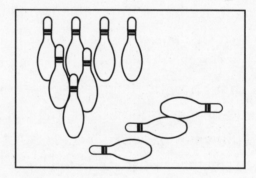

You can represent this situation as:

$$\frac{3}{10} \rightarrow \frac{\text{numerator}}{\text{denominator}}$$

$$\rightarrow \frac{\text{the number of bowling pins knocked down}}{\text{the total number of bowling pins}}$$

The Student Bowler Association (SBA) is an organization of student bowlers in Grades 3 through 8. Each of the SBA bowling teams consists of two student bowlers. Each team is asked to design two flags to represent the two players on the team. Each team flag must be labeled and evenly divided into thirds, fourths, fifths, sixths, eighths, or twelfths. Each flag has the same dimensions as shown.

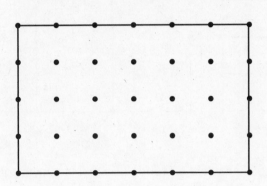

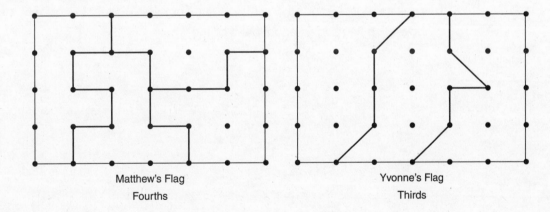

If labels aren't provided, use the word "unit" to describe the dimensions.

1. Describe the dimensions and total area of the flag.

Team members Yvonne and Matthew each designed a flag and labeled them "Fourths" and "Thirds."

Matthew's Flag
Fourths

Yvonne's Flag
Thirds

They showed their flags to team members Dante and Miko. Dante looked at the flags and said, "Your flags don't seem correct. Look at our flags."

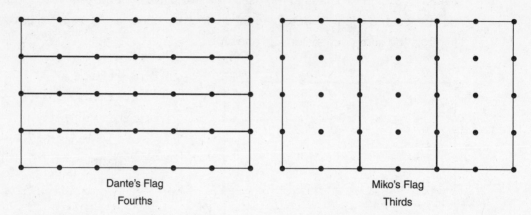

Dante's Flag
Fourths

Miko's Flag
Thirds

Ashley looked at all four flags and said, "You are all correct! Each flag shows *equal* parts of a whole."

2. For each question, explain why Ashley's statement is correct.

    a. How are both Matthew's and Dante's flags of fourths correct? Explain your answer by describing how each flag shows equal parts of the whole.

    b. How are both Yvonne's and Miko's flags of thirds correct? Explain by describing how each flag shows equal parts of the whole.

Let's analyze another fractional representation.

3. A rectangular flag is divided into 24 equal parts, and 15 of those parts are shaded.

   a. Represent the portion of the flag that is shaded as a fraction. Then describe what each number of the fraction represents.

   b. Does the shaded portion of the rectangular flag shown represent $\frac{15}{24}$? Explain your reasoning.

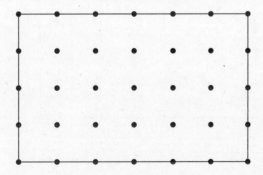

   c. Shade a different representation for $\frac{15}{24}$. Explain how you know you are correct.

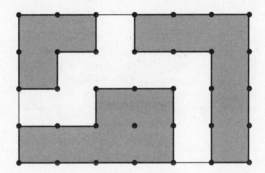

Fractions can be represented in different ways as long as they have the same equal number of units dividing the whole. This means the way the model of the fraction looks does not affect the value of the fraction.

4. Draw three different flags for each fraction. Show how you know you have equal parts by writing how many square units are in each part. Then describe how you made your flags. Extra grids are included for workspace.

   a. Halves

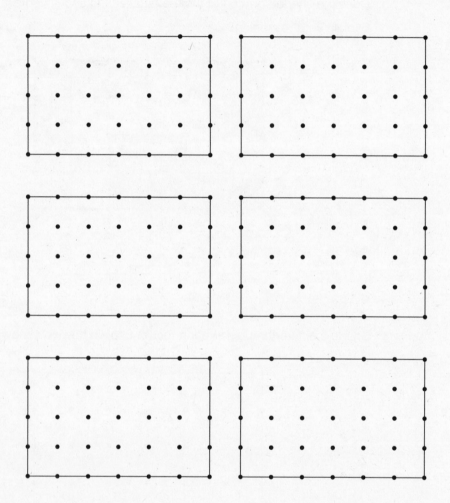

b. Thirds

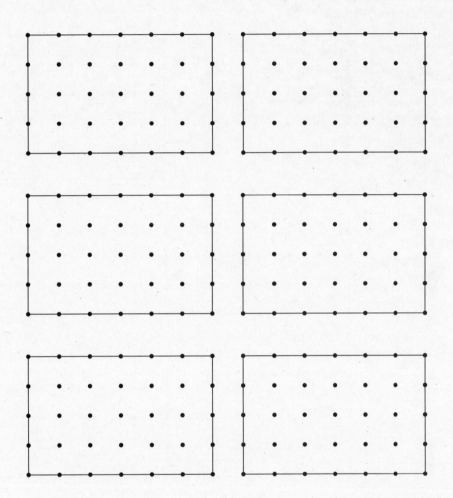

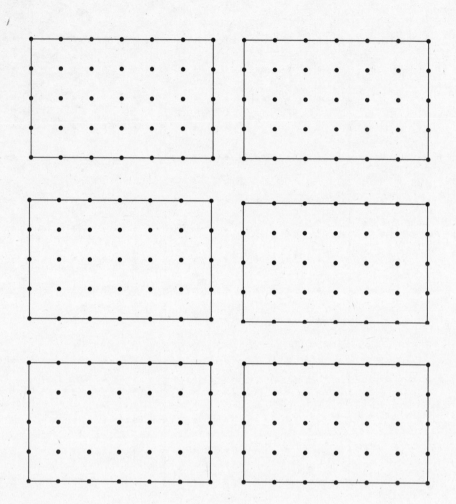

d. Sixths

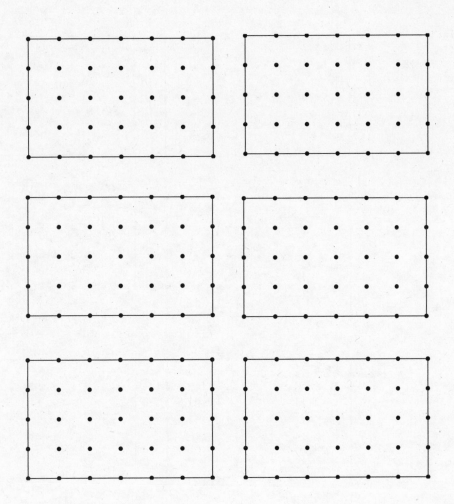

e. Eighths

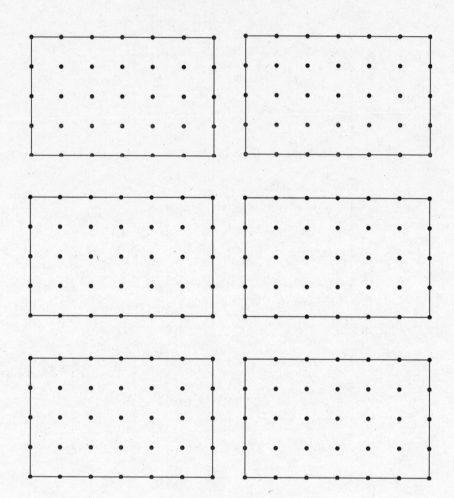

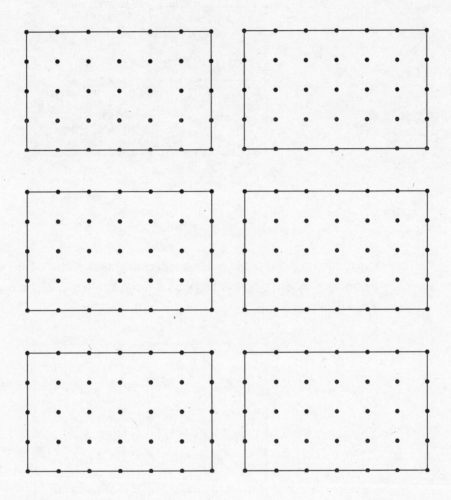

Problem 2 Who's Correct?

1. Carmen designed a flag and shaded half of it. Did she correctly label her flag?
   Explain your reasoning.

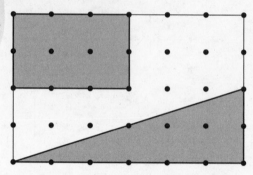

2. Katy wondered if she could make a flag using fifths. Katy had an idea and drew these
   lines on her flag and said her flag was divided into fifths. Is she correct?
   Explain your reasoning.

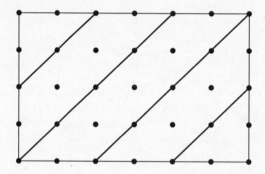

3. What do you think? Can you make fifths in the rectangular flag shown? If so, draw the flag. Explain your reasoning.

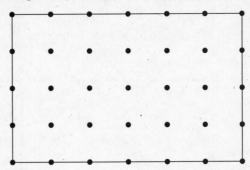

1. Use these flag pieces to answer each question.

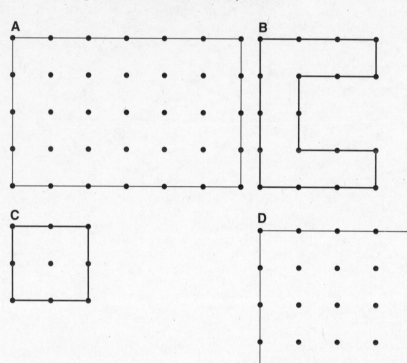

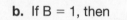

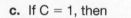

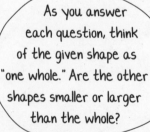

a. If A = 1, then   B = _____,   C = _____,   D = _____.

b. If B = 1, then   A = _____,   C = _____,   D = _____.

c. If C = 1, then   A = _____,   B = _____,   D = _____.

d. If D = 1, then   A = _____,   B = _____,   C = _____.

As you answer each question, think of the given shape as "one whole." Are the other shapes smaller or larger than the whole?

Problem 4 Fractions of a Set

1. The seventh grade class is collecting books for the local children's hospital library. They have collected:

- 16 books about animals
- 8 books about sports
- 20 books about different cultures
- 10 biographies
- 6 mysteries
- 12 books about ancient civilizations

Represent each book type in the collection of books as a fraction.

Problem 5 Fundraising Goals

The eighth-grade class at Carnegie Middle School decided to sell pom-poms at all the sporting events. The money from the sales will be donated to the local children's hospital. Each homeroom set a different goal, displayed at the top of each thermometer. The total money raised so far by each homeroom, including today's donations, is shaded.

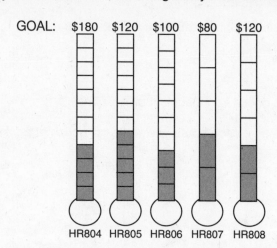

GOAL: $180 $120 $100 $80 $120

HR804 HR805 HR806 HR807 HR808

Yolanda is in charge of announcing the progress of the pom-pom fundraiser during the morning announcements. She announces that Homeroom 805 (HR 805) has raised the most money so far.

1. Do you think Yolanda is correct? Explain why or why not. If you think Yolanda is incorrect, determine which homeroom has raised the most money.

2. Complete the table shown using the information from the fundraising thermometers.

Homeroom	Fractional Part of the Goal Completed as of Today	Money Raised (in dollars)
HR 804		
HR 805		
HR 806		
HR 807		
HR 808		

a. Is it better to announce the fractional part of money raised or the actual amount of money raised? Why?

b. If HR 804 raises $\frac{11}{12}$ of their goal, how much money would they have raised?

c. If HR 807 raises $\frac{3}{5}$ of their goal, how much money would they have raised?

d. If HR 805 raises $\frac{7}{12}$ of their goal, how much money would they have raised?

3. Let's consider the same thermometers, but this time all the homerooms have the same goal. How much money has each homeroom raised?

a. Homeroom 804

b. Homeroom 805

c. Homeroom 806

d. Homeroom 807

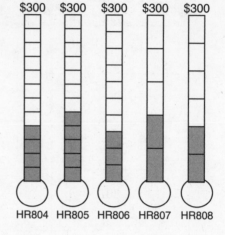

e. Homeroom 808

 Be prepared to share your solutions and methods.

Don't forget you just calculated the fractional part of each thermometer's shaded region in the previous table.

3

3.2

YOU MEAN THREE CAN BE ONE?

Fractional Representations

Learning Goals

In this lesson, you will:

▶ Create different fractional representations using pattern blocks.

▶ Write fractional statements for different representations given the whole.

▶ Determine fractional representations given the whole.

▶ Determine fractional representations given parts of the whole.

Pattern blocks can be used to show fractions. Pattern blocks are a relatively new mathematical model that was invented in the 1960s. You will use pattern blocks in this lesson. What shapes are the pattern blocks? Have you ever used pattern blocks before?

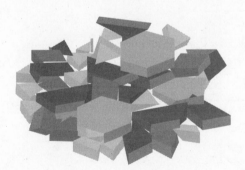

Problem 1   Hexagonal Fractions

1. Complete the table shown. Use your yellow hexagon to represent the whole, or 1.

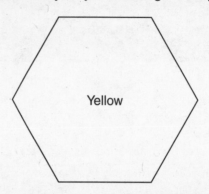

Yellow

Shape	Name of Shape	Fractional Part of Whole	Number of Fractional Parts to Make a Whole
red		——	——
blue		——	——
green		——	——

You can place different pattern blocks on top of the yellow hexagon to create another representation for the whole. For example, you can create the design shown.

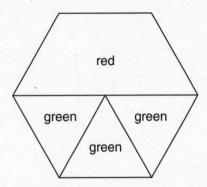

As you saw from the table you completed, a red trapezoid covers $\frac{1}{2}$ of the hexagon, and a green triangle covers $\frac{1}{6}$ of the trapezoid. So, in this example, the red trapezoid covers $\frac{1}{2}$ of the hexagon, and 3 triangles cover $\frac{1}{2}$ of the hexagon. The fraction sentence for this representation would be $1 = \frac{1}{2} + \frac{1}{6} + \frac{1}{6} + \frac{1}{6}$.

2. Create different representations for the yellow hexagon. Follow the example shown.

- Start with the yellow hexagon.
- Cover the yellow hexagon with other pattern blocks.
- Record your designs.
- Write a fraction sentence to describe your design.
- Repeat the process to create as many representations as possible.

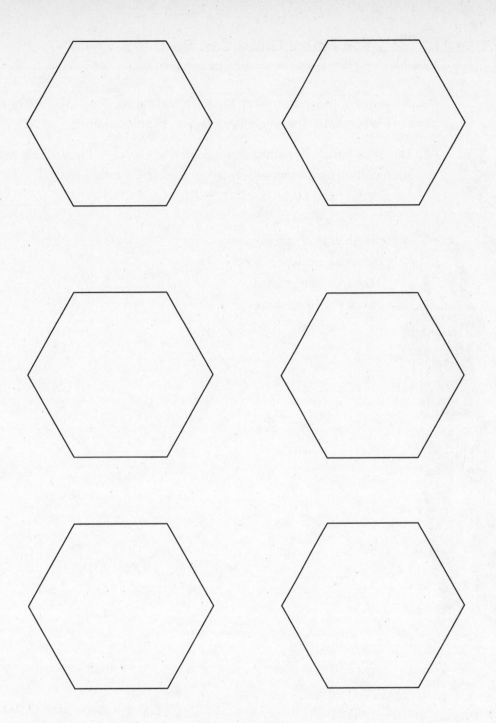

3. How did you know you had determined all the combinations?

Problem 2   You Mean Three Can Be One?

Recall the title of this lesson: "You Mean Three Can Be One?" You will now determine the parts of a whole when the whole is more than one hexagon.

1. The three hexagons shown represent the whole, or 1. Determine what fractional part each pattern block shape represents. Explain your reasoning.

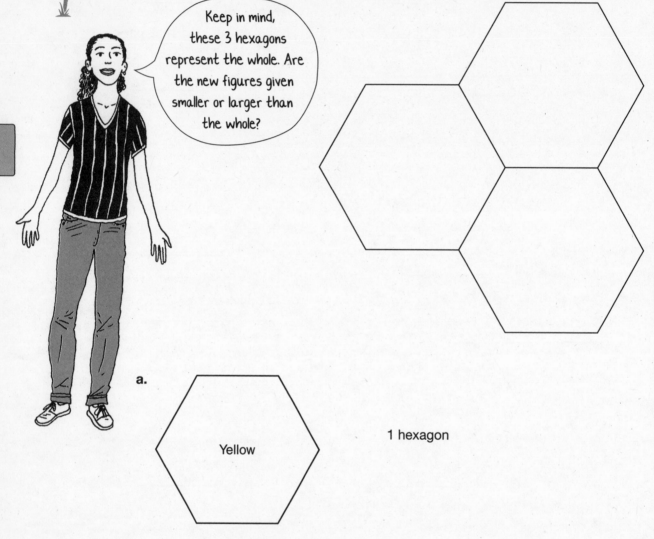

Keep in mind, these 3 hexagons represent the whole. Are the new figures given smaller or larger than the whole?

a.

Yellow

1 hexagon

b.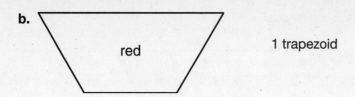

1 trapezoid

c.

1 rhombus

d.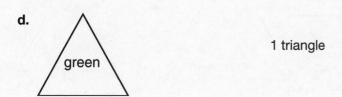

1 triangle

2. Complete each statement.

a.

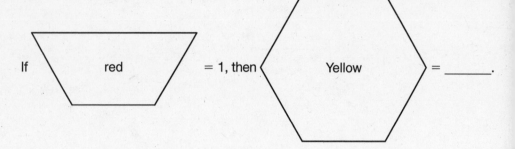

If | red | = 1, then | Yellow | = _____.

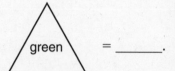

green = _____.

blue = _____.

b.

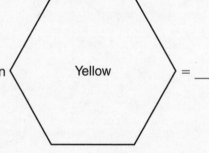

If | blue | = 1, then | Yellow | = _____.

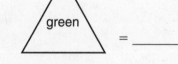

green = _____.

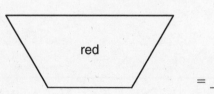

red = _____.

c.

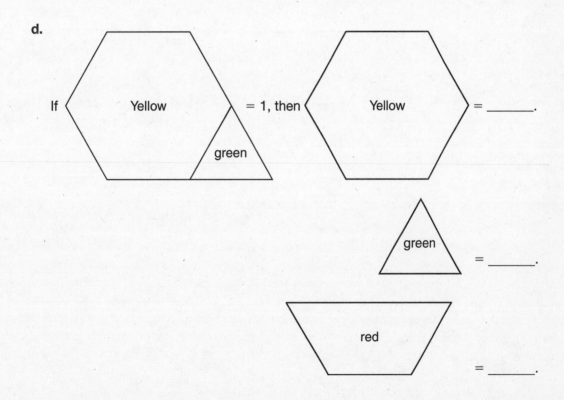

If [green triangle] = 1, then [Yellow hexagon] = _____.

[blue rhombus] = _____.

[red trapezoid] = _____.

d.

If [Yellow hexagon with green triangle] = 1, then [Yellow hexagon] = _____.

[green triangle] = _____.

[red trapezoid] = _____.

e.

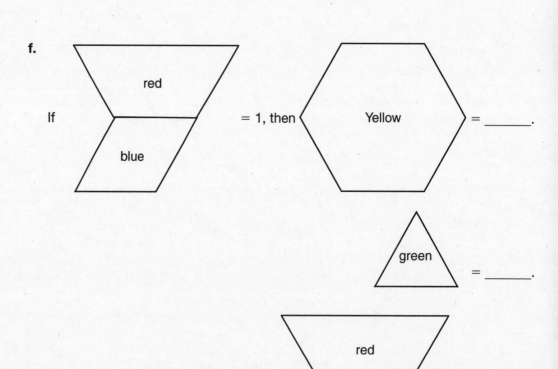

If [green / green] = 1, then Yellow = _____.

green = _____.

red = _____.

f.

If [red / blue] = 1, then Yellow = _____.

green = _____.

red = _____.

3. Build and sketch each representation for the description given.

a. A triangle that is two-thirds red, one-ninth green, and two-ninths blue.

Now, think in reverse. What will the whole look for each description?

3

b. A parallelogram that is three-fourths blue and one-fourth green.

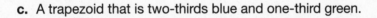

c. A trapezoid that is two-thirds blue and one-third green.

d. A parallelogram that is one-half red and one-half blue.

e. A triangle that is one-third green and two-thirds red.

f. Create a puzzle for your partner to solve using three pattern block types. Make sure it is possible to create.

4. Determine each fractional representation by drawing a model.

a.

If  is 1, what is $\frac{3}{4}$?

b.

If ●　●　●　● is 1, what is $\frac{3}{4}$?

c. If |———|———|———| is 1, what is $\frac{3}{4}$?

d.

If  is $\frac{2}{3}$, what is 1?

e.

If 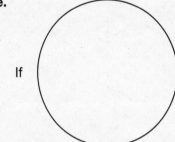 is $1\frac{1}{2}$, what is 1?

f.

If ⬢ is $1\frac{1}{2}$, what is 1?

g. If ├──────┼──────┼──────┤ is $1\frac{1}{2}$, what is 1?

h.

If

$\boxed{}$

is 2, what is $\frac{1}{2}$?

Talk the Talk

1. Describe a method for determining the value of a fractional part of any set.

Be prepared to share your solutions and methods.

ROCKET STRIPS

3.3

Dividing a Whole into Fractional Parts

Learning Goals

In this lesson, you will:

▶ Create equal parts of a whole.

▶ Determine if fractions are equal.

▶ Graph fractions on a number line.

Key Terms

▶ unit fraction

▶ equivalent fractions

3

Is there more news in a newspaper or are there more advertisements? In addition to supplying news stories, newspapers routinely sell advertisement space on each page. With your partner, take a section from a newspaper and measure the size of each article in the section's first four pages. Then, measure the size of each advertisement in the first four pages. What do you notice?

Problem 1   Newspaper Column Preparation

You signed up to participate in the school newspaper club. During the first meeting, faculty advisors Ms. Foster and Ms. Shu showed everyone copies of last year's publication of the *Rocket*. The teachers have already planned out the sections for this year's *Rocket*.

Matthew volunteered to create the "Random Acts of Kindness" section. The section will appear along the right side of the paper's back page. The newspaper is printed on $8 \frac{1}{2}$-inch by 11-inch paper.

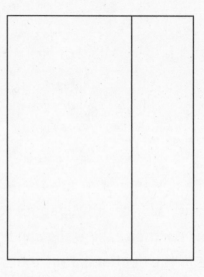

Matthew plans to put a box in each homeroom and ask students to nominate classmates for the monthly recognition of random kindness acts. Students must tell what nice act their nominee performed on a nomination slip. In preparation for completing his section, help Matthew plan the layout of the column; do not worry about the top or bottom margin of the page.

1. To begin, cut eight strips of paper the length of a newspaper page. Remember, the *Rocket* is printed on $8 \frac{1}{2}$-inch by 11-inch paper. Each strip of paper should be 1 inch wide. The strip represents one whole column. Do not fold the first strip, and label it as 1 whole.

> The strips are provided for you at the end of this lesson.

2. Take one of your paper strips and fold it carefully in half to divide the strip into two equal parts like the one shown. Label each folded part of the paper strip with the appropriate fraction, and draw a line to mark your fold. The strip shown will represent a column that recognizes two students.

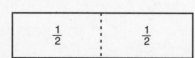

3. Take another paper strip and fold it carefully in half two times. Unfold and draw lines to mark your folds. Then, label each folded part of the paper strip with the appropriate fraction.

   How many students can be recognized in this column?

4. Take another paper strip and fold it in half three times. Be very careful to fold accurately. Unfold and draw lines to mark your folds. Then, label each folded part of the paper strip with the appropriate fraction.

   How many students can be recognized in this column?

5. Take another paper strip and fold it very carefully in half, four times. Unfold and draw lines to mark your folds. Then, label each folded part of the paper strip with the appropriate fraction.

   How many students can be recognized in this column?

6. Take another paper strip and fold it carefully into three *equal* sections. Unfold and draw lines to mark your folds. Then, label each folded part of the paper strip with the appropriate fraction.

   How many students can be recognized in this column?

7. Take the next paper strip and fold it into thirds, and then fold the strip in half. Unfold and draw lines to mark your folds. Then, label each folded part of the paper strip with the appropriate fraction.

   How many students can be recognized in this column?

8. Finally, take your last paper strip and fold it into thirds. Then, fold in half, and then fold in half once more. Unfold and draw lines to mark your folds. Then, label each folded part of the paper strip with the appropriate fraction.

   How many students can be recognized in this column?

Arrange your strips in a column so that all of the left edges are lined up and the strips are ordered from the strip with the smallest parts to the strip with the largest parts.

9. As the number of students who can be recognized in the column increases, describe what happens to the space for each student.

A **unit fraction** is a fraction that has a numerator of 1 and a denominator that is a positive integer.

10. List the unit fractions for each strip you created in ascending order.

> To list a set in ascending order means to list the set from least to greatest. To list a set in descending order means to list the set from greatest to least.

11. Explain how understanding the size of a unit fraction helps you determine the size of the whole.

If you folded the paper strips carefully, you will notice that some of the folds line up with each other. Fractions that represent the same part-to-whole relationship are **equivalent fractions.**

12. Show that $\frac{1}{2}$ is equivalent to $\frac{6}{12}$. Draw on the paper strips to represent halves and twelfths. Then, shade the strips to represent $\frac{1}{2}$ and $\frac{6}{12}$.

13. Make a collection of equivalent fractions using your fraction strips. Then, complete the graphic organizer by writing all the equivalent fractions for each.

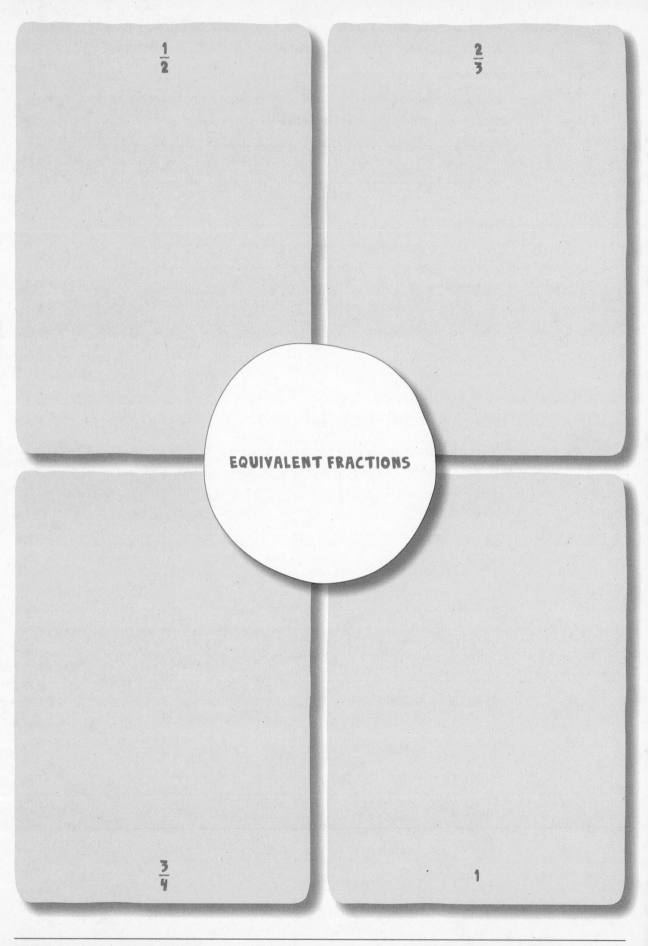

$\frac{1}{2}$

$\frac{2}{3}$

EQUIVALENT FRACTIONS

$\frac{3}{4}$

1

14. What do you notice in the collection of equivalent fractions? Give an example to justify your answer.

Talk the Talk

1. What do you notice about the numerator and denominator of the equivalent fractions?

2. What do you need to do to both the numerator and the denominator of a fraction in order to write another equivalent fraction?

Be prepared to share your solutions and methods.

3

3

3

3.4 GETTING CLOSER
Benchmark Fractions

Learning Goals

In this lesson, you will:

▶ Estimate fractions by using benchmark fractions.

▶ Order fractions in ascending order.

▶ Compare fractions.

Key Terms

▶ benchmark fractions

▶ inequality

3

Have you ever heard car companies compare the gas mileage of their vehicles to their competitors? Do you ever wonder how car companies get information, like gas mileage, about their vehicles and their competitor's vehicles? The Environmental Protection Agency (EPA) runs cars on test tracks under controlled conditions to determine fuel efficiencies. The gas-mileage results of these tests are used as *benchmarks* for consumers. Benchmarks are all around us and are not limited to just cars, but can be used for comparisons of almost any item. Can you think of other benchmarks you may have encountered?

Problem 1 Graphing Rocket Strips

Label each number line to represent the fractional part provided. Then plot each fraction.

As you get ready to label each number line, think about how you folded your strips in the Rocket Strips lesson. This will help you get the number line evenly spaced.

To get fourths, you folded the strip in half first, so mark $\frac{2}{4}$ on the number line first. Then mark $\frac{1}{4}$ and finally $\frac{3}{4}$.

1. fourths

0 ———————————————— 1

    a. $\frac{1}{4}$

    b. $\frac{3}{4}$

2. twelfths

0 ———————————————— 1

    a. $\frac{5}{12}$ **b.** $\frac{11}{12}$

    c. $\frac{1}{12}$ **d.** $\frac{7}{12}$

3. sixteenths

0 ———————————————— 1

    a. $\frac{10}{16}$ **b.** $\frac{1}{16}$

    c. $\frac{7}{16}$ **d.** $\frac{15}{16}$

4. eighths

0 ———————————————— 1

    a. $\frac{5}{8}$ **b.** $\frac{7}{8}$

    c. $\frac{1}{8}$ **d.** $\frac{3}{8}$

Problem 2   Benchmark Fractions

Benchmark fractions are common fractions you can use to estimate the value of fractions.

Three common benchmark fractions are 0, $\frac{1}{2}$, and 1.

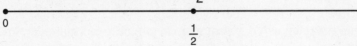

$$0 \qquad\qquad\qquad \frac{1}{2} \qquad\qquad\qquad 1$$

A fraction is close to 0 when the numerator is very small compared to the denominator.

A fraction is close to $\frac{1}{2}$ when the numerator is about half the size of the denominator.

A fraction is close to 1 when the numerator is very close in size to the denominator.

1. Use each number line you completed in Problem 1 to write a fraction that is:

   a. less than $\frac{1}{2}$.

   b. exactly $\frac{1}{2}$.

   c. greater than but not equal to $\frac{1}{2}$.

   d. close to but not equal to 0.

   e. exactly 1.

   f. close to but not equal to 1

   g. exactly 0.

Even though you used 4 different number lines, how are the fractions you wrote for each question similar?

2. Name the closest benchmark fraction for each fraction given.

   a. $\frac{4}{9}$

   b. $\frac{8}{9}$

   c. $\frac{6}{100}$

   d. $\frac{5}{67}$

   e. $\frac{7}{15}$

   f. $\frac{7}{12}$

   g. $\frac{5}{6}$

   h. $\frac{14}{27}$

   i. $\frac{12}{13}$

   j. $\frac{1}{17}$

   k. $\frac{5}{11}$

   l. $\frac{3}{7}$

3. Write the unknown numerator or denominator so that each fraction is close to but less than $\frac{1}{2}$.

a. $\dfrac{(\quad)}{12}$

b. $\dfrac{(\quad)}{27}$

c. $\dfrac{8}{(\quad)}$

d. $\dfrac{7}{(\quad)}$

e. $\dfrac{(\quad)}{13}$

f. $\dfrac{9}{(\quad)}$

4. Write the unknown numerator or denominator so that each fraction is close to but less than 1.

a. $\dfrac{(\quad)}{17}$

b. $\dfrac{11}{(\quad)}$

c. $\dfrac{(\quad)}{8}$

d. $\dfrac{(\quad)}{18}$

e. $\dfrac{13}{(\quad)}$

f. $\dfrac{(\quad)}{10}$

5. Rewrite each expression using benchmark fractions. Then, estimate the sum. Explain your reasoning.

a. $\dfrac{8}{9} + \dfrac{6}{7}$

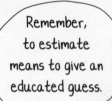

Remember, to estimate means to give an educated guess.

b. $\dfrac{1}{11} + \dfrac{8}{17}$

c. $\dfrac{10}{11} + \dfrac{11}{12} + \dfrac{12}{13} + \dfrac{13}{14} + \dfrac{14}{15}$

6. If three fractions that are greater than $\frac{1}{2}$ but less than 1 are added together, what can you say about their sum? Explain your reasoning.

7. If two fractions that are less than $\frac{1}{2}$ but greater than 0 are added together, what can you say about their sum? Explain your reasoning.

8. If seven fractions that are slightly less than 1 are added together, what can you say about their sum? Explain your reasoning.

Problem 3 Inequalities

You can use the inequality symbols < (less than) or > (greater than) to write a mathematical sentence that compares two numbers. An **inequality** is a statement that one number is less than or greater than another number.

1. Compare each pair of fractions using benchmark fractions. Insert a > or < symbol to make the inequality true. Explain your reasoning.

   a. $\dfrac{11}{12}$ _____ $\dfrac{5}{9}$

   b. $\dfrac{5}{9}$ _____ $\dfrac{5}{7}$

   c. $\dfrac{7}{13}$ _____ $\dfrac{5}{11}$

   d. $\dfrac{5}{10}$ _____ $\dfrac{7}{10}$

2. Determine a fraction that keeps each list in ascending order.

   a. $\dfrac{3}{7}$, ____ , $\dfrac{6}{7}$

   b. $\dfrac{1}{4}$, ____ , $\dfrac{2}{4}$

   c. $\dfrac{3}{8}$, ____ , $\dfrac{3}{4}$

   d. $\dfrac{1}{4}$, ____ , $\dfrac{5}{9}$

3. List the fractions shown in ascending order.

a. $\dfrac{1}{8}, \dfrac{1}{11}, \dfrac{1}{9}, \dfrac{1}{4}, \dfrac{1}{7}, \dfrac{1}{5}$

b. $\dfrac{4}{5}, \dfrac{4}{10}, \dfrac{4}{12}, \dfrac{4}{7}$

c. $\dfrac{3}{8}, \dfrac{3}{11}, \dfrac{3}{9}, \dfrac{3}{4}, \dfrac{3}{7}, \dfrac{3}{5}$

4. What do the fractions in each part of Question 3 have in common? Explain how you determined the order of the fractions in each.

5. Write the fractions shown in ascending order. Use what you know about benchmark fractions to determine the order. Explain your reasoning.

$\dfrac{5}{9}, \dfrac{7}{13}, \dfrac{2}{7}, \dfrac{10}{11}$

6. Lynn was trying to figure out which fraction was larger, $\frac{1}{2}$ or $\frac{1}{5}$. Her aunt said, "In fractions, larger is smaller and smaller is larger. So $\frac{1}{2}$ is larger than $\frac{1}{5}$." However, Lynn looked at the pairs of fractions shown and wasn't sure if that rule still worked.

Example 1

$\frac{8}{9}$ $\frac{1}{2}$

Example 2

$\frac{11}{12}$ $\frac{1}{5}$

Lynn said, "Ninths are smaller than halves, and twelfths are smaller than fifths, but something seems wrong about what my aunt said."

a. Explain to Lynn which fraction is larger in each pair and why.

b. Explain when her aunt's statement is true.

Problem 4 Who's Correct?

1. The sixth-grade students are designing logo patches using solids and patterns. The designs of four different students in Group 1 are shown.

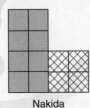

Nakida

Agnes

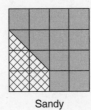

Sandy

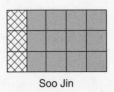

Soo Jin

Nakida says that she has the greatest fractional part of plaid in her design. The other students disagree. Settle the argument by determining the fractional part that is plaid for each student's patches. Who has the greatest fractional part plaid? Explain your reasoning.

2. The four students in Group 2 designed the patches shown.

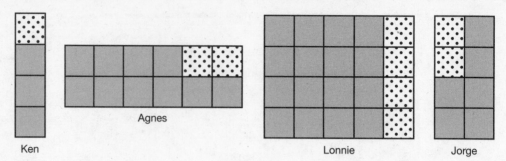

Ken

Agnes

Lonnie

Jorge

a. Agnes said that she has the greatest fractional part in polka dots. Put the students' patches in order from the smallest fractional part of polka dots to the largest fractional part of polka dots.

b. Is Agnes correct in claiming she has a design with the greatest fractional part in polka dots? Explain your reasoning.

3. Complete the table. List the fractional parts of each pattern for each student.

Student	Solid	Polka Dot
Ken		
Agnes		
Lonnie		
Jorge		

Be prepared to share your solutions and methods.

3.5 WHAT'S MY CUT?
Equivalent Fractions

Learning Goals

In this lesson, you will:

▶ Determine equal portions of a whole.

▶ Determine equivalent fractions.

▶ Calculate equivalent fractions using a form of 1.

▶ Simplify fractions.

▶ Order fractions.

Key Terms

▶ simplest form

▶ Multiplicative Identity Property

3

Today, you can take your coins to the grocery store to have them counted by a machine. You can exchange your coins for a cash voucher, gift cards, or you can even donate your coins to charity.

Careful, though. Unless you're donating your money, these machines usually take a "cut" of about 10 cents for every one of your dollars that it counts.

One of the largest transactions recorded for one of these machines was in San Dimas, California. A customer turned in over $8000 worth of coins! What was the machine's "cut"?

Problem 1 Pizza Cuts

1. Coach Finley buys pizzas to share with everyone who participated in the volleyball intramural program. She buys 21 pizzas to share among the 28 students who are sitting at tables of four.

   a. How many pizzas should each table receive if she wants each table to receive the same amount of pizza? Explain your reasoning.

   b. Coach Finley suggests dividing each pizza into fourths. Draw a diagram that represents the problem. Then, explain her reasoning.

   c. What fractional part of a pizza will each student receive?

d. Mario suggests dividing the pizzas in half. Will Mario's method work? Why or why not? If Mario's suggestion is not possible, explain what he can do to make his suggestion work. Draw a diagram that supports your explanation.

e. Sydney tries to divide his group's pizzas into thirds. Will Sydney's method work? Why or why not? If Sydney's method is not possible, explain what he can do to make his method work. Draw a diagram that supports your explanation.

3

f. Natalie tries to divide her group's pizzas into eighths. Will Natalie's method work? Why or why not? If it is not possible, explain what she can do to make her method work. Draw a diagram that supports your explanation.

g. Name the student(s) whose method did not require your suggestion. Then, name the fractional part of the pizzas each student at the table will receive.

h. Juanita claims that dividing the pizzas into any number of equal-sized pieces will work to divide the pizzas equally among the 28 students. Is she correct? Explain your reasoning and offer a solution if Juanita's method does not work.

2. Casey and Jamal are talking about pizza parties they had in each of their classes. Casey said, "In my class, four people shared three pizzas." Jamal said, "In my class, three people shared two pizzas."

a. Which student's classmates each got more pizza? Use a drawing or diagram to explain your reasoning. Assume the pizzas are the same size.

All this talk of pizza is making me hungry!

Problem 2 Equivalent Fractions

Throughout this chapter, you have encountered equivalent fractions. Recall that equivalent fractions are fractions that represent the same part-to-whole relationship.

When determining equivalent fractions, you must multiply the numerator and the denominator of a fraction by the same number. This process is the same as multiplying the given fraction by a fraction with the same numerator and denominator, such as $\frac{3}{3}$.

Recall that any fraction whose numerator and denominator are the same number is equivalent to 1. Multiplying any number by 1 does not change that number.

> To change a fraction to an equivalent fraction with a larger numerator and denominator, you multiply the fraction by a form of 1. For example,
>
> $$\frac{5}{8} \times \frac{3}{3} = \frac{15}{24}.$$

1. Complete each number sentence with the correct fraction to make it true. Explain your reasoning. Use your fraction strips if you need help determining the missing fraction to make equivalent fractions.

   a. $\dfrac{5}{6} \times \dfrac{(\quad)}{(\quad)} = \dfrac{15}{18}$

   b. $\dfrac{3}{4} \times \dfrac{(\quad)}{(\quad)} = \dfrac{15}{20}$

   c. $\dfrac{5}{8} \times \dfrac{(\quad)}{(\quad)} = \dfrac{15}{(\quad)}$

   d. $\dfrac{9}{27} \times \dfrac{(\quad)}{(\quad)} = \dfrac{(\quad)}{27}$

2. You just multiplied each fraction by the same number. What number was it?

The **Multiplicative Identity Property** states: $a \times 1 = a$, where a is a nonzero number.

3. Complete each equation to make the fractions equivalent. Explain your reasoning. Use your fraction strips if you need help determining equivalent fractions.

a. $\dfrac{1}{4} = \dfrac{(\quad)}{16}$

b. $\dfrac{2}{3} = \dfrac{(\quad)}{6}$

c. $\dfrac{7}{16} = \dfrac{(\quad)}{32}$

d. $\dfrac{(\quad)}{12} = \dfrac{3}{4}$

e. $\dfrac{1}{18} = \dfrac{1}{(\quad)}$

4. Write the first 10 equivalent fractions of each using what you know about equivalent fractions. The first example is done for you.

a. $\dfrac{1}{4}, \dfrac{2}{8}, \dfrac{3}{12}, \dfrac{4}{16}, \dfrac{5}{20}, \dfrac{6}{24}, \dfrac{7}{28}, \dfrac{8}{32}, \dfrac{9}{36}, \dfrac{10}{40}$

b. $\dfrac{3}{5},$

c. $\dfrac{2}{3},$

d. $\dfrac{5}{8},$

e. How did you determine the order to list your equivalent fractions?

To change a fraction to an equivalent fraction with a smaller numerator and denominator, you must divide the numerator and denominator by a form of 1.

For example, $\frac{15}{24} \div \frac{3}{3} = \frac{5}{8}$.

Whenever you determine an equivalent fraction whose numerator and denominator are smaller than the original fraction's numerator and denominator, the new fraction is simpler. When a fraction cannot be simplified further, the fraction is in *simplest form,* or completely simplified. **Simplest form** is a way of writing a fraction so that the numerator and denominator have no common factors other than 1.

You can say a fraction is in a simpler form in several ways:

"$\frac{1}{2}$ is simpler than $\frac{4}{8}$."

"$\frac{1}{2}$ is a simplified form of $\frac{4}{8}$."

"$\frac{4}{8}$ in simplest form is $\frac{1}{2}$."

Sometimes it is read:

"$\frac{1}{2}$ is the simplified form of $\frac{4}{8}$."

"$\frac{1}{2}$ is in lowest, or simplest, terms."

5. Determine if each fraction is simplified completely. If the fraction is not simplified completely, write the fraction in simplest form.

a. $\frac{9}{24} = \frac{9 \div 3}{24 \div 3} = \frac{3}{8}$

b. $\frac{6}{12} = \frac{6 \div 3}{12 \div 3} = \frac{2}{4}$

c. $\frac{18}{27} = \frac{18 \div 3}{27 \div 3} = \frac{6}{9}$

6. Circle the fractions that are simplified completely. How do you know?

$\frac{9}{13}$ $\frac{10}{32}$ $\frac{9}{12}$ $\frac{12}{144}$ $\frac{7}{12}$ $\frac{33}{55}$

Recall that the factors of a number are those numbers that divide into the number with no remainder.

7. How can you use factors of a number to simplify fractions?

8. Write each fraction in simplest form.

a. $\frac{6}{9}$

b. $\frac{9}{12}$

c. $\frac{8}{24}$

d. $\frac{12}{15}$

e. $\frac{18}{36}$

f. $\frac{14}{42}$

g. Explain how you simplified each fraction.

9. Ms. Glick asked her students to simplify $\frac{24}{36}$. Jose, Sara, and Clifton's methods are shown. Analyze each method and solution to determine if it is correct. If one of the methods is incorrect, what would you tell the student to do to correct his or her method?

Jose:

I simplified $\frac{24}{36}$ by first dividing both the numerator and denominator by 2. I then continued dividing by 2 until the fraction could not be evenly divided by $\frac{2}{2}$.

$$\frac{24}{36} = \frac{24 \div 2}{36 \div 2} = \frac{12}{18} = \frac{12 \div 2}{18 \div 2} = \frac{6}{9}$$

Sara:

I divided both the numerator and denominator by the GCF of 12 and got a quotient of $\frac{2}{3}$.

$$\frac{24}{36} = \frac{24 \div 12}{36 \div 12} = \frac{2}{3}$$

Clifton:

I wrote the prime factorization of the numerator and denominator, and then I divided out the common prime factors.

$$\frac{24}{36} = \frac{2 \times 2 \times 2 \times 3}{2 \times 2 \times 3 \times 3} = \frac{2}{3}$$

10. Simplify each fraction using prime factorization.

    a. $\frac{15}{20}$ **b.** $\frac{8}{24}$

    c. $\frac{24}{28}$ **d.** $\frac{20}{24}$

    e. $\frac{24}{30}$ **f.** $\frac{8}{15}$

11. Simplify each fraction using the GCF. State the GCF used.

    a. $\frac{24}{28}$ **b.** $\frac{45}{56}$

    c. $\frac{33}{77}$ **d.** $\frac{16}{32}$

    e. $\frac{63}{72}$ **f.** $\frac{72}{99}$

Problem 3 Frac-O

Frac-O is played with two players. The object of the game is to be the first player to arrange five fraction cards on the game board in ascending order. To begin, cut apart the 16 Frac-O fraction cards.

Directions:

1. Shuffle the fraction cards. Deal one card face down on each of the five spaces on each player's game board.

2. Put the remaining cards face down in a pile. Turn the top card over and place it in a discard pile.

3. Each player turns over the five cards on his or her game board. You may NOT change the order of the cards at any point during the game.

4. Players take turns as follows:

   a. The first player takes either the top card from the face down pile or the top card from the discard pile.

   b. The player decides whether to keep the card or put it face up in the discard pile.

   c. If the player keeps the card, he or she must replace one of the five cards on the game board with the card drawn. The replaced card now goes face up on the discard pile.

5. If all the facedown cards are used, then shuffle the discard pile and continue.

6. The winner is the first person to have all five cards in ascending order.

Good Luck!

Be prepared to share your solutions and methods.

3

$\dfrac{3}{5}$	$\dfrac{1}{12}$	$\dfrac{3}{4}$	$\dfrac{1}{5}$
$\dfrac{1}{3}$	$\dfrac{11}{12}$	$\dfrac{4}{7}$	$\dfrac{5}{6}$
$\dfrac{3}{8}$	$\dfrac{1}{4}$	$\dfrac{7}{9}$	$\dfrac{2}{3}$
$\dfrac{4}{9}$	$\dfrac{3}{7}$	$\dfrac{4}{5}$	$\dfrac{5}{8}$

3

3

Frac-O Game Board

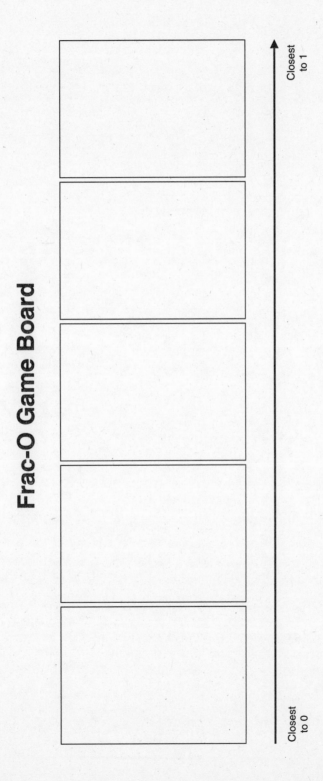

3

TRAIL MIX

3.6 Adding and Subtracting Fractions with Like and Unlike Denominators

Learning Goals

In this lesson, you will:

▶ Write number sentences to represent 1.

▶ Create models to represent addition and subtraction of fractions.

▶ Add and subtract fractions with common denominators.

▶ Add and subtract fractions with unlike denominators.

Key Terms

▶ common denominator

▶ least common denominator (LCD)

It goes by many names in the world. In Germany, it is called Studentenfutter (shtoo-DEN-ten-foot-er) and in Denmark it is called studentenhavre, which, loosely translated, means "student oats." It has even been called gorp! But generally in the United States, this healthy and high energy snack is called trail mix. What types of trail mixes have you had? Do you have a nickname for trail mix? What is usually in the trail mix you eat?

Problem 1 Number Sentences for 1

There are many ways to represent 1.

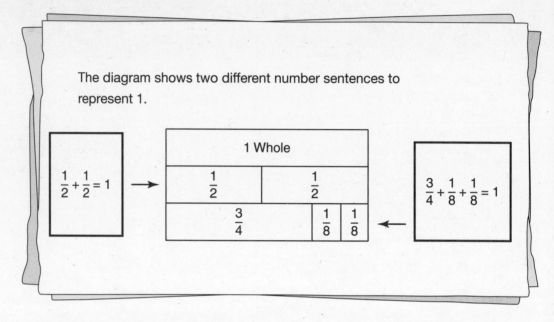

1. Using your fraction strips, write six addition sentences that equal 1. You can use some fractions with the same denominator, but you must use at least one fraction with a different denominator in each of your addition sentences.

Find your fraction strips. You will need them for this lesson!

a. 1 =

b. 1 =

c. 1 =

d. 1 =

e. 1 =

f. 1 =

Two or more fractions have a *common denominator* if the denominators in each fraction are the same. A **common denominator** is a whole number that is a common multiple of the denominators of the fractions. The **least common denominator, LCD,** is the least common multiple of the denominators of two or more fractions.

2. Use your fraction strips and the six addition sentences you wrote in Question 1 to help you write addition sentences with each fraction having a common denominator. Does your new number sentence equal 1? How do you know?

a. 1 =

b. 1 =

c. 1 =

d. 1 =

e. 1 =

f. 1 =

Problem 2 A Trail Trip!

1. The teachers at Riverside Middle School decide to make trail mix for an upcoming field trip to the Natural History Museum. They have decided on three different recipes.

Sweet & Nutty Trail Mix	Popcorn Trail Mix	Fruity Trail Mix
$\frac{2}{3}$ cup almonds	$1\frac{3}{4}$ cups popped popcorn	$\frac{1}{3}$ cup dried cherries
$\frac{1}{2}$ cup raisins	$\frac{2}{3}$ cup honey	$\frac{1}{3}$ cup raisins
$\frac{3}{4}$ cup pumpkin seeds	$\frac{1}{3}$ cup dried cherries	$\frac{5}{8}$ cup walnuts
$\frac{1}{6}$ cup honey	$\frac{1}{8}$ cup pumpkin seeds	$\frac{1}{2}$ cup dried blueberries
	$\frac{3}{4}$ cup chocolate chips	$\frac{2}{3}$ cup banana chips

a. How many cups of raisins are needed to make one batch of each trail mix?

b. Can you determine the total amount of raisins if you put the $\frac{1}{2}$ fraction strip and the $\frac{1}{3}$ fraction strip end to end? Why or why not?

You can use other strips to help you solve the problem from part (a). Consider the fraction strip model and the corresponding fraction sentence.

$\frac{1}{2}$			$\frac{1}{3}$	
$\frac{1}{6}$	$\frac{1}{6}$	$\frac{1}{6}$	$\frac{1}{6}$	$\frac{1}{6}$

$$\begin{array}{r} \frac{1}{2} = \frac{3}{6} \\ + \frac{1}{3} = \frac{2}{6} \\ \hline \frac{5}{6} \end{array}$$

c. What fraction represents the length of $\frac{1}{2}$ and $\frac{1}{3}$ from the model shown?

d. Explain the corresponding fraction sentence.

When fractions do not share a common denominator, they are sometimes called unlike fractions.

2. Write a rule for adding unlike fractions.

3. For each question, write the addition sentence. Then, sketch the fraction strip representation. Finally, write the fraction sentence to calculate the sum and explain your reasoning.

   a. How many total cups of honey are needed to make one batch of all three trail mixes?

   Strips: Fraction Sentence:

   b. How many total cups of dried cherries are needed to make one batch of all three trail mixes?

   Strips: Fraction Sentence:

   c. How many total cups of pumpkin seeds are needed to make one batch of all three trail mixes?

   Strips: Fraction Sentence:

Problem 3   What Is the Difference?

1. You can also use fraction strips to help you determine the difference in a problem. Consider the following question:

   a. How many more cups of pumpkin seeds are used in the Sweet & Nutty Trail Mix than in the Popcorn Trail Mix? Sketch the fraction strip that you think represents the difference.

   b. Write the mathematical sentence that describes the sketch you drew. What operation will you use to calculate the difference?

   c. What is the difference?

2. For each question, write the subtraction sentence. Then, use your fraction strips to model the mathematical sentence. Finally, write the corresponding fraction sentence to determine the difference and explain your reasoning.

a. How many more cups of dried cherries are used for the Popcorn Trail Mix than the Fruity Trail Mix?

Strips: Fraction Sentence:

b. How many more cups of raisins are used for the Sweet & Nutty Trail Mix than the Fruity Trail Mix?

Strips: Fraction Sentence:

c. How many more cups of honey are used in the Popcorn Trail Mix than the Sweet & Nutty Trail Mix?

Strips: Fraction Sentence:

Problem 4   The Rules

You have seen that adding or subtracting unlike fractions is different from adding or subtracting fractions with common denominators. The table describes characteristics of like and unlike denominators and the process for working with both like and unlike denominators.

	Like Denominators	Unlike Denominators
Description of the Whole	Wholes have the same number of parts.	Wholes are evenly divided into different number of parts.
Process for Adding or Subtracting	Add or subtract the numerators to calculate the sum or difference, keeping the denominators the same.	First, write the fractions as equivalent fractions that have the same denominator. It is most efficient to use the least common denominator (LCD). Then, add or subtract the numerators, keeping the common denominator the same.

1. Why is it more efficient to use the least common denominator?

To determine the sum or difference of two fractions, first determine the least common denominator. Then add or subtract, and finally, simplify the result if possible.

$$\frac{5}{6} = \frac{5}{6} \times \frac{(1)}{(1)} = \frac{5}{6}$$

$$-\frac{1}{3} = \frac{1}{3} \times \frac{(2)}{(2)} = \frac{2}{6} \qquad\qquad LCD = \underline{\quad 6 \quad}$$

$$= \frac{3}{6} = \frac{1}{2}$$

2. Determine the least common denominator for each, and then calculate the sum or difference. Finally, simplify the result, if possible.

a.
$$\frac{1}{6} = \frac{1}{6} \times \frac{()}{()} = \frac{()}{()}$$
$$+\frac{2}{5} = \frac{2}{5} \times \frac{()}{()} = \frac{()}{()}$$
$$= \frac{()}{()}$$

LCD = _____

b. $\frac{11}{12} - \frac{2}{3}$

c. $\frac{1}{12} + \frac{1}{4}$

d. $\frac{13}{15} - \frac{2}{3}$

e. $\frac{1}{8} + \frac{2}{5}$

f. $\frac{7}{11} + \frac{2}{5}$

g. $\frac{17}{18} - \frac{2}{3}$

3. How did you determine each LCD?

4. Casey's group added $\frac{2}{3}$ and $\frac{1}{4}$ and got a sum of $\frac{11}{12}$. Casey wondered how adding thirds and fourths could result in twelfths. Is the group correct?

   Explain the process to Casey.

Be prepared to share your solutions and methods.

3.7 TRAIL MIX EXTRAVAGANZA

Improper Fractions and Mixed Numbers

Have you ever gone to a bakery? Almost anyone who has lived near a bakery seems to have loved the wonderful smell of baking bread, biscuits, and rolls in the early morning hours. Ordinarily, most baking requires a lot of different amounts of ingredients. Do you think bakers use fractions for baking?

Problem 1   Fractions Greater Than 1

1. A recipe calls for $3\frac{1}{8}$ cups of flour, $1\frac{1}{2}$ cups of salt, and $\frac{1}{8}$ cup of vegetable oil. What do you notice about the fractions shown?

A number such as $3\frac{1}{8}$ is called a **mixed number** because it has a whole number part, the 3, and a fraction part, the $\frac{1}{8}$.

Mixed Number	Fraction Sentence	Improper Fraction
$3\frac{1}{8}$	$= \ 1 + 1 + 1 + \frac{1}{8}$	
	$= \ \frac{8}{8} + \frac{8}{8} + \frac{8}{8} + \frac{1}{8} \quad =$	$\frac{25}{8}$

An **improper fraction** is a fraction whose numerator is greater than the denominator.

2. Complete the table shown by writing a mixed number, a fraction sentence, or an improper fraction.

Mixed Number	Fraction Sentence	Improper Fraction
	$\frac{4}{4} + \frac{4}{4} + \frac{1}{4}$	
		$\frac{17}{5}$
$2\frac{2}{3}$		
		$\frac{29}{8}$
	$\frac{7}{7} + \frac{7}{7} + \frac{7}{7} + \frac{7}{7} + \frac{3}{7}$	
		$\frac{19}{6}$
$5\frac{1}{2}$		

Dontrell noticed a strategy for changing an improper fraction to a mixed number. He said, "If I divide the denominator into the numerator, I get the whole number part of the mixed number. Then, the remainder is the numerator of the fractional part of the mixed number. Finally, I keep the same denominator."

He demonstrated his thinking in the calculation shown.

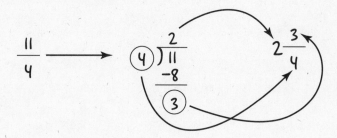

3. Explain why Dontrell's strategy is correct.

4. Write each improper fraction as a mixed number. If necessary, simplify the fractional part of the mixed number.

a. $\frac{25}{6}$

b. $\frac{22}{9}$

c. $\frac{42}{5}$

d. $\frac{34}{7}$

e. $\frac{34}{8}$

f. $\frac{84}{10}$

g. $\frac{45}{4}$

h. $\frac{28}{3}$

5. Determine the mixed number and improper fraction for each point plotted on the number line.

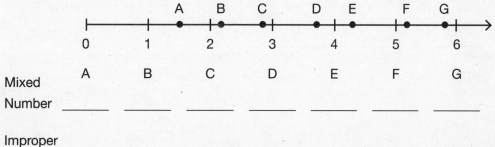

	A	B	C	D	E	F	G
Mixed Number	_____	_____	_____	_____	_____	_____	_____
Improper Fraction	_____	_____	_____	_____	_____	_____	_____

6. Estimate each sum using what you know about benchmark fractions. Then, calculate the sum. Write each sum as a mixed number in simplest terms.

Estimating first is a good habit to get into.

a. $\frac{3}{4} + \frac{2}{3}$

b. $\frac{7}{8} + \frac{5}{6}$

c. $\frac{7}{9} + \frac{5}{6}$

d. $\frac{3}{5} + \frac{7}{10}$

e. $\frac{5}{8} + \frac{2}{3}$

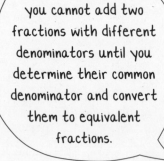

Don't forget that you cannot add two fractions with different denominators until you determine their common denominator and convert them to equivalent fractions.

f. $\frac{1}{4} + \frac{5}{6}$

Dontrell wondered if he could use his method backward to change a mixed number to an improper fraction. He wrote the steps shown to convert $2\frac{3}{5}$ and $3\frac{4}{7}$ to improper fractions.

$$2\frac{3}{5} = \frac{10}{5} + \frac{3}{5} = \frac{13}{5}$$

$$3\frac{4}{7} = \frac{21}{7} + \frac{4}{7} = \frac{25}{7}$$

Dontrell explained, "So, if I multiply the whole number by the denominator and then add the numerator of the fraction, I get the numerator of the improper fraction. Finally, I need to keep the denominator the same to complete an improper fraction."

7. Draw a model to verify Dontrell's reasoning.

8. Write each mixed number as an improper fraction. If necessary, simplify the improper fractions.

    a. $3\frac{2}{5}$

                                              b. $4\frac{5}{8}$

    c. $2\frac{3}{7}$

                                              d. $5\frac{2}{5}$

    e. $8\frac{1}{3}$

                                              f. $6\frac{2}{9}$

Problem 2 Add and Subtract Mixed Numbers

1. Ms. Hadley decided to create a new trail mix recipe with a tropical flavor that would make more individual servings. She named it Hawaiian Trail Mix Extravaganza. The recipe is shown.

Hawaiian Trail Mix Extravaganza

$3\frac{3}{8}$ cups of macadamia nuts $2\frac{1}{3}$ cups of almonds

$2\frac{1}{4}$ cups of pumpkin seeds $1\frac{2}{3}$ cups of sunflower seeds

$3\frac{3}{8}$ cups of dried cherries $2\frac{5}{6}$ cups of honey

$4\frac{5}{8}$ cups of popped popcorn $4\frac{1}{2}$ cups of raisins

$1\frac{2}{3}$ cups of corn syrup $2\frac{3}{4}$ cups of granola

a. Draw a diagram to represent the amount of pumpkin seeds in the mix. Then, draw a diagram to represent the amount of sunflower seeds in the mix.

b. How many full cups of seeds (both pumpkin and sunflower) does the recipe require?

c. What fractional parts of a cup of seeds (both pumpkin and sunflower) does the recipe require?

d. Add the fractions and simplify if possible.

e. How many total cups of pumpkin and sunflower seeds are in the mix?

2. Determine each amount.

a. the total amount of nuts (macadamia nuts and almonds) in the recipe

b. the total amount of fruit (dried cherries and raisins) in the recipe

c. the total amount of corn syrup and honey

d. the total amount of popcorn and granola

Problem 3 What is the Difference?

Kaye and Lakea each determined that the Hawaiian Trail Mix Extravaganza recipe uses $1\frac{7}{8}$ more popcorn than granola.

1. Kaye and Lakea each set up the same subtraction problem, but calculated the solutions differently. Analyze each method.

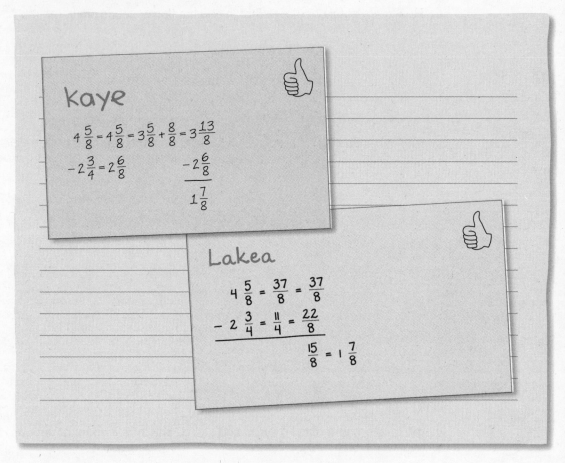

Kaye

$4\frac{5}{8} = 4\frac{5}{8} = 3\frac{5}{8} + \frac{8}{8} = 3\frac{13}{8}$

$-2\frac{3}{4} = 2\frac{6}{8} \qquad -2\frac{6}{8}$

$\qquad\qquad\qquad\qquad 1\frac{7}{8}$

Lakea

$4\frac{5}{8} = \frac{37}{8} = \frac{37}{8}$

$-2\frac{3}{4} = \frac{11}{4} = \frac{22}{8}$

$\qquad\qquad\quad \frac{15}{8} = 1\frac{7}{8}$

a. Describe the calculations performed by Kaye and Lakea.

b. Which method do you prefer? Explain your reasoning.

2. Complete each mixed number so it is equivalent to the one given.

a. $8\frac{2}{3} = 7\frac{(\quad)}{3}$

b. $9\frac{4}{5} = 8\frac{(\quad)}{5}$

c. $3\frac{1}{3} = 2\frac{(\quad)}{3}$

d. $4\frac{3}{7} = (\quad)\frac{(\quad)}{7}$

e. $6\frac{5}{9} = 5\frac{14}{(\quad)}$

f. $3\frac{1}{4} = 2\frac{(\quad)}{4}$

3. Solve each problem shown. Show the work you did to calculate the difference.

a. How many more cups of pumpkin seeds are needed than cups of sunflower seeds to make the Hawaiian Trail Mix Extravaganza?

b. How many more cups of raisins are used than cups of granola?

c. How many more cups of honey are used than cups of corn syrup?

4. Adam is subtracting the following two mixed numbers: $3\frac{5}{8}$ from $5\frac{1}{8}$. His work is shown.

$$4\not{5}\,\frac{\not{1}^{11}}{8}$$
$$-\;3\frac{5}{8}$$
$$\overline{\quad 1\frac{6}{8} = 1\frac{3}{4}\quad}$$

Is Adam correct? If not, explain to him what he did incorrectly and how he can correct his mistake.

Be prepared to share your solutions and methods.

PIZZAS BY THE SLICE— OR THE RECTANGLE!

3.8

Parts of Parts

Learning Goals

In this lesson, you will:

▶ Create models to represent parts of parts.

▶ Analyze various methods for multiplying fractions.

▶ Multiply fractions.

Chances are that if you walk down any major street in New York City, you'll run into a pizza parlor selling pizzas by the slice. In fact, the first pizza parlor that opened in the United States can be found in New York's Little Italy. Back in 1905, Gennaro Lombardi originally opened up a grocery store, but decided to begin making pizzas to offer to his customer. Today, Lombardi's is still a success. How do you think pizzas and fractions interact? Why do you think pizza parlors give customers the option of buying pizza by the slice or as a whole pie?

Problem 1   Multiplying Fractions

The sixth-grade students are making extra-large rectangular pizzas to sell at home basketball games. One extra-large pizza costs $24, but customers can buy part of extra-large pizzas.

1. Create a model to determine the amount of pizza each person bought. Then, write your answer below your model. Make sure your answer is in simplest form. Finally, determine how much each person paid.

   a. Christine bought $\frac{1}{4}$ of $\frac{1}{2}$ of a pizza. How much pizza did Christine buy? How much did she pay?

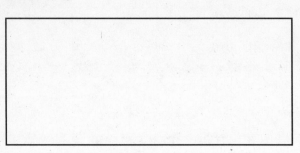

   b. Antoine bought $\frac{3}{4}$ of $\frac{1}{2}$ of a pizza. How much pizza did Antoine buy? How much did he pay?

   c. Paul bought $\frac{2}{3}$ of $\frac{1}{4}$ of a pizza. How much pizza did Paul buy? How much did he pay?

d. Katy bought $\frac{1}{3}$ of $\frac{1}{2}$ of a pizza. How much pizza did Katy buy? How much did she pay?

e. Sifi bought $\frac{2}{3}$ of $\frac{3}{4}$ of a pizza. How much pizza did Sifi buy? How much did she pay?

f. Gary bought $\frac{1}{2}$ of $\frac{2}{3}$ of a pizza. How much pizza did Gary buy? How much did he pay?

The expression $\frac{1}{2}$ of $\frac{2}{3}$ means to multiply $\frac{1}{2}$ and $\frac{1}{3}$. Any time you see two numbers or fractions with the word "of" between them, remember that you must multiply the numbers or fractions together to get a product. When you multiply a fraction by a fraction, you are calculating a part of a part. You can represent the product of two fractions using an area model.

Let's consider an area model for $\frac{1}{4} \times \frac{1}{2}$ and what it represents.

To represent $\frac{1}{4}$ along one side of the square, divide the square into four equal parts along the vertical line. Then shade $\frac{1}{4}$.

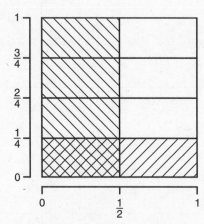

To represent $\frac{1}{2}$ along the other side, divide the square along the horizontal line into two equal parts. Then, shade $\frac{1}{2}$.

$$\frac{1}{4} \times \frac{1}{2} = \frac{1}{8}$$

The area of the overlapping region is the product of the fractions.

Can you set up the model to show $\frac{1}{4}$ along the horizontal line and the $\frac{1}{2}$ along the vertical line?

2. Represent each product using an area model. Then, state the product.

a. $\frac{3}{4} \times \frac{1}{2}$

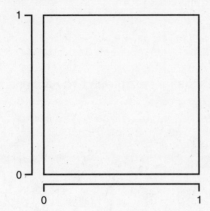

b. $\frac{2}{3} \times \frac{3}{4}$

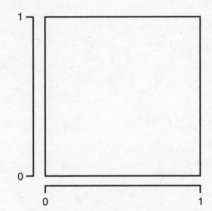

c. $\frac{1}{2} \times \frac{2}{3}$

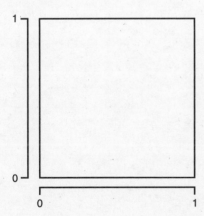

3. Review the products calculated in Questions 1 and 2. Write a rule to calculate the product of two fractions.

4. Let's explore several correct methods for multiplying two fractions.

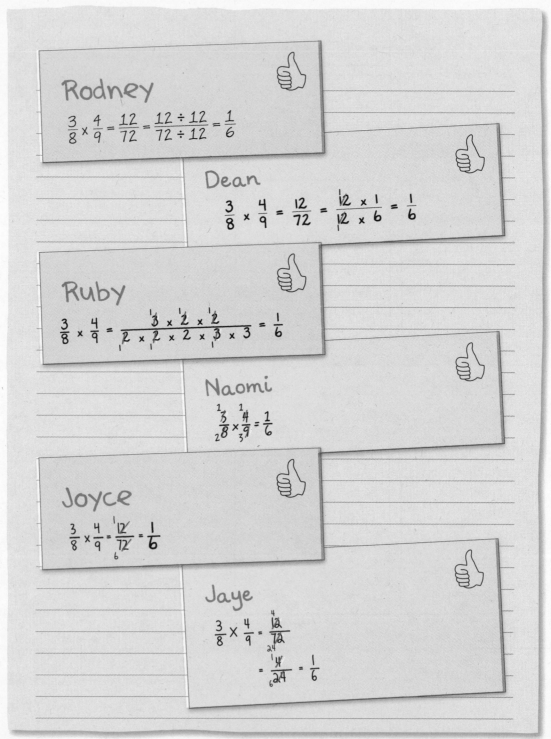

Rodney

$\frac{3}{8} \times \frac{4}{9} = \frac{12}{72} = \frac{12 \div 12}{72 \div 12} = \frac{1}{6}$

Dean

$\frac{3}{8} \times \frac{4}{9} = \frac{12}{72} = \frac{\cancel{12} \times 1}{\cancel{12} \times 6} = \frac{1}{6}$

Ruby

$\frac{3}{8} \times \frac{4}{9} = \frac{\cancel{3}^1 \times \cancel{2}^1 \times \cancel{2}^1}{\cancel{2}_1 \times \cancel{2}_1 \times 2 \times \cancel{3}_1 \times 3} = \frac{1}{6}$

Naomi

$\frac{\cancel{3}^1}{\cancel{8}_2} \times \frac{\cancel{4}^1}{\cancel{9}_3} = \frac{1}{6}$

Joyce

$\frac{3}{8} \times \frac{4}{9} = \frac{\cancel{12}^1}{\cancel{72}_6} = \frac{1}{6}$

Jaye

$\frac{3}{8} \times \frac{4}{9} = \frac{\cancel{12}^4}{\cancel{72}_{24}}$

$= \frac{\cancel{4}^1}{\cancel{24}_6} = \frac{1}{6}$

a. How are the methods alike?

b. How are the methods different?

c. Which method do you prefer? Why?

5. Angel noticed that when he multiplies two fractions, the product is less than each of the two fractions he multiplied. Ashton didn't think Angel's products were correct because he learned that when multiplying, the product gets bigger. Who is correct? What can you tell the other person so that he can correct his misinterpretation? Explain your reasoning.

6. Estimate each product. Use what you know about benchmark fractions and estimation to explain your reasoning.

a. $\frac{1}{2} \times 3\frac{11}{12}$

b. $1\frac{1}{2} \times 4\frac{1}{6}$

c. $3\frac{1}{2} \times 2\frac{9}{10}$

d. $2\frac{1}{2} \times \frac{5}{9}$

Problem 2   Hawaiian Trail Mix For Everyone!

Hawaiian Trail Mix Extravaganza

$3\frac{3}{8}$ cups of macadamia nuts $2\frac{1}{3}$ cups of almonds

$2\frac{1}{4}$ cups of pumpkin seeds $1\frac{1}{3}$ cups of sunflower seeds

$3\frac{3}{8}$ cups of dried cherries $2\frac{5}{6}$ cups of honey

$4\frac{5}{8}$ cups of popped popcorn $4\frac{1}{2}$ cups of raisins

$1\frac{2}{3}$ cups of corn syrup $2\frac{3}{4}$ cups of granola

Feeds 12 People

Remember Ms. Hadley's Hawaiian Trail Mix Extravaganza? It was quite a success, and some teachers are making more batches. Calculate how many cups are needed to make multiple batches. Show your work for each.

1. The sixth-grade teachers want to make three batches of Hawaiian Trail Mix Extravaganza.

   a. How many cups of almonds must they use?

   b. How many cups of popped popcorn do they need?

   c. How many cups of raisins should they buy?

2. Let's look at two methods for multiplying fractions.

Dawson is thinking about how to determine $3\frac{2}{3} \times 2\frac{1}{4}$. He is trying to remember a model he used when he learned how to multiply whole numbers.

He multiplied 25×34 first to remember the method, and then applied the same strategy to multiply the mixed numbers.

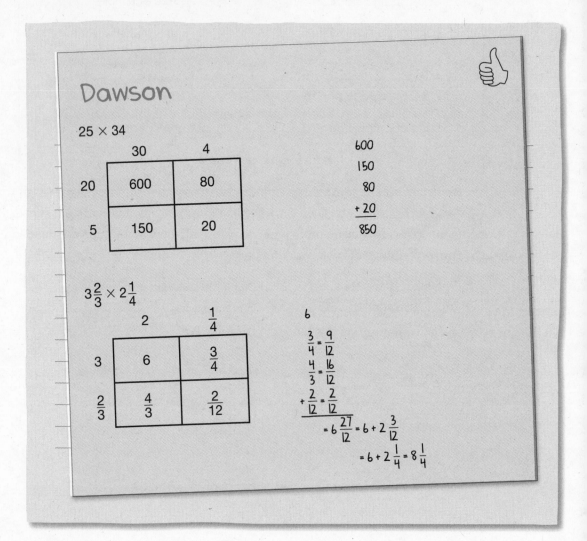

a. Describe the model Dawson used to calculated the product of two mixed numbers.

b. Lezlee's correct method is shown. Describe how she calculated the product of two mixed numbers.

Lezlee

$$3\frac{2}{3} \times 2\frac{1}{4}$$
$$\frac{11}{3} \times \frac{9}{4} = \frac{33}{4}$$
$$= 8\frac{1}{4}$$

c. Which method do you prefer? Why?

3. Calculate each product. Show your work. Do not leave your answer as an improper fraction.

a. $2\frac{1}{2} \times 3\frac{2}{5}$

b. $4\frac{1}{5} \times 2\frac{1}{7}$

c. $2\frac{2}{3} \times 4\frac{1}{4}$

d. $1\frac{3}{4} \times 2\frac{2}{5}$

e. $1\frac{1}{2} \times \frac{5}{6}$

f. $4\frac{1}{2} \times \frac{1}{6}$

g. $3\frac{3}{4} \times 2$

h. $2\frac{5}{8} \times 3$

Be prepared to share your solutions and methods.

In this lesson, you will learn about dividing fractions. Take a look at the model shown:

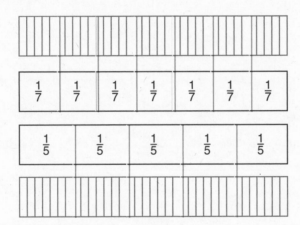

You can use this model to divide certain fractions. For example, to determine $\frac{3}{7} \div \frac{3}{5}$, count the number of sections in the top bar from left to right until you reach the right edge of $\frac{3}{7}$. There are 15 equal sections. Now count the number of sections in the bottom bar from left to right until you reach the right edge of $\frac{3}{5}$. There are 21 equal sections. This means that your answer is $\frac{15}{21}$, or $\frac{5}{7}$.

How does this work? Maybe when you have completed this lesson you can figure it out.

Problem 1   Division: Please Explain Yourself!

Division of whole numbers means to ask how many groups of a certain size are contained in a number.

The expression 12 ÷ 3 means you are trying to determine how many groups of 3 are in 12. A physical model and number line model are shown.

Physical Model   **Number Line Model**

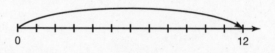

1 group of 12   1 group of 12

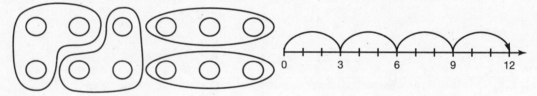

4 groups of 3   4 groups of 3

$$12 \div 3 = 4$$

There are 4 groups of 3 in 12.

When you divide with fractions, you are asking the same question.

The expression $2 \div \frac{1}{2}$ is asking how many halves are in 2.

Physical Model

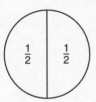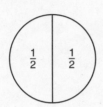

Number Line Model

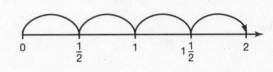

There are four $\frac{1}{2}$ parts in 2, so $2 \div \frac{1}{2} = 4$.

The expression $\frac{1}{2} \div 2$ is asking how many groups of 2 are in $\frac{1}{2}$.

Physical Model

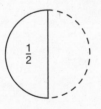

Number Line Model

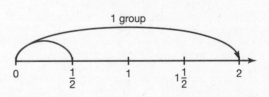

There is $\frac{1}{4}$ of a group of 2 in $\frac{1}{2}$, so $\frac{1}{2} \div 2 = \frac{1}{4}$.

How do the models compare?

1. Write a sentence to describe what the division expression is asking. Then, draw a diagram to represent the division problem. Finally, calculate the quotient, and write a sentence to describe your answer. Use your fraction strips to help you draw the model.

   a. $\frac{3}{4} \div \frac{1}{4}$

   b. $\frac{3}{2} \div \frac{1}{4}$

   c. $3 \div \frac{3}{4}$

d. $\frac{1}{2} \div \frac{1}{8}$

e. $\frac{3}{4} \div \frac{1}{8}$

2. How can you check each of your answers in Question 1 to make sure you were correct? Explain your reasoning.

3. Jamilla is throwing a small party. She has 4 pizzas and decides that everyone at her party should receive a serving size that is $\frac{3}{5}$ of a pizza. Jamilla says she has $6\frac{2}{3}$ servings, but Devon says she has $6\frac{2}{5}$ servings. Draw a diagram of the situation, and solve for the quotient to determine who is correct. Then explain why one person is not correct.

4. Calculate each product. Show your work.

    a. $\frac{1}{3} \times \frac{3}{1}$ **b.** $\frac{2}{3} \times \frac{3}{2}$

    c. $13 \times \frac{1}{13}$ **d.** $\frac{7}{8} \times \frac{8}{7}$

    e. $\frac{1}{5} \times \frac{5}{1}$ **f.** $\frac{6}{9} \times \frac{9}{6}$

5. What do you notice about each product in Question 4?

When you reverse the numbers in the numerator and denominator of a fraction, you form a new fraction called the *reciprocal*. The **reciprocal** of a number is also known as the *multiplicative inverse* of the number. The **multiplicative inverse** of a number $\frac{a}{b}$ is the number $\frac{b}{a}$, where a and b are nonzero numbers. The product of any nonzero number and its multiplicative inverse is 1. The fractions you multiplied in Question 4 are reciprocals of each other.

The **Multiplicative Inverse Property** states: $\frac{a}{b} \times \frac{b}{a} = 1$, where a and b are nonzero numbers.

6. Which number is its own reciprocal?

7. Which number has no reciprocal? Explain your reasoning.

8. Alexa wrote the reciprocal of the mixed number incorrectly. Explain why she is incorrect and provide the correct reciprocal.

Alexa

Given $3\frac{8}{5}$

The reciprocal is $3\frac{5}{8}$.

Karen said, "I wish everything could be as easy as dividing by 1." She tried her "dividing by 1" method on the division of fraction problem.

$$\frac{5}{8} \div \frac{3}{4}$$

"If I can turn the divisor of $\frac{3}{4}$ into one, then the problem can be solved. I can multiply both fractions by the reciprocal of $\frac{3}{4}$, which is $\frac{4}{3}$, to create 1."

9. Analyze Karen's method for dividing fractions. Describe the steps in the dashed circles.

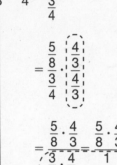

$$\frac{5}{8} \div \frac{3}{4} = \frac{\frac{5}{8}}{\frac{3}{4}}$$

Division is rewritten as a fraction.

$$= \frac{\frac{5}{8} \cdot \frac{4}{3}}{\frac{3}{4} \cdot \frac{4}{3}}$$

_____

$$= \frac{\frac{5}{8} \cdot \frac{4}{3}}{\frac{3}{4} \cdot \frac{4}{3}} = \frac{\frac{5}{8} \cdot \frac{4}{3}}{1}$$

_____

$$= \frac{5}{8} \cdot \frac{4}{3} = \frac{20}{24} = \frac{5}{6}$$

I see a shortcut! I can change ÷ to · if I invert and multiply the divisor.

10. Write a rule based on Karen's method that you can use to calculate the quotient in the division of fraction problem.

11. Calculate each quotient. Show your work. Make sure your answer is in simplest form and make certain none of your answers are improper fractions.

a. $\frac{3}{4} \div \frac{1}{3}$

b. $\frac{3}{8} \div \frac{1}{4}$

c. $\frac{5}{6} \div \frac{2}{3}$

d. $\frac{7}{8} \div \frac{3}{4}$

e. $\frac{11}{12} \div \frac{2}{3}$

f. $\frac{9}{10} \div \frac{3}{5}$

12. Draw a diagram for each problem. Then, match the expression with each problem. Finally, solve the problem.

Number Sentences
$\frac{5}{8} \div 2 \qquad \frac{5}{8} \div \frac{1}{4} \qquad \frac{5}{8} \times \frac{1}{2} \qquad \frac{5}{8} \times \frac{1}{4}$

a. Georgianne has $\frac{5}{8}$ cups of raisins. Each batch of trail mix requires $\frac{1}{4}$ cup of raisins. How many batches of trail mix can she make?

b. Georgianne has $\frac{5}{8}$ of a batch of trail mix. She plans to share the trail mix equally with her friend Jackie. How much of the batch will each receive?

c. Georgianne has to travel $\frac{5}{8}$ of a mile to the store. She can walk $\frac{1}{4}$ of a mile in an hour. How many hours will it take her to travel to the store?

d. Georgianne has to travel $\frac{5}{8}$ of a mile. She is going to bike halfway and skate halfway. How far will she bike?

13. Draw a diagram for each problem situation. Then, write the appropriate number sentence.

a. How many students can be served with 4 cups of trail mix if each student gets $\frac{1}{2}$ of a cup of trail mix?

b. How many $\frac{1}{4}$-cup servings of trail mix can you make with 4 cups?

c. How many $\frac{1}{3}$-cup trail mix servings can you make with 4 cups?

d. Do you notice a pattern? Explain your reasoning.

14. You have 4 cups of trail mix. If each student receives:

    a. $\frac{2}{3}$ cup, how many students are there?

    b. $\frac{2}{5}$ cup, how many students are there?

    c. $\frac{4}{5}$ cup, how many students are there?

    d. $\frac{4}{7}$ cup, how many students are there?

15. What pattern do you notice? Explain your reasoning.

16. How many students are there if:

    a. you have $\frac{1}{2}$ cup of trail mix and each student gets $\frac{1}{4}$ cup?

    b. you have $\frac{1}{3}$ cup of trail mix and each student gets $\frac{1}{6}$ cup?

    c. you have $\frac{2}{3}$ cup of trail mix and each student gets $\frac{1}{6}$ cup?

    d. you have $\frac{3}{5}$ cup of trail mix and each student gets $\frac{1}{10}$ cup?

    e. you have $\frac{2}{3}$ cup of trail mix and each student gets $\frac{2}{9}$ cup?

    f. you have $\frac{2}{3}$ cup of trail mix and each student gets $\frac{3}{9}$ cup?

17. What pattern do you notice in Question 16? Explain your reasoning.

Talk the Talk

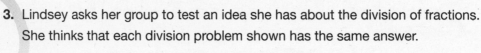

1. How is the quotient of $12 \div \frac{1}{3}$ related to the quotient of $12 \div \frac{2}{3}$? Explain your reasoning.

2. Determine the quotient for each. Then, describe any patterns that you notice.

$6 \div \frac{1}{2}$ $\qquad$ $6 \div \frac{1}{4}$ $\qquad$ $6 \div \frac{1}{8}$ $\qquad$ $6 \div \frac{1}{16}$

3. Lindsey asks her group to test an idea she has about the division of fractions. She thinks that each division problem shown has the same answer.

$8 \div 6$

$\frac{8}{9} \div \frac{6}{9}$

$\frac{8}{5} \div \frac{6}{5}$

$\frac{8}{11} \div \frac{6}{11}$

$\frac{8}{3} \div \frac{6}{3}$

Is Lindsey correct? Explain why or why not.

Be prepared to share your solutions and methods.

3.10 DIVIDE YOUR TIME WELL, AND YOUR TRAIL MIX, AND YOUR . . .

Mixed Number Division

Learning Goals

In this lesson, you will:

▶ Determine how many groups of a certain size are in a number.

▶ Create a representation for division problems involving mixed numbers.

▶ Divide fractions involving mixed numbers.

Gosh! You go to school every day and you probably get homework in most of your classes. Then, you might have practice for band, or for sports. Then, you probably have chores to do like take out the trash or do the dishes—or even clean your room! Oh—and then you have to update your status on your personal web page, and send emails to friends, or chat with others online. So, when do you find time to relax? Chances are that if you have time to relax, then you have divided your time well.

Adults and businesses are no different. Typically, your teachers need to divide their teaching time into roll call, lecture time, discussion, and practice for multiple classes. Businesses usually divide money for a budget, and they need to divide the workload among employees. What other occupations need to divide money or time well? How do you end up dividing your time so that you have time to relax?

Problem 1   Making Bags of Trail Mix

Let's consider how to make a bag of trail mix that is greater than 1 pound.

If you have $5\frac{2}{3}$ pounds of trail mix, how many bags can you make so that each bag contains $1\frac{5}{6}$ pounds?

Analyze each student method.

Carla's Method:

I drew a model for $5\frac{2}{3}$.

How did Carla know she needed to divide her model into $\frac{1}{6}$'s?

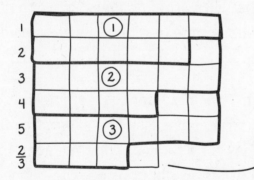

I knew that I needed $1\frac{5}{6}$ groups, so I divided my model to show $\frac{1}{6}$'s. Because $1\frac{5}{6} = \frac{11}{6}$, I then marked off groups of $\frac{11}{6}$.

3 groups of $\frac{11}{6}$

and one $\frac{1}{6}$ part left over.

The remaining $\frac{1}{6}$ part is actually $\frac{1}{11}$ of a group.
So, I can make $3\frac{1}{11}$ bags of trail mix.

Karen's Method:

I wrote a division sentence, and then converted both mixed numbers to improper fractions.

$$5\frac{2}{3} \div 1\frac{5}{6} = \frac{17}{3} \div \frac{11}{6}$$
$$= \frac{17}{3} \cdot \frac{6}{11} = \frac{34}{11}$$
$$= 3\frac{1}{11}$$

So, I can make $3\frac{1}{11}$ bags of trail mix.

1. Karen converted the mixed numbers to improper fractions. How did Carla represent this same step?

2. Describe how Karen changed from division to multiplication.

Problem 2 How Many?

Solve each problem. Show your work and be sure to label your answer.

1. The cook in the school cafeteria made $47\frac{1}{2}$ cups of mashed potatoes. If there are $1\frac{1}{4}$ cups of mashed potatoes in a serving, how many servings did she make?

2. Ashley had $18\frac{1}{3}$ feet of ribbon. She cut it into 6 equal lengths. How long is each piece of ribbon?

3. Nicole bought $10\frac{5}{8}$ pounds of walnuts. The cookie recipe she is using calls for $1\frac{1}{4}$ cups of walnuts. How many batches can she make?

4. The students in Mr. Rivera's shop class volunteered to make doll houses for the school fundraiser. The blueprints call for the side pieces of the dollhouse to be $12\frac{1}{4}$ inches long.

   a. If Mr. Rivera has 6 boards that are 98 inches long, how many side pieces can be cut?

   b. If the blueprint for the dollhouse is $\frac{1}{4}$ the actual size, how long is the side piece represented on the blueprint?

5. One of the most beautiful hiking trails in the United States is Glacier Gorge in Rocky Mountains National Park. The hiking trail through Glacier Gorge is $9\frac{3}{5}$ miles round trip.

   a. If you hike $1\frac{3}{5}$ miles an hour, how many hours will the round trip take?

   b. If you need to rest every $\frac{1}{2}$ mile, how many rest stops will you need?

   c. If you mountain bike the trail, you can complete the trail in $3\frac{1}{5}$ hours. What is the average number of miles per hour you will travel on your bike?

6. In the 6th-grade yearbook, each page has 11 inches of vertical space.

a. If each photo is $2\frac{1}{2}$ inches long, how many photos can you stack?

$2\frac{1}{2} = \frac{2}{5} \times \frac{11}{1} = \frac{22}{5} = 4\frac{2}{5}$ <u>photos you</u> can stack

b. The width of each page in the yearbook is $8\frac{1}{2}$ inches. If each photo is $2\frac{1}{2}$ inches wide, how many photos will fit across the page?

c. How many total pictures will fit on 1 yearbook page?

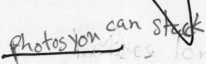

7. The school cafeteria buys large boxes of raisins that weigh $19\frac{1}{2}$ ounces. How many servings can they make if each serving is:

a. $1\frac{1}{2}$ oz?

b. $\frac{3}{4}$ oz?

c. 3 oz?

Talk the Talk

1. Explain how to divide any two fractions including mixed numbers.

2. Estimate each quotient first, and then calculate the quotient.

    a. $8\frac{3}{4} \div \frac{1}{2}$

    b. $8\frac{3}{4} \div 2$

    c. $8\frac{3}{4} \div 3\frac{1}{2}$

    d. $8\frac{3}{4} \div 9\frac{1}{2}$

Estimating first really helps me think about my answer and check my work.

3. Notice that each dividend in Question 2 was the same. As the divisor increased, what happened to your quotient?

Be prepared to share your solutions and methods.

Chapter 3 Summary

Key Terms		Properties

Key Terms

- ► fraction (3.1)
- ► numerator (3.1)
- ► denominator (3.1)
- ► unit fraction (3.3)
- ► equivalent fractions (3.3)
- ► benchmark fractions (3.4)
- ► inequality (3.4)
- ► simplest form (3.5)
- ► common denominator (3.6)
- ► least common denominator (LCD) (3.6)
- ► mixed number (3.7)
- ► improper fraction (3.7)
- ► reciprocal (3.9)
- ► multiplicative inverse (3.9)

Properties

- ► Multiplicative Identity Property (3.5)
- ► Multiplicative Inverse Property (3.9)

3

3.1 Dividing a Whole into Fractional Parts

A fraction represents a part of a whole object or unit. The numerator represents the number of parts of the whole. The denominator represents how many parts make up the whole.

Example

The flag design shown is made up of 24 square units. Three square units are striped, so $\frac{3}{24}$ of the flag design is striped.

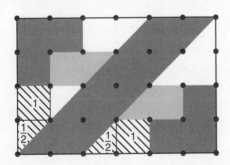

Your brain is divided into two sides. The left side of your brain controls the right side of your body, and the right side of your brain controls the left side of your body. Interestingly, both the left and right side are used when you do math!

3.1 Dividing a Set into Fractional Parts

A fraction can also represent a part of a set.

Example

There are 19 students in your class. Ten of the students are boys. If 10 of the 19 students are boys, there must be 9 girls. So $\frac{9}{19}$ of the students in your class are girls.

3.2 Identifying Parts of Wholes

To determine the value of a fractional part of any whole, set, unit, or group, identify the number of parts in the whole, and then determine the value of the fractional part of the whole.

Example

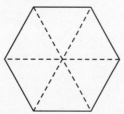

Each triangle shown is $\frac{1}{6}$ of the hexagon.

3.3 Plotting Fractions on a Number Line

A unit fraction is a fraction that has a numerator of 1 and a denominator that is a positive integer. Two fractions are equivalent when they each represent the same part-to-whole relationship. A fraction can be represented on a number line by plotting a point.

Example

Plot $\frac{1}{12}, \frac{1}{6}, \frac{1}{4}, \frac{1}{3}, \frac{1}{2}$.

3.4 Estimating Fractions Using Benchmark Fractions

Benchmark fractions, such as 0, $\frac{1}{2}$, and 1, are common fractions that can be used to estimate the value of other fractions. A fraction is close to 0 when the numerator is very small compared to the denominator. A fraction is close to $\frac{1}{2}$ when the numerator is about half of the denominator. A fraction is close to 1 when the numerator is very close to the denominator.

Example

$\frac{4}{9}$ is less than but close to $\frac{1}{2}$

$\frac{1}{8}$ is close to 0

$\frac{6}{7}$ is less than but close to 1

3.4 Comparing and Ordering Fractions Using Benchmark Fractions

Benchmark fractions can be helpful when comparing and ordering fractions.

Example

To order the fractions $\frac{6}{11}$, $\frac{4}{8}$, $\frac{15}{16}$, $\frac{3}{7}$ and $\frac{1}{5}$ from least to greatest, follow the steps shown.

- $\frac{6}{11} \approx \frac{1}{2}$, but is greater than $\frac{1}{2}$
- $\frac{4}{8} = \frac{1}{2}$
- $\frac{15}{16} \approx 1$
- $\frac{3}{7} \approx \frac{1}{2}$, but is less than $\frac{1}{2}$
- $\frac{1}{5} \approx 0$

So, the fractions in order from least to greatest are $\frac{1}{5}$, $\frac{3}{7}$, $\frac{4}{8}$, $\frac{6}{11}$ and $\frac{15}{16}$.

3.5 Writing Equivalent Fractions

Equivalent fractions are fractions that represent the same part-to-whole relationship. To write an equivalent fraction, multiply or divide the numerator and the denominator by the same number, which is a form of 1. When the numerator and the denominator of a fraction do not share any common factors, you can say that the fraction is in simplest form.

Example

To write $\frac{27}{42}$ in simplest form, divide the fraction by a form of 1.

The GCF of 27 and 42 is 3. So, divide the numerator and denominator by $\frac{3}{3}$.

$\frac{27}{42} \div \frac{3}{3} = \frac{9}{14}$

3.6 Adding and Subtracting Fractions with Like and Unlike Denominators

To add or subtract fractions, first write the fractions with a common denominator. Then, add or subtract the numerators while keeping the denominator the same.

Example

$$\frac{1}{5} + \frac{5}{6} - \frac{1}{2}$$

LCD: 30

$$
\begin{aligned}
\frac{1}{5} &= \frac{6}{30} \\
+\frac{5}{6} &= \frac{25}{30} \\
-\frac{1}{2} &= \frac{15}{30} \\
\hline
&\ \ \frac{16}{30} = \frac{8}{15}
\end{aligned}
$$

3.7 Writing Improper Fractions as Mixed Numbers

To write an improper fraction as a mixed number, divide the numerator by the denominator to determine the whole number part. The remainder then becomes the numerator of the fractional part of the mixed number. The denominator does not change.

Example

To write $\frac{35}{16}$ as a mixed number, follow the steps shown.

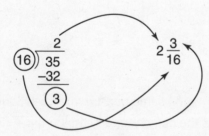

3.7 Writing Mixed Numbers as Improper Fractions

To write a mixed number as an improper fraction, multiply the whole number by the denominator, and then add the numerator of the fraction to get the numerator of the improper fraction. The denominator does not change.

Example

To write $4\frac{7}{9}$ as an improper fraction, follow the steps shown.

$$4\frac{7}{9} = \frac{36}{9} + \frac{7}{9} = \frac{43}{9}$$

3.7 Adding and Subtracting Mixed Numbers

To add or subtract mixed numbers, first write the fractional parts with a common denominator. Then, add or subtract the whole numbers and fractional parts separately. Simplify if necessary.

Example

$$7\frac{1}{8} + 3\frac{6}{7} - 5\frac{1}{2}$$

Add the first two mixed numbers.

$$7\frac{1}{8} = 7\frac{7}{56}$$
$$+3\frac{6}{7} = 3\frac{48}{56}$$
$$\overline{\qquad 10\frac{55}{56}}$$

Then, subtract the third mixed number from the total.

$$10\frac{55}{56} = 10\frac{55}{56}$$
$$-5\frac{1}{2} = \ 5\frac{28}{56}$$
$$\overline{\qquad 5\frac{27}{56}}$$

3.8 Using an Area Model to Represent a Part of a Part

Multiplying two fractions is the same as determining a part of a part. Shade each fraction on a square. The overlapping region represents the product of the fractions.

Example

The area model shown represents $\frac{2}{5} \times \frac{1}{3}$.

The product is $\frac{2}{15}$.

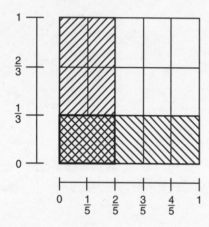

$$\frac{2}{5} \times \frac{1}{3} = \frac{2}{15}$$

3.8 Multiplying Fractions

To calculate the product of two fractions, multiply their numerators, and then multiply their denominators. Simplify the result if necessary. Mixed numbers should be written as improper fractions before multiplying.

Example

$$2\frac{5}{8} \times 3\frac{1}{2}$$

$$2\frac{5}{8} \times 3\frac{1}{2} = \frac{21}{8} \times \frac{7}{2}$$

$$= \frac{147}{16}$$

$$= 9\frac{3}{16}$$

3.9 Dividing Fractions

The reciprocal, or multiplicative inverse, of a number $\frac{a}{b}$ is $\frac{b}{a}$, where a and b are nonzero numbers. The product of any nonzero number and its multiplicative inverse is 1. To calculate the quotient of two fractions, multiply the dividend by the reciprocal of the divisor. Simplify the result if necessary.

Example

$$\frac{6}{7} \div \frac{2}{5}$$

$$\frac{6}{7} \div \frac{2}{5} = \frac{6}{7} \times \frac{5}{2}$$

$$= \frac{30}{14}$$

$$= 2\frac{2}{14}$$

$$= 2\frac{1}{7}$$

3.10 Dividing Mixed Numbers

To divide any two fractions including mixed numbers, first, convert any mixed numbers to improper fractions. Then, change the division problem to multiplication and take the reciprocal of the divisor. Finally, multiply the two fractions and write the answer in simplest form.

Example

$$3\frac{1}{2} \div 8\frac{5}{8} = ?$$

$$\downarrow \qquad \downarrow$$

$$\frac{7}{2} \div \frac{69}{8} \qquad \text{Convert the mixed numbers to improper fractions.}$$

$$\downarrow \qquad \downarrow$$

$$\frac{7}{2} \times \frac{8}{69} \qquad \text{Change the division to multiplication and take the reciprocal of the divisor.}$$

$$\downarrow \qquad \downarrow$$

$$\frac{7}{2} \times \frac{8}{69} = \frac{56}{138} \qquad \text{Multiply the fractions and write the answer in simplest form.}$$

$$= \frac{28}{69}$$

3

4 DECIMALS

A rush hour traffic jam clogs a freeway in Southern California. According to the Census Bureau, the average commute time in Los Angeles was 29.5 minutes per day in 2008.

4

4.1 MINTY FRESH— COINS?

Introduction to Decimals

Learning Goals

In this lesson, you will:

▶ Understand decimals as parts of wholes.

▶ Represent decimals on a hundredths grid.

▶ Write decimals.

▶ Represent decimals on a number line.

Key Term

▶ decimal

Do you ever wonder where the coins you carry come from? In the United States, there are six U.S. Mint facilities. Each facility has a special responsibility for creating money. The U.S. Mints in Philadelphia, Pennsylvania, and Denver, Colorado, are responsible for creating all of the coins in circulation. In fact, in 2009, these two mints created approximately 2,300,000,000 pennies! What do you think the money value is for 2,300,000,000 pennies?

Problem 1   Say Hello to Decimals

Decimals are another way to show parts of a whole. A **decimal** is a number that is written in a system based on multiples of 10. You need to use a decimal point to separate the whole number and the decimal. For example, look at the decimal shown.

0.3

You can use tenths and hundredths grids to show the connection between fractions and decimals. You can also write equivalent forms of fractions and decimals.

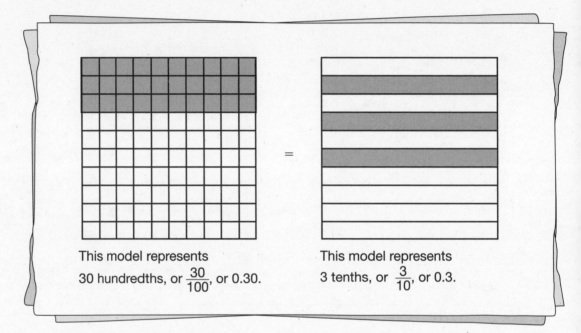

This model represents 30 hundredths, or $\frac{30}{100}$, or 0.30.

This model represents 3 tenths, or $\frac{3}{10}$, or 0.3.

1. Look at the shaded portion in the hundredths grid shown. What is the decimal value of the shaded portion? Explain your reasoning.

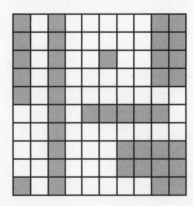

2. Each grid represents 1 whole. Write a decimal that represents each shaded portion in the tenths or hundredths grid.

a.

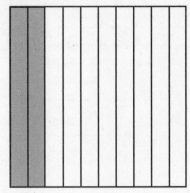

b.

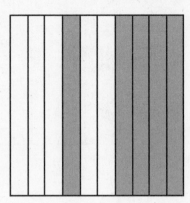

c.

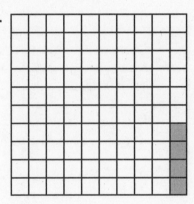

d.

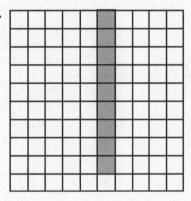

e.

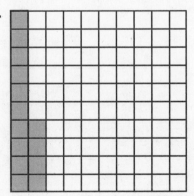

f.

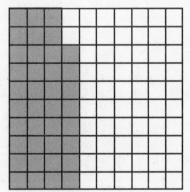

g.

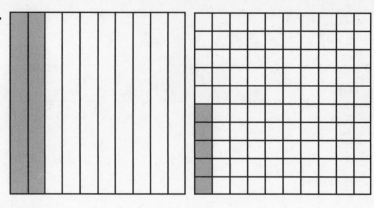

h.

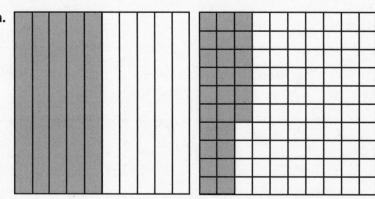

i.

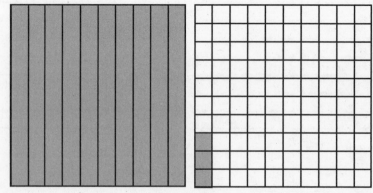

j.

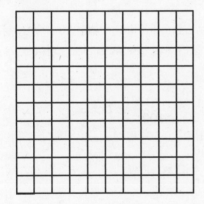

3. Use the hundredths grid to represent each decimal. Then, write an equivalent fraction for each decimal.

a. 0.05

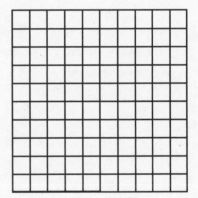

b. 0.75

c. 0.2

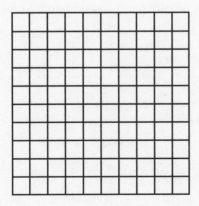

d. 0.22

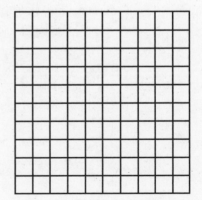

e. 0.36

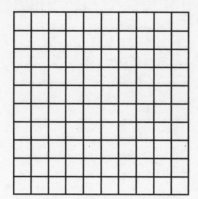

f. 0.4

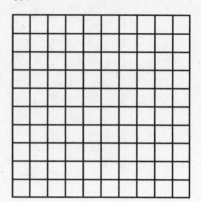

Problem 2   Writing Decimals in Expanded Form and as a Power of Ten

As you learned, you can write decimals using fractions with 10 or power of 10 (such as 100; 1000; 10,000 . . .) in the denominator. For instance, you can use decimals to write amounts of money.

One dime	$= \dfrac{1}{10}$, or $\dfrac{10}{100}$ of a dollar	$= \$0.10$
Five dimes	$= \dfrac{5}{10}$, or $\dfrac{50}{100}$ of a dollar	$= \$0.50$
One penny	$= \dfrac{1}{100}$ of a dollar	$= \$0.01$
Five pennies	$= \dfrac{5}{100}$ of a dollar	$= \$0.05$

For example, you can represent 5 dollars and 87 cents using decimals.

Five dollars	$= \dfrac{500}{100}$ dollars	$= \$5.00$
Eight dimes	$= \dfrac{80}{100}$ of a dollar	$= \$0.80$
+ Seven pennies	$= \dfrac{7}{100}$ of a dollar	$= \$0.07$

$$\frac{587}{100} = 5\frac{87}{100} = \$5.87$$

When you write a decimal, you are writing a representation of a fraction with denominators of 10, 100, 1000, 10,000...

The place value of the number corresponds to the denominator of the equivalent fraction. The value in the place-value chart is the numerator.

Thousands	Hundreds	Tens	Ones	Decimal point	Tenths	Hundredths	Thousandths	Ten-Thousandths
1000	100	10	1	.	0.1	0.01	0.001	0.0001
1000	100	10	1		$\frac{1}{10}$	$\frac{1}{100}$	$\frac{1}{1000}$	$\frac{1}{10,000}$

Each position of a number in a decimal is 10 times the value of the position to its right.

Let's consider the decimal 6702.8451. The decimal can be written in expanded form:

$$6000 + 700 + 2 + \frac{8}{10} + \frac{4}{100} + \frac{5}{1000} + \frac{1}{10,000}$$

and powers of ten:

6 thousands + 7 hundreds + 2 ones + 8 tenths
+ 4 hundredths + 5 thousandths + 1 ten-thousandths.

4

1. Write each decimal in expanded form and as powers of ten.

    a. 47.568 = _____

    _____

    b. 52.479 = _____

    _____

2. Write each as a decimal.

    a. Five hundredths   **b.** Fifty

    c. Five and five tenths   **d.** Five hundred

    e. Six and six hundredths   **f.** Six hundred

    g. Six thousandths   **h.** Sixty and six tenths

    i. Four millionths   **j.** Four and four thousandths

    k. Four tenths   **l.** Four ten-thousandths

3. Write each decimal in words.

   a. 5.360

   b. 0.27

   c. 0.00007

4. Plot a point on the number line to represent each decimal.

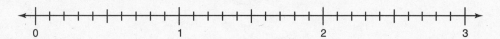

   a. 0.25   **b.** 1.38   **c.** 0.5   **d.** 2.3

   e. 0.56   **f.** 2.92   **g.** 1.75   **h.** 1.1

5. Use the number line to plot the points.

   a. Label the number line, and then plot points to represent 0.3 and 0.4 on the number line.

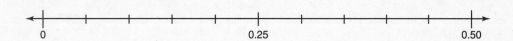

   b. Plot points to represent four decimals between 0.3 and 0.4. Then, label each decimal.

6. Write four decimals between 0.45 and 0.46.

Be prepared to share your solutions and methods.

4

YOU BE THE JUDGE

4.2

Comparing, Ordering, Estimating, and Rounding Decimals

Learning Goals

In this lesson, you will:

▶ Compare decimal representations.

▶ Order decimals.

▶ Estimate sums and differences of decimals.

▶ Estimate decimals to benchmark numbers.

▶ Round decimals.

Key Terms

▶ benchmark decimal

▶ round

Before Melvil Dewey, finding a book in a library was an adventure. It was even more of an adventure to organize the library. Libraries used to be organized by assigning a specific place on a specific bookshelf. However, this process was hard to maintain as more books were added to libraries. So in 1876, Mr. Dewey invented an organizational classification of books using numbers and decimals. There have been 21 revisions to the Dewey Decimal System since then, but it all started with Mr. Dewey and his idea for organizing libraries.

How do you think the Dewey Decimal System adjusts for new modern technologies? Do you think the Dewey Decimal System will survive as more books are being released electronically?

4

Problem 1   Comparing Decimals

1. Look at the decimals shown. First, shade the decimal squares in the hundredths grids for each decimal. Then, compare the decimals by writing >, <, or = in the circles between the two decimals.

a.

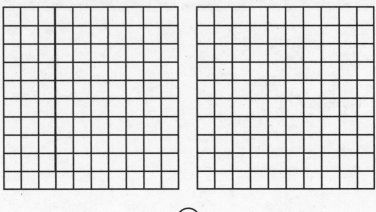

0.39   0.29

b.

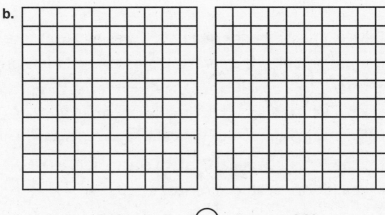

0.03   0.30

c.

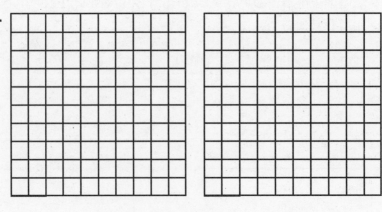

0.2   0.20

d.

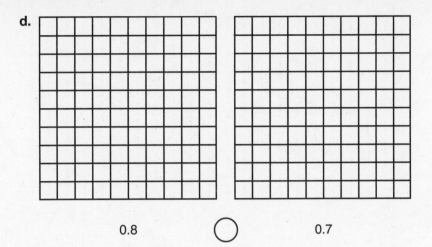

0.8 $\bigcirc$ 0.7

e.

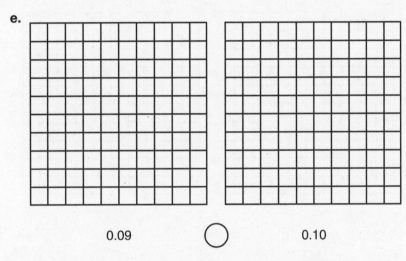

0.09 $\bigcirc$ 0.10

f.

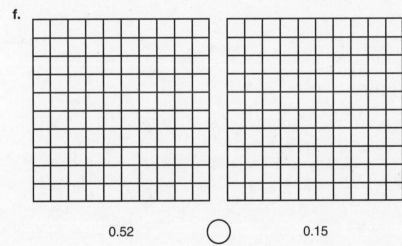

0.52 $\bigcirc$ 0.15

g.

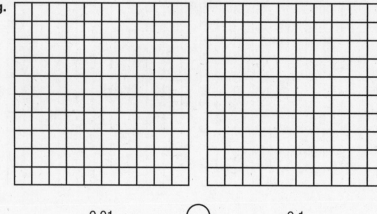

0.01   ◯   0.1

h.

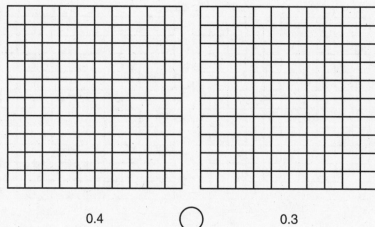

0.4   ◯   0.3

You are babysitting your neighbor Remlee, who is in the fourth grade. Remlee is doing her homework and asks you whether her work is correct.

Remlee's homework:

Circle the greater decimal in each pair shown.

1. 0.32   (0.45)

2. (0.35)   0.4

3. 0.6   (0.09)

4. (0.999)   1.00

2. Explain to Remlee whether or not her homework is correct. If Remlee has correct answers, tell her which answers are correct. If Remlee has incorrect answers, instruct her how to correct her answers. You can use pictures or diagrams in your explanation.

4

Problem 2   Putting Books Back at the Library

1. Janet is helping Ms. Woods reshelf books in the library. Ms. Woods asks Janet to put the following mathematics books in order from greatest to least on the mathematics shelf.

516.84	512.78
512.35	512.04
516.24	513.64
513.98	516.09
512.36	513.99

   a. Order the decimals shown for Janet.

   b. How did you decide which decimal was greatest? How did you determine the next decimal of greatest value?

2. Koto and Sam are trying to decide which book to put next on the shelf. They are putting books back from greatest to least. They came across two books with the following decimals: 512.07 and 512.70. Koto said, "These two books are the same number because zeros don't count for anything." Sam said, "That doesn't make sense. If they were the same number, then these books would be the same, and they aren't." Explain to Koto why her thinking is incorrect.

3. Ms. Woods had another set of books for Koto and Sam to order from greatest to least. Each book had one of the decimals shown on its spine.

512.36   512.375

512.0781   512.4

Koto picked up the book labeled 512.0781 and said, "This book has the greatest decimal," and she ordered the books in the following way:

512.0781, 512.375, 512.36, 512.4

Again, Sam said, "That doesn't seem correct." Koto replied "I ordered them by the number of digits each book has. 512.0781 has seven digits, so it must be the greatest decimal."

a. Explain to Koto why her ordering is incorrect.

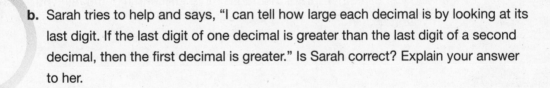

b. Sarah tries to help and says, "I can tell how large each decimal is by looking at its last digit. If the last digit of one decimal is greater than the last digit of a second decimal, then the first decimal is greater." Is Sarah correct? Explain your answer to her.

4

?

4. Write a rule that states how to determine when a decimal is greater than another decimal.

5. Tony says, "I can write each decimal as a mixed number or fraction, and then decide which is greater." Is Tony correct?

6. Do you think that Tony's method is more efficient than the rule you wrote? Explain your reasoning.

Problem 3 So Who Won the Race?

 Coach Henderson asked Rosa to keep track of the times in the 400-meter dash. Rosa recorded the times in the table shown.

Runner	Time (seconds)
1	53.18
2	53.09
3	53.01
4	54.13
5	52.18
6	53.75
7	51.28
8	53.99
9	52.99
10	56.98

1. List the runners' times in order from fastest to slowest.

Runner	Time (seconds)

Yvonne and Regina are asked to be judges at the sixth grade track meet. They recorded these results for the 200-meter dash. The runners' names and their times are shown. The runner who completes the run with the fastest time is the winner.

Runner	Time (in seconds)
Felicia	26.98
Carla	25.8
Nia	25.23
Vonetta	25.16
Ronnie	25.3
Danielle	27.78

2. Yvonne and Regina disagree on who won the meet. Yvonne claims Ronnie is first because 25.3 is the fastest time. Regina insists Vonetta is the winner because 25.16 is the fastest time. Help them settle their disagreement.

   a. Explain which runner has the fastest time in the 200-meter dash, and then explain how the incorrect student can correct her statement.

   b. List the runners in order from fastest time to slowest time so that all the medals and ribbons can be correctly awarded.

   Gold Medal/First Place   _____

   Silver Medal/Second Place   _____

   Bronze Medal/Third Place   _____

   Ribbon/Fourth Place   _____

   Ribbon/Fifth Place   _____

   Ribbon/Sixth Place   _____

Problem 4 Getting Close

Benchmark decimals are common decimals you can use to estimate the value of other decimals. For example, 0, 0.5, and 1 are benchmark decimals that can be used to compare decimals. Remember, an estimate is not about being exactly correct, but it provides a "ballpark figure," something that is near to and could be, but is not expected to be exact.

> We did something similar with benchmark fractions.

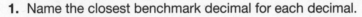

0	0.5	1

When you estimate the value of a decimal, analyze the digits to the right of the decimal point. For instance,

0.00459999 is close to 0

0.49997865 is close to 0.5

0.899999 is close to 1

1. Name the closest benchmark decimal for each decimal.

  a. 0.00009789   **b.** 0.9000001

  c. 0.50012   **d.** 0.90009

  e. 0.00999   **f.** 0.4123

  g. 0.09   h. 0.41

  i. 0.80004   **j.** 0.000099

2. Write three different decimals for each.

    a. close to 1, but less than 1

    b. close to 1, but greater than 1

    c. close to 0.5, but less than 0.5

    d. close to 0.5, but greater than 0.5

    e. close to 0

3. Estimate each sum or difference. Explain how you determined your answer.

    a. $0.948 - 0.518765$

    b. $0.0004998 + 0.5997$

    c. $0.524 + 0.4987 + 0.00999$

d. $0.0000348 + 0.9999 + 0.4999$

e. $0.0000999 + 0.0006$

f. $0.9999 + 0.000999 - 0.4876$

4. Determine which number or decimal shown is closer to 4.0827 and circle it.

    a. Is this decimal closer to 4 or 5?

    b. Is this decimal closer to 4.0 or 4.1?

    c. Is this decimal closer to 4.08 or 4.09?

    d. Is this decimal closer to 4.082 or 4.083?

    e. How did you decide each of your answers?

To **round** a decimal to a given place value, look at the digit to the right of the place to which you want to round the decimal. If the digit to the right is 4 or less, round down. If the digit to the right is 5 or greater, round up.

5. Round each decimal to the given place value in the table.

Number	Rounded to the Nearest Ten	Rounded to the Nearest One	Rounded to the Nearest Tenth	Rounded to the Nearest Hundredth	Rounded to the Nearest Thousandth
23.1768					
45.3455					
125.3578					
435.9008					
236.0895					

Be prepared to share your solutions and methods.

4.3 THE ANCIENT SPANIARDS DIDN'T COUNT THE THUMBS!

Fraction-Decimal Equivalents

Learning Goal

In this lesson, you will:

▶ Write fractions as decimals.

Key Terms

▶ terminating decimal
▶ repeating decimal

Before 2001, the U.S. stock markets used to report the change in stock values as fractions whose denominators were 16. Does that seem like a strange way to report money values? If so, perhaps you should know that the U.S. stock markets derived its trading system from the ancient Spanish trading system.

About 400 years ago, Spaniards traded items in denominations of eight (which is a factor of 16) because those items could be easily counted on their fingers. Wait a minute! People have *10* fingers, right? Well, for some reason, the Spaniards didn't use their thumbs to count! That's the reason why the ancient Spanish trading system reported items in eighths. Can you think of other items or statistics that use decimals *and* fractions?

4

Problem 1   Writing Fractions as Decimals

Remember the Rocket Strips you created in the Fractions chapter? You can use your fractions strips to determine equivalent decimals.

1. Use a straightedge and the chart to determine the decimal that is equal to or approximately equal to the fractions given. Write the decimal to the nearest hundredth.

						1						
		$\frac{1}{2}$							$\frac{1}{2}$			
	$\frac{1}{3}$				$\frac{1}{3}$					$\frac{1}{3}$		
	$\frac{1}{4}$			$\frac{1}{4}$			$\frac{1}{4}$			$\frac{1}{4}$		
$\frac{1}{5}$		$\frac{1}{5}$			$\frac{1}{5}$		$\frac{1}{5}$			$\frac{1}{5}$		
$\frac{1}{6}$		$\frac{1}{6}$		$\frac{1}{6}$		$\frac{1}{6}$		$\frac{1}{6}$		$\frac{1}{6}$		
$\frac{1}{7}$		$\frac{1}{7}$		$\frac{1}{7}$		$\frac{1}{7}$		$\frac{1}{7}$		$\frac{1}{7}$	$\frac{1}{7}$	
$\frac{1}{8}$		$\frac{1}{8}$	$\frac{1}{8}$		$\frac{1}{8}$		$\frac{1}{8}$		$\frac{1}{8}$		$\frac{1}{8}$	$\frac{1}{8}$
$\frac{1}{9}$	$\frac{1}{9}$	$\frac{1}{9}$	$\frac{1}{9}$	$\frac{1}{9}$	$\frac{1}{9}$	$\frac{1}{9}$	$\frac{1}{9}$	$\frac{1}{9}$				
$\frac{1}{10}$	$\frac{1}{10}$	$\frac{1}{10}$	$\frac{1}{10}$	$\frac{1}{10}$	$\frac{1}{10}$	$\frac{1}{10}$	$\frac{1}{10}$	$\frac{1}{10}$	$\frac{1}{10}$			
$\frac{1}{12}$	$\frac{1}{12}$	$\frac{1}{12}$	$\frac{1}{12}$	$\frac{1}{12}$	$\frac{1}{12}$	$\frac{1}{12}$	$\frac{1}{12}$	$\frac{1}{12}$	$\frac{1}{12}$	$\frac{1}{12}$	$\frac{1}{12}$	
$\frac{1}{16}$	$\frac{1}{16}$	$\frac{1}{16}$	$\frac{1}{16}$	$\frac{1}{16}$	$\frac{1}{16}$	$\frac{1}{16}$	$\frac{1}{16}$	$\frac{1}{16}$	$\frac{1}{16}$	$\frac{1}{16}$	$\frac{1}{16}$	$\frac{1}{16}$

```
0.0    0.1    0.2    0.3    0.4    0.5    0.6    0.7    0.8    0.9    1.0
```

a. $\frac{6}{10} =$ _____

b. $\frac{3}{5} =$ _____

c. $\frac{3}{12} =$ _____

d. $\frac{5}{8} =$ _____

e. $\frac{1}{8} =$ _____

f. $\frac{7}{12} =$ _____

g. $\frac{1}{3} =$ _____

h. $\frac{5}{6} =$ _____

i. $\frac{2}{3} =$ _____

j. $\frac{3}{7} =$ _____

Problem 2   Making Fractions and Decimal Equivalents

As you learned, decimals are numbers that are written in a system based on multiples of 10.

Fraction		Tenths	Hundredths	Thousandths	Ten-Thousandths
$\frac{3}{10}$	0.	3			
$\frac{71}{100}$	0.	7	1		
$\frac{305}{1000}$	0.	3	0	5	
$\frac{24}{10,000}$	0.	0	0	2	4

Fractions that do not have a denominator of 10 or a power of 10 also have decimal equivalents.

> Remember, to write an equivalent fraction, multiply or divide the fraction by a form of 1.

The examples show you how to write an equivalent fraction with a power of 10 in the denominator, and then its decimal equivalent.

$$\overset{\times 2}{\underset{\times 2}{\frac{1}{5}}} = \frac{2}{10} = 0.2 \qquad \overset{\times 25}{\underset{\times 25}{\frac{3}{4}}} = \frac{75}{100} = 0.75$$

$$\overset{\div 4}{\underset{\div 4}{\frac{12}{400}}} = \frac{3}{100} = 0.03 \qquad \overset{\div 6}{\underset{\div 6}{\frac{54}{600}}} = \frac{9}{100} = 0.09$$

4

1. Rewrite each fraction as a decimal.

Fraction	Equivalent Fraction with Denominator as a Power of 10	Decimal
$\frac{2}{5}$	$\frac{(\quad)}{10}$	
$\frac{7}{20}$	$\frac{(\quad)}{100}$	
$\frac{13}{25}$	$\frac{52}{(\quad)}$	
$\frac{3}{8}$	$\frac{(\quad)}{1000}$	
$\frac{54}{200}$	$\frac{(\quad)}{100}$	

2. Write each fraction as a decimal.

a. $\frac{7}{10}$ b. $\frac{7}{100}$ c. $\frac{7}{1000}$ d. $\frac{7}{10,000}$

e. $\frac{59}{10}$ f. $\frac{59}{100}$ g. $\frac{59}{1000}$ h. $\frac{59}{10,000}$

3. What patterns do you notice about the decimals in Question 2?

4. Write each decimal as a fraction or mixed number.

a. 2.208 b. 0.00009 c. 0.9023

5. For each pair of decimals shown, write another decimal between them.

  a. 0.6 and 0.62

  b. 0.62 and 0.63

  c. 0.632 and 0.633

  d. 2.633 and 2.6331

Some fractions have denominators that are not factors of 10 or a power of 10.

Fractions such as $\frac{1}{3}$, $\frac{2}{7}$, and $\frac{4}{9}$ are not easily converted to equivalent decimals by changing their denominator to a 10, 100, or 1000.

In this case, you can change a fraction to a decimal by using the meaning of the fraction bar. The fraction bar, which separates the numerator from the denominator, means divide.

$$\frac{3}{8} \text{ means 3 divided by 8}$$

$$\begin{array}{r} 0.375 \\ 8\overline{)3.000} \\ -24 \\ \hline 60 \\ -56 \\ \hline 40 \\ -40 \\ \hline 0 \end{array}$$

so $\frac{3}{8} = 0.375$

This decimal, 0.375, is called a **terminating decimal** because there is a remainder of 0. So, the denominator divides evenly into the numerator.

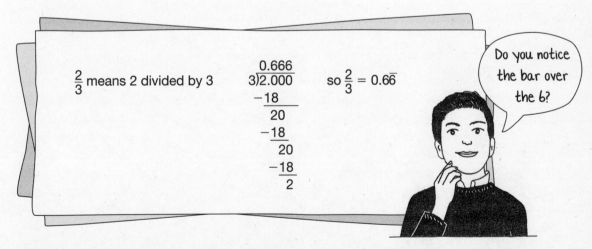

$$\frac{2}{3} \text{ means 2 divided by 3}$$

$$\begin{array}{r} 0.666 \\ 3\overline{)2.000} \\ -18 \\ \hline 20 \\ -18 \\ \hline 20 \\ -18 \\ \hline 2 \end{array}$$

so $\frac{2}{3} = 0.6\overline{6}$

Do you notice the bar over the 6?

The bar over the 6 means that the 6 repeats without ending. This decimal, $0.6\overline{6}$ is called a *repeating decimal*. A **repeating decimal** is a decimal in which a digit or a group of digits repeats without end. So, the denominator does not divide evenly into the numerator.

6. Convert each fraction to a decimal. Round each decimal to the nearest thousandth.

a. $\dfrac{1}{8}$

b. $\dfrac{3}{10}$

c. $\dfrac{3}{5}$

d. $\dfrac{2}{7}$

e. $\dfrac{1}{3}$

f. $\dfrac{4}{9}$

g. $\dfrac{13}{25}$

h. $\dfrac{7}{20}$

7. Convert each fraction to a decimal. Round each decimal to the nearest hundredth.

a. $\dfrac{1}{9}$

b. $\dfrac{2}{9}$

c. $\dfrac{3}{9}$

d. $\dfrac{4}{9}$

e. $\dfrac{5}{9}$

f. $\dfrac{6}{9}$

g. $\dfrac{7}{9}$

h. $\dfrac{8}{9}$

i. $\dfrac{9}{9}$

Be prepared to share your solutions and methods.

WHEN LESS IS BETTER
Adding and Subtracting Decimals

4.4

Learning Goals

In this lesson, you will:

▶ Estimate the sum and difference with decimals.

▶ Add and subtract decimals.

In many sports, getting the most points usually results in a win. From gymnastics competitions to diving events, from soccer goals scored to baskets made, the higher the point total, the better the chance at victory.

However, in racing competitions, *less* time is a better time. Run the race in the shortest amount of time and you're guaranteed to win! What other sports or activities guarantee success with fewer times or points?

4

Problem 1 Estimating Sums and Differences of Decimals

1. Estimate the sums or differences to the nearest whole number. Explain how you determined your estimate.

a. 5.804 + 126.009 + 56.2345

b. 459.6 − 12.436

c. 68.998 − 9.908

d. 87.36 + 13.004 + 10.998

Estimating computations before doing the actual computation on paper or by calculator helps you check your answers. If you estimate first, you will know what answer to expect. Then, if your answer is not close to your estimate, you will know there is a mistake somewhere in your calculation.

2. Paul always estimates the total of his purchases at the supermarket. He estimates to ensure he has enough money to pay for his purchases. He also estimates to check that the cashier hasn't made a mistake when ringing up his total.

Today, Paul has these items in his grocery cart.

Bread	$3.25
Peanut Butter	$5.16
Jelly	$2.97
Hot Dogs	$4.86
Hot Dog Buns	$2.42
Mustard	$1.25
Soda	$4.99
Chips	$1.50

a. About how much money does Paul need to pay for his purchases? Explain your reasoning.

b. The cashier said that his total is $39.90. Could the cashier be correct?

c. If Paul only has $20, what can he buy from his list?

3. Amy, Tonya, Emilia, and Dannie are forming a relay team for the sixth grade track meet. Each runner's best time is shown in the table.

Runner	200-Meter Time (seconds)
Amy	27.68
Tonya	28.1
Emilia	26.25
Dannie	28.95

Four other teams have total best times of:

Team A: 120.9 seconds

Team B: 110.5 seconds

Team C: 108.88 seconds

Team D: 125.6 seconds

a. What is the approximate total time for Amy, Tonya, Emilia and Dannie's team to run the 200-meter relay?

b. Which team(s) can Amy, Tonya, Emilia, and Dannie feel confident they can beat?

c. Which team(s) will run a close race against Amy, Tonya, Emilia, and Dannie?

d. Do they have a chance of breaking the school record of 108.25 seconds? If yes, by how many seconds will they need to reduce their best total time to beat the school record?

4. Jennie is a student worker at her college. Jennie tracks the hours she works in a table that she submits to the payroll department each Friday. Her time card for this week is shown.

Day	Hours
Monday	4.75
Tuesday	5.5
Wednesday	6.25
Thursday	2.15
Friday	1.6
Total	

a. Estimate the amount of hours Jennie worked this week.

b. Jennie's younger brother added her hours and claimed that she worked about 14 hours this week. His calculations are shown.

Jennie knew she worked more than 14 hours. What did her brother do when calculating the hours Jennie worked? What instructions could Jennie give her brother to correct his calculation?

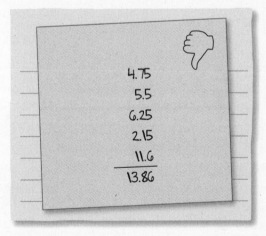

Problem 2   Adding and Subtracting Decimals

When you add or subtract decimals, it is important to add the digits in like place values. Let's consider adding decimals.

> $3.421 + 9.5 + 12.85$
>
> First, estimate the answer so you know the approximate sum.
>
> $3 + 10 + 13 = 26$
>
> Then, line up the decimals so that like place values are in the same column. You can use the decimal point as a reference point to help you align numbers in the correct place value column.
>
> $$\begin{array}{r} 3.421 \\ 9.5 \\ +12.85 \\ \hline 25.771 \end{array}$$
>
> The estimate of 26 and the sum of 25.771 are reasonably close, so the sum appears to be correct.

1. Determine the difference of $18.45 - 3.9$ using the information you know for adding decimals.

Use Questions 2, 3, and 4 from Problem 1 to answer each question.

2. How much money did Paul actually spend at the supermarket? If he gave the cashier $30.00, how much change should he receive?

3. What is the total sum of the best times for Amy, Tonya, Emilia, and Dannie?

4. What is the difference between Amy, Tonya, Emilia, and Dannie's total best time and the school record?

5. How many hours did Jennie actually work? If student workers can only work 25 hours each week, how many more hours could she have worked?

When you added fractions, you learned that the fractions must have the same denominator. When you add decimals, you must add the digits with the same place value.

Add 0.25 + 0.375

	Ones	.	Tenths	Hundredths	Thousandths					
	0	.	2	5		=	$\dfrac{25}{100}$	=	$\dfrac{250}{1000}$	
+	0	.	3	7	5	=	$\dfrac{375}{1000}$	=	$\dfrac{375}{1000}$	
	0	.	6	2	5			=	$\dfrac{625}{1000}$	

Decimal forms and fraction forms lead to the same solution.

6. Phillipa can run one mile in 17.4 minutes. She wants to improve her time by 2.6 minutes. What would be her new running time?

7. The cheerleaders have 26.3 yards of blue ribbon, 38.2 yards of white ribbon, and 48.9 yards of red ribbon. What is the total amount of ribbon the cheerleaders have?

8. It is 639.18 miles from Atlanta to Washington, D.C., and 881.46 miles from Atlanta to New York City.

   a. How much farther is it from Atlanta to New York City than it is from Atlanta to Washington, D.C.?

   b. If a bus goes from Atlanta to Washington, D.C. and then proceeds to New York City, and finally returns to Atlanta, how many miles has it traveled?

9. Chris completed a 100-meter breaststroke swimming race in 92.54 seconds. Michael completed the 100-meter breaststroke swimming race in 105.32 seconds. How much faster was Chris's time than Michael's?

10. Ginger completed a race 6.875 seconds behind Will, who completed the race in 53.786 seconds. What was Ginger's time?

11. Amy finished the first half of her relay in 87.924 seconds and the second half in 79.06 seconds. How long did it take her to complete the entire relay?

Problem 3   Wipe Out the Sevens

1. Use your calculator to wipe out the sevens from each number. Write the decimal or number you can subtract to wipe out the seven(s), and change them to a zero without changing the other digits. Then, write the difference.

a. 5.927 − _____ = _____

b. 769.333 − _____ = _____

c. 27.328 − _____ = _____

d. 476.0574 − _____ = _____

e. 3.407682 − _____ = _____

f. 79.7856 − _____ = _____

g. 124.27744 − _____ = _____

h. 4870.7672 − _____ = _____

i. 79.767676 − _____ = _____

j. 9.857777 − _____ = _____

Be prepared to share your solutions and methods.

4.5

I JUST SPENT ONE WEEK GOING TO WORK!

Multiplying Decimals

Learning Goals

In this lesson, you will:

▶ Use hundredths and decimal grids to multiply two decimals.

▶ Multiply decimals by whole numbers.

▶ Multiply two decimals.

▶ Use fractions to calculate the products of decimals.

▶ Calculate the product of decimals using fractional forms.

▶ Estimate the product of decimals.

Do you walk or take the bus to school? You and millions of other students and adults start your day by commuting to school or work. Because so many people commute every morning, traffic is common in most cities every weekday. According to the U.S. Census Bureau, the average commute time in Los Angeles was 29.5 minutes every single day in 2008. Over the course of one year, the average Los Angeles commuter can expect to spend 4.9 days commuting to work every year! How long does it take for you to get to school? How can you calculate how many minutes, hours, or days it would take you to get to school over the course of one year?

4

Problem 1 Modeling Decimal Multiplication

You can use tenth or hundredth square grids to model multiplication of decimals by whole numbers.

3×0.2

$3 \times 0.2 = 0.2 + 0.2 + 0.2$

$\qquad = 0.6$

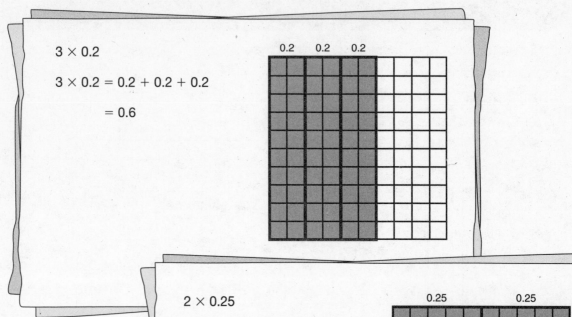

2×0.25

$2 \times 0.25 = 0.25 + 0.25$

$\qquad = 0.50$

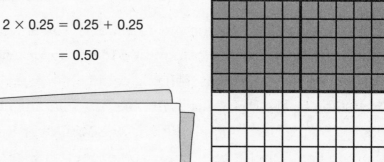

5×0.3

$5 \times 0.3 = 0.3 + 0.3 + 0.3 + 0.3 + 0.3$

$\qquad = 1.5$

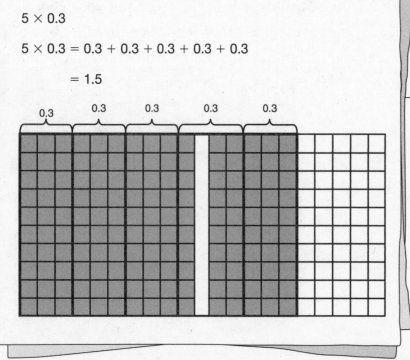

1. Use the hundredths grid to calculate the product of each expression. Show your work.

   a. 4×0.2

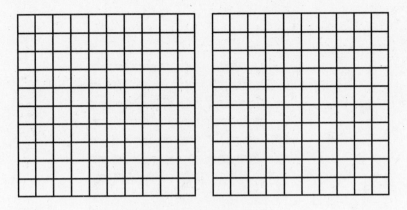

   b. 5×0.2

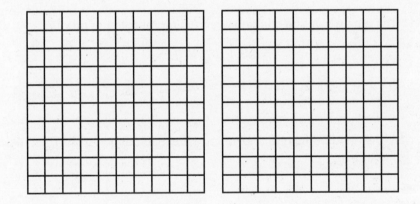

   c. 9×0.3

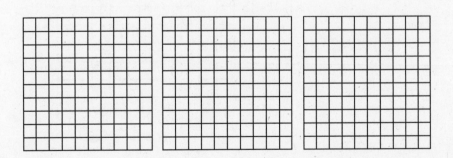

Similarly to how you used area models to multiply fractions, you can also use hundredth grids to multiply two decimals.

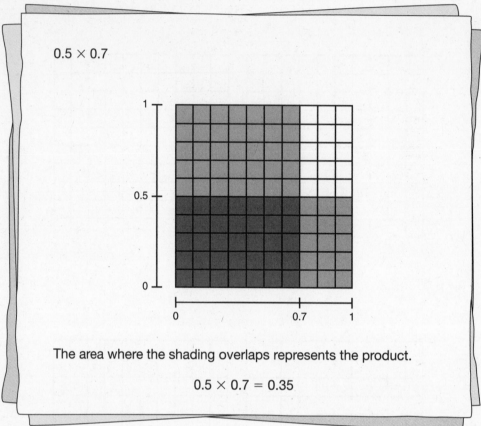

0.5×0.7

The area where the shading overlaps represents the product.

$$0.5 \times 0.7 = 0.35$$

2. Use the hundredths grid shown to model each expression. Then, calculate each product.

   a. 0.2×0.8

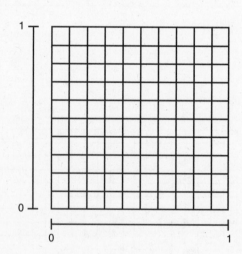

b. 0.3×0.6

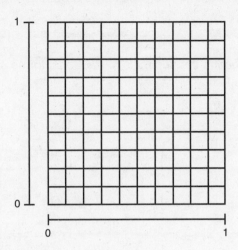

c. 1.0×0.6

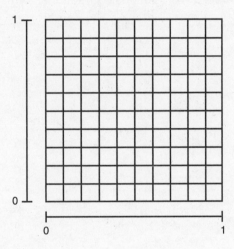

d. 0.7×0.7

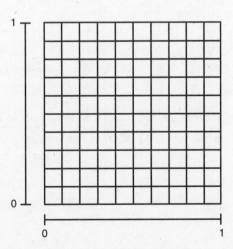

You can use fractions to calculate the products of decimals.

Change the decimals to fractional forms using 10, 100, or 1000 in the denominators.

$$4.5 \times 0.9 = 4\frac{5}{10} \times \frac{9}{10}$$

$$= \frac{45}{10} \times \frac{9}{10} = \frac{405}{100}$$

$$= 4\frac{5}{100} = 4.05$$

Remember to convert any mixed number to an improper fraction before multiplying.

3. Calculate each product using fractional forms of each number.

a. 2.5×1.3

b. 2.6×1.003

c. 2.37×2.5

4. What do you notice about the number of decimal places in the product compared to the number of decimal places in the factors?

5. Emily is buying supplies for her camping trip. She wants to pack light and healthy snacks. She notices these choices at the health food store.

On Sale Today	
Delicious Apples	$1.26/lb
Trail Mix	$5.65/lb
Peanuts	$2.45/lb.
Oatmeal Mix	$0.87/lb.
Fruit Rolls	$4.35/lb.
Raisins	$5.59/lb.

Emily decides to buy:

- 2.6 lbs of trail mix
- 0.4 lbs of fruit rolls

a. First, estimate the cost of each item that Emily will purchase.

b. Next, write each decimal in fraction form with a denominator of 10, 100, or 1000. Then, multiply the two fractions. Compare the product you calculate to your estimate.

c. How much did Emily spend on trail mix and fruit rolls?

Problem 2   Estimating Products of Decimals

Estimation can also help you with multiplication of decimals. If you do not need the exact product, you can estimate to determine the approximate product. If you have an estimate, you can use it to decide whether your answer is correct. An estimate can also help you place your decimal point correctly in the product.

Kenny said, "I can never remember the rule for multiplying decimals, so I use estimation when I forget."

Suppose Kenny has to multiply 32.64 × 7.3.

He estimates his two numbers.

32.64 is close to 30
7.3 is close to 7
7 × 30 = 210

So he knows his product is close to 210, but larger since he rounded down. Next, he calculates the product of 32.64 × 7.3.

$$
\begin{array}{r}
32.64 \\
\times \quad 7.3 \\
\hline
9792 \\
228480 \\
\hline
238.272
\end{array}
$$

Kenny knows the product will be larger than 210, so he knows he must place the decimal point after the 8. The product is 238.272.

1. Try Kenny's rule to determine the correct decimal place in each multiplication problem.

   a. $52.6 \times 0.83 = 43658$ **b.** $7.9 \times 0.6 = 474$

   c. $0.94 \times 24.9 = 23406$

2. Casey thought that using a pattern would help her understand how to calculate the product in a decimal multiplication problem.

   a. Complete the table

Problem	Product	Problem	Product	Problem	Product
32 × 100		3.2 × 100		0.32 × 100	
32 × 10		3.2 × 10		0.32 × 10	
32 × 1		3.2 × 1		0.32 × 1	
32 × 0.1		3.2 × 0.1		0.32 × 0.1	
32 × 0.01		3.2 × 0.01		0.32 × 0.01	
32 × 0.001		3.2 × 0.001		0.32 × 0.001	

   b. Describe any patterns that you notice.

3. Use the fact that 26 × 31 = 806 to calculate each product. Do not use your calculator.

    a. 2.6 × 31

    b. 2.6 × 3.1

    c. 0.26 × 3.1

    d. 2.6 × 0.31

    e. 0.26 × 31

    f. 2.6 × 0.031

    g. 0.026 × 0.31

    h. 0.26 × 0.31

    i. How can some of the problems have the same product? Explain your reasoning.

    j. How can you tell without multiplying which problems will have the same product?

4. Sandy asked, "When I was in third grade, I added a zero to a number when multiplying by 10, and I added two zeros to a number when multiplying by 100. Now that I am in the sixth grade, why can't I just add a zero to a decimal when multiplying by 10?"

a. Is 3.2×10 equal to 3.20? Is 3.2×100 equal to 3.200? Is Sandy's statement correct?

b. Can you explain to Sandy the similarities and differences between these number sentences.

$32 \times 10 = 320$

$3.2 \times 10 = 32$

$3.2 \times 100 = 320$

$32 \times 100 = 3200$

When multiplying decimals, the number of decimal places in the product is equal to the sum of the decimal places in the factors.

5. Paula thought she had the multiplication of decimals rule memorized when she multiplied 3.65 × 4.22 and got 15.403 on her calculator.

   She said, "I thought there should be four decimal places, but the calculator has only three places."

   a. Explain to Paula why the calculator is correct.

   b. How could the estimate of 3.65 × 4.22 have helped Paula understand?

6. You did your homework on multiplying decimals, but when you were walking to school, it started raining and some of the decimal points got washed away. Insert decimal points to make each multiplication sentence correct.

   a. 368 × 526 = 19.3568

   b. 8962 × 9121 = 81.742402

   c. 75.6 × 98.75 = 7465500

   d. 152 × 152 = 231.04

   e. 5875 × 2569 = 0.15092875

 Be prepared to share your solutions and methods.

ORGANIZED ESTIMATION

Long Division of Whole Numbers

Unfortunately, natural and human-made disasters happen—sometimes without a moment's warning. The threats of earthquakes, brush fires, tornados, and blizzards are a few examples of disasters. These events can be very scary.

When disaster strikes, the U.S. government helps its citizens by sending food, money, and people to help victims. The Federal Emergency Management Agency, commonly known as FEMA, was created to help disaster victims. When a disaster occurs, FEMA's director must act quickly to divide up money and resources. At times, FEMA also coordinates volunteers from other disaster-relief agencies to provide food, shelter, and recovery.

Have you or your family ever been the victim of a natural disaster? Do you think there are formulas or guidelines that FEMA and other recovery agencies should use to divide and distribute aid and resources to communities?

Problem 1 Organized Guessing

Before you divide decimals, let's look back at what you have already learned about division of whole numbers. In elementary school, you learned that division helps you determine how many times one number is contained in another number. In other words, you determined the *quotient* given a *dividend* and a *divisor*. The **dividend** is the number or decimal that is being divided into equal groups. The **divisor** is the number or decimal that divides the dividend. Finally, the **quotient** is the result of the division sentence. Quotients can be whole numbers, decimals, or fractions.

You can also think of division as the number of times you can subtract the divisor from the dividend.

We called this a fact family in elementary school.

$$\text{divisor} \overline{)\text{dividend}}^{\text{quotient}}$$

or

(quotient) (divisor) = dividend

Remember that multiplication and division are inverse operations!

Let's consider a few different examples to understand how division works.

Example 1: 48 ÷ 6

John's solution:

I know that 6 X 8 = 48, so 48 ÷ 6 = 8.

Example 2: 582 ÷ 6

Christopher's solution:

This is not a fact I memorized! I used a combination of estimating and organized guessing.

	Multiplication Sentence	Reasoning
1st guess	6 × 100 = 600	too big
2nd guess	6 × 50 = 300	too small
3rd guess	6 × 70 = 420	still too small
4th guess	6 × 80 = 480	still too small
5th guess	6 × 90 = 540	getting closer
6th guess	6 × 95 = 570	getting closer
7th guess	6 × 96 = 576	getting closer
8th guess	6 × 97 = 582	finally!

So, $6\overline{)582}^{\,97}$

1. Once Christopher's 6th guess was completed, how do you think guesses 7 and 8 were made?

If the division problem is longer or more difficult than Example 2, then guessing could be very time consuming.

Example 3: 34,098 ÷ 6

Lori's solution:

I used an organized estimation strategy.

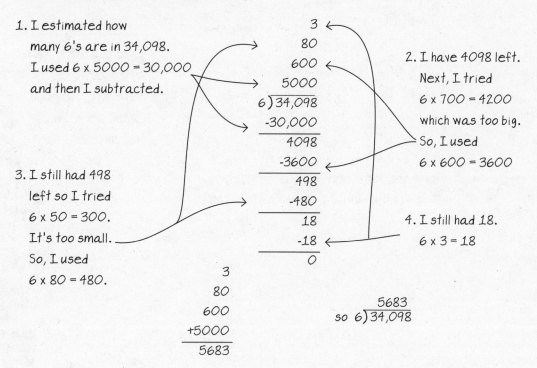

1. *I estimated how many 6's are in 34,098. I used 6 x 5000 = 30,000 and then I subtracted.*

2. *I have 4098 left. Next, I tried 6 x 700 = 4200 which was too big. So, I used 6 x 600 = 3600*

3. *I still had 498 left so I tried 6 x 50 = 300. It's too small. So, I used 6 x 80 = 480.*

4. *I still had 18. 6 x 3 = 18*

$$
\begin{array}{r}
3 \\
80 \\
600 \\
5000 \\
6\overline{)34,098} \\
-30,000 \\
\hline
4098 \\
-3600 \\
\hline
498 \\
-480 \\
\hline
18 \\
-18 \\
\hline
0
\end{array}
$$

$$
\begin{array}{r}
3 \\
80 \\
600 \\
+5000 \\
\hline
5683
\end{array}
$$

so $6\overline{)34,098}^{\,5683}$

2. In each step, why did Lori subtract after she determined each estimate?

Rob and Morgan agreed with Lori's logic, but each shortened the process.

Example 4:

Rob's solution:

$$
\begin{array}{r}
\left.\begin{array}{r}
3 \\
80 \\
600 \\
5000
\end{array}\right\} 5683 \\
6\overline{)34{,}098} \\
-30{,}000 \\
\hline
4098 \\
-3600 \\
\hline
498 \\
-480 \\
\hline
18 \\
-18 \\
\hline
0
\end{array}
$$

Example 5:

Morgan's solution:

$$
\begin{array}{r}
5683 \\
6\overline{)34{,}098} \\
-30 \\
\hline
40 \\
-36 \\
\hline
49 \\
-48 \\
\hline
18 \\
-18 \\
\hline
\end{array}
$$

You can use double lines at the end of a long division problem when the last difference is 0.

3. Compare Rob's and Morgan's strategies. What are the similarities and differences?

Problem 2   More Long Division Strategies

Carnegie Middle School conducted a month-long food and clothing drive to assist in disaster relief. They collected the following items for distribution.

- 3,312 cans of food
- 9472 blankets
- 19,456 batteries
- 26,112 bottles of water

If the students want to make 256 disaster-relief shipping crates, how many bottles of water will they put in each shipping crate?

1. Analyze each solution.

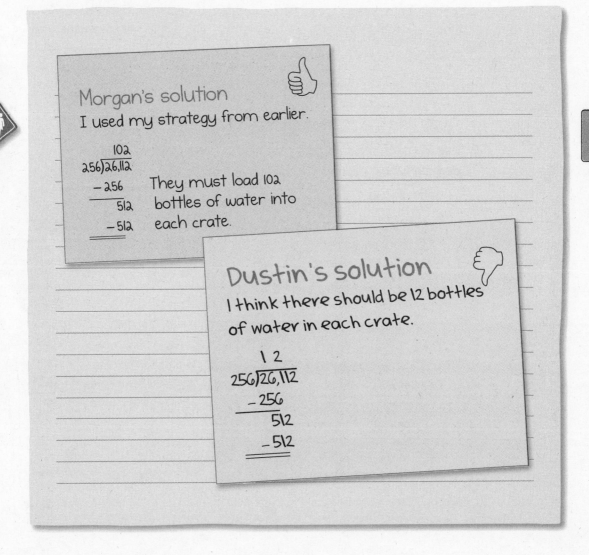

Morgan's solution
I used my strategy from earlier.

$$
\begin{array}{r}
102 \\
256\overline{)26{,}112} \\
-256 \\
\hline
512 \\
-512 \\
\hline
\end{array}
$$

They must load 102 bottles of water into each crate.

Dustin's solution
I think there should be 12 bottles of water in each crate.

$$
\begin{array}{r}
12 \\
256\overline{)26{,}112} \\
-256 \\
\hline
512 \\
-512 \\
\hline
\end{array}
$$

a. What did Dustin do incorrectly?

b. How could Dustin have checked his work to know that his answer was incorrect?

c. There should have been 3 digits in Dustin's quotient. How could he have determined that before he started dividing?

Think about the number of digits in your answer first. This will help you determine if your quotient is correct.

2. Use Morgan's method of long division to determine how many of each item must be loaded into each of the 256 shipping crates.

   a. cans of food

   b. blankets

c. batteries

Problem 3   What's Left Over?

1. How many digits are in each quotient?

    a. 75,915 ÷ 63   **b.** 87,618 ÷ 859

    c. 66,794 ÷ 26   **d.** 56,280 ÷ 56

    e. 179,120 ÷ 20   **f.** 118,352 ÷ 569

2. Fill in the missing digits in each long division problem. Then, rewrite each quotient using fractions instead of remainders.

"R" stands for remainder.

    a.
```
       □2□ R3□
   76)9384
      −76
       17□
      −152
        2□4
       −□28
         3□
```

    b.
```
       □9 R3□
   85)□5□7
      −680
        79□
       −□□5
         3□
```

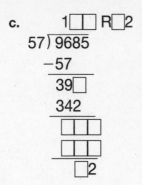

c.

```
      1□□ R□2
57) 9685
   -57
    39□
    342
    □□□
    □□□
     □2
```

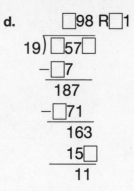

d.

```
        □98 R□1
19) □57□
   -□7
    187
   -□71
    163
    15□
     11
```

3. The Red Cross disaster relief fund collected 3551 winter coats to distribute to flood victims. If there are 23 distribution centers, how many coats can be sent to each center? Marla's calculations are shown.

```
        9
   154 ——
        23
23) 3551
  -23
   125
  -115
   101
   -92
     9
```

Marla said, "The Red Cross can send $154\frac{9}{23}$ coats to each center."

Madison replied, "You cannot have a fraction of a coat. So, each center will receive 154 coats and there will be 9 coats left over. So, the answer should be written as 154 R 9."

Who's correct and why?

In division problems, the remainder can mean different things in different situations. Sometimes the remainder can be ignored, and sometimes the remainder is the answer to the problem. Sometimes the answer is the number without the remainder, and sometimes you need to use the next whole number up from the correct answer. In other words, you can *round down* if you don't use the remainder, and you can *round up* if you use the next whole number larger than your answer.

4. The Carnegie Middle School is hosting a picnic for any fifth-grader who will be attending school next year as a sixth-grader. The hospitality committee is planning the picnic for 125 students. Each fifth-grader will get a sandwich, a drink, and a dessert.

a. The hospitality committee is ordering large sandwiches that each serve 8 people. If 125 fifth-graders are coming to the picnic, how many sandwiches should the committee buy? Jodi thought they should order 15 sandwiches, but Rhonda thought they needed 16 sandwiches. Who's correct? Explain your reasoning and why the other person is not correct.

b. The committee is planning to have frozen fruit bars for dessert. If frozen fruit bars come in boxes of 12, how many boxes of frozen fruit bars should they order? Will there be any extra frozen fruit bars? If so, how many?

> Think about what the remainder means in terms of each problem situation.

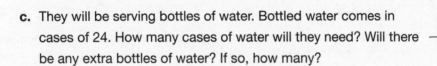

c. They will be serving bottles of water. Bottled water comes in cases of 24. How many cases of water will they need? Will there be any extra bottles of water? If so, how many?

d. The fifth-graders will take a bus from the elementary school to the middle school on the afternoon of the picnic. If each bus seats 32 passengers, how many buses will be needed to transport the students? How many seats will be empty?

5. Throughout the year, local businesses collected 28,654 pairs of eyeglasses for disaster victims. If they have requests from 236 relief organizations, how many pairs of eyeglasses can each organization receive? How many pairs, if any, will be left over?

6. The Annual Book Drive collected 96,120 books. There were 32 schools that requested books for their students and libraries.

   a. How many books will each school receive? How many books, if any, will be left over?

   b. One of the receiving schools decided to give their share of the books to the students to take home. If the school has 213 students, what is the maximum number of books each person can receive? How many books, if any, will be left over?

7. The local firefighters collect toys to distribute at various give-away events. They have 4569 toys and will sponsor 129 give-away events. How many toys can they give away at each event? How many toys, if any, will be left over?

 Be prepared to share your solutions and methods.

4.7 LOS ANGELES COMMUTE DIDN'T TOP THE LIST?

Dividing Decimals

Learning Goals

In this lesson, you will:

▶ Estimate quotients of division of decimals.

▶ Divide decimals.

4

Previously you read, the average Los Angeles commuter had a commute time of 29.5 minutes. However, this average commute time did not top the list. According to the 2008 U.S. Census Bureau, New York City area commuters had, on average, the longest commute time. In fact, it was expected that New Yorkers would spend a total of 7.23 days in commuting time in one year. About how much time do New Yorkers spend daily commuting to work using the U.S. Census Bureau information?

Problem 1 Dividing with Decimals

You can use hundredths grids to model dividing decimals.

Let's consider 3.57 ÷ 3.

First represent 3.57. Shade three hundredths grids to represent 3, five columns in the fourth grid to represent five tenths, and then shade seven more squares in the fourth grid to represent seven hundredths.

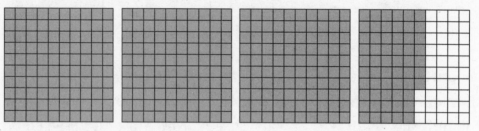

Next, divide the shaded model into three equal groups. To do this, divide the three hundredths grids into three equal groups. Then, divide the 57 hundredths into three equal groups.

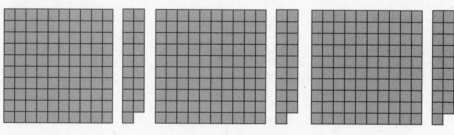

Group 1   Group 2   Group 3

One whole grid and 19 small squares are in each group.

Therefore, 3.57 ÷ 3 = 1.19

Let's consider 3.9 ÷ 1.3.

Shade three tenths grids and nine columns of a fourth grid to represent 3.9.

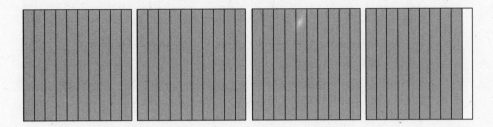

Divide the grids and tenths into equal groups of 1.3.

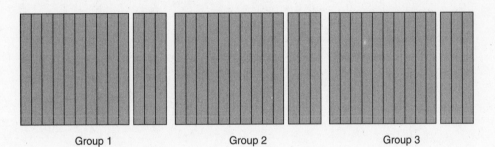

Group 1   Group 2   Group 3

There are three equal groups of 1.3.

3.9 ÷ 1.3 = 3

1. Tracy thought that if 39 ÷ 13 = 3 and 3.9 ÷ 1.3 = 3, there must be a relationship. What do you think? Explain your reasoning.

> Remember, when you divide fractions, rewrite the division sentence as a multiplication sentence and convert the divisor to its reciprocal.

You want to buy ribbon to make track medallions. You find a web site that sells 4.8 meters of red, white, and blue striped ribbon for $20.16, or 7.2 meters of blue ribbon for $30.60. To compare the costs, you need to calculate the price for 1 meter of ribbon for both prices. First, rewrite the decimal numbers as mixed numbers. Then, rewrite the mixed numbers as improper fractions. Finally, divide the improper fraction. Make sure to put your answer in decimal form.

Striped Ribbon: $20.16 \div 4.8$

$$20.16 = 20\frac{16}{100} = \frac{2016}{100}$$

$$4.8 = 4\frac{8}{10} = \frac{48}{10}$$

$$\frac{2016}{100} \div \frac{48}{10} = \frac{2016}{100} \times \frac{10}{48} = \frac{20{,}160}{4800} = 4\frac{960}{4800}$$

$$= 4\frac{20}{100} = \$4.20/\text{meter}$$

2. Use this method to divide 30.60 by 7.2.

3. Based on your results, which type of ribbon is the better or cheaper buy? Explain your answer.

If you multiply both the dividend and the divisor by the same number, the quotient remains unchanged.

$12 \div 3 = 4$

$(12 \times 10) \div (3 \times 10) = 4$

$(12 \times 100) \div (3 \times 100) = 4$

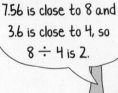

The quotient remains the same because you are dividing by a form of 1.

You can use this information to change any divisor into a whole number to make the division of a decimal easier to solve.

Multiply both numbers by the least power of 10 that makes the divisor into a whole number. Then, divide as with whole numbers.

$7.56 \div 3.6$ or $3.6\overline{)7.56}$

$(7.56 \times 10) \div (3.6 \times 10)$ or $36\overline{)75.6}$

If I estimate that 7.56 is close to 8 and 3.6 is close to 4, so 8 ÷ 4 is 2.

$$
\begin{array}{r}
2.1 \\
36\overline{)75.6} \\
-72 \\
\hline
36 \\
-36 \\
\hline
0
\end{array}
$$

4

4. Rewrite each division problem so the divisor is a whole number. Explain how you determined your answer.

    a. $48 \div 8.6$

    b. $59.5 \div 0.17$

c. $6.2 \div 0.02$

5. Look at these division problems.

$7\overline{)56}$ $70\overline{)560}$ $700\overline{)5600}$ $7000\overline{)56{,}000}$

    a. How are the divisors and dividends in the last three problems related to the first problem?

    b. Calculate all four quotients. What do you notice about them?

    c. What happens to the quotient when the dividend and divisor are multiplied by the same number?

6. Which of the division expressions shown has the same quotient as $475 \div 25$? How do you know?

    a. $4.75 \div 0.25$

    b. $47.5 \div 0.025$

    c. $0.475 \div 0.25$

    d. $0.0475 \div 0.0025$

e. Write another division expression that has the same quotient as the division expression in Question 6.

7. Look at the table of division problems. What patterns do you see?

60	÷	1000	=	0.06	
60	÷	100	=	0.6	
60	÷	10	=	6	
60	÷	1	=	60	

60	÷	0.1	=	600
60	÷	0.01	=	6000
60	÷	0.001	=	60,000

8. You are helping your parents research hybrid cars. You learn that on a long-distance trip, the Sentar traveled 571.95 miles on 12.3 gallons of gas. You also learn that the Eventar traveled 753.48 miles on 15.6 gallons of gas. Determine which car got better gas mileage.

4

9. Estimate the quotients for each expression shown. Make sure to show your work.

   a. 7.5 ÷ 0.8   **b.** 98.3 ÷ 23   **c.** 99.2 ÷ 1.6

   d. 10.35 ÷ 0.45   **e.** 24.6 ÷ 0.6   **f.** 7.4 ÷ 25

   g. Divide each problem using your calculator. Round your answers to the nearest thousandth. Compare your estimates to the actual calculations.

10. Place the decimal point in each quotient to make the division sentence true. Use estimation with powers of 10.

a. $23.4 \div 0.9 = 260$ **b.** $5.51 \div 0.16 = 344375$ **c.** $10.25 \div 8.2 = 125$

Problem 2   Who's Correct?

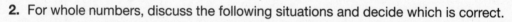

1. Jared started his homework and did the first two problems.

$$1.3 \div 0.25 = 0.52$$
$$39.6 \div 0.11 = 36$$

Adam said immediately that his answers were wrong.

How did Adam know there was a mistake just by looking at the two problems and not doing any calculations?

2. For whole numbers, discuss the following situations and decide which is correct.

a. If the divisor is less than the dividend, then the quotient is always ⎢greater than or less than⎥ one.

b. If the divisor is greater than the dividend, then the quotient is always ⎢greater than or less than⎥ one.

Be prepared to share your solutions and methods.

Chapter 4 Summary

Key Terms

- decimals (4.1)
- benchmark decimal (4.2)
- round (4.2)
- terminating decimal (4.3)

- repeating decimal (4.3)
- dividend (4.6)
- divisor (4.6)
- quotient (4.6)

4.1 Writing Decimals

Decimals are another way to represent parts of a whole. The place value names for the places to the right of the decimal are tenths, hundredths, thousandths, ten-thousandths, and so on.

Example

The decimal three and fifty-two thousandths is shown.

$$3.052$$

The decimal three and fifty two thousandths is shown in expanded form:

$$3 + \frac{5}{100} + \frac{2}{1000}$$

The same decimal is shown as powers of ten:

3 ones + 0 tenths + 5 hundredths + 2 thousandths

Have you ever heard that humans only use a portion of their brain? Well, it's not true! When you are solving difficult math problems, your WHOLE brain is engaged!

Representing Decimals on a Tenths Grid and a Hundredths Grid

Tenths grids and hundredths grids can be used to model decimals and show the connection between fractions and decimals. An entire hundredths grid represents one whole. Each small square represents one-hundredth. An entire tenths grid also represents one whole. Each bar represents one-tenth.

Example

The decimal 0.42 is represented on a hundredths grid and a tenths and hundredths grid.

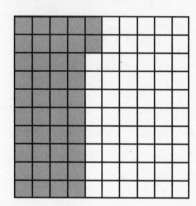 = 0.42

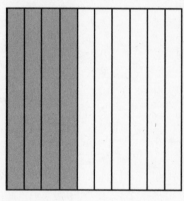 = 0.42

4.1 Representing Decimals on a Number Line

A decimal can be plotted as a point on a number line. This representation is often helpful for comparing and ordering decimals.

Example

The decimals 0.9, 1.25, and 1.3 are plotted on the number line.

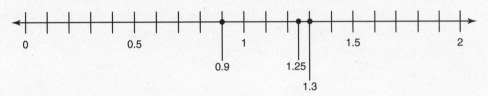

A decimal between 1.25 and 1.3 is 1.27.

4.2 Comparing and Ordering Decimals

To compare two decimals, compare the digits in each place value from left to right. If the digits in a place value are the same, then move to the right and compare the next place value until you find two different digits to compare.

Example

The decimals 43.27, 43.532, 43.58, 53.58 are ordered from least to greatest.

4.2 Estimating Decimals Using Benchmark Decimals

Benchmark decimals, such as 0, 0.5, and 1, are common decimals that can be used to estimate the value of decimals.

Example

Because the digit in the tenths place is a nine, the decimal 0.9299 is close to 1.

4.2 Rounding Decimals

To round a decimal to a given place value, look at the digit to the right of the place where you want to round the decimal. If the digit to the right is 4 or less, round down. If the digit to the right is 5 or greater, round up.

Example

To round 68.2468 to the nearest hundredth, look at the digit in the thousandths place. The digit in the thousandths place is 6. Because 6 is greater than 5, round up. So, 68.2468 rounded to the nearest hundredth is 68.25.

4.3 Writing Fractions as Decimals

To write a fraction as a decimal, rewrite the denominator as a power of ten, or divide the numerator by the denominator.

Example

a. Write $\frac{7}{25}$ as a decimal.

$$\overset{\times 4}{\overgroup{\frac{7}{25} = \frac{28}{100}}} = 0.28$$
$$\underset{\times 4}{\undergroup{}}$$

$$\frac{7}{25} = 0.28$$

b. Write $\frac{6}{7}$ as a decimal. Round to the nearest thousandth.

$$
\begin{array}{r}
0.8571 \\
7{\overline{\smash{\big)}\,6.0000}} \\
\underline{-5.6} \\
40 \\
\underline{-35} \\
50 \\
\underline{-49} \\
10 \\
\underline{-7} \\
3
\end{array}
$$

So, $\frac{6}{7} \approx 0.857$.

4.4 Estimating Sums and Differences of Decimals

To estimate the sum or difference of decimals, first round each decimal to the nearest whole number. Then, add or subtract.

Example

Estimate $45.42 + 124.924 - 99.02$.

$$45.42 + 124.924 - 99.02 = 45 + 125 - 99$$
$$= 71$$

4.4 Adding and Subtracting Decimals

When adding or subtracting decimals, be sure to line up the decimal points. Doing so helps to ensure that the digits in the same place value are being added or subtracted correctly.

Examples

a. $8.964 + 12.05$

$$\begin{array}{r} 8.964 \\ +12.05 \\ \hline 21.014 \end{array}$$

b. $125.03 - 6.1032$

$$\begin{array}{r} 125.0300 \\ -\ 6.1032 \\ \hline 118.9268 \end{array}$$

4

4.5 Multiplying Decimals

When multiplying decimals, the number of decimal places in the product is equal to the sum of the decimal places in the factors. Estimating the product helps to check if a product is reasonable.

Example

The estimate of the product for the expression 6.13×9.87 to the nearest whole number is shown. Then, the product of the multiplication expression is shown.

Estimate: $6.13 \times 9.87 \approx 6 \times 10$

$$= 60$$

Actual product:
$$
\begin{array}{r}
6.13 \\
\times 9.87 \\
\hline
4291 \\
49040 \\
+551700 \\
\hline
60.5031
\end{array}
$$

$6.13 \times 9.87 = 60.5031$

Estimating first made it easier to determine where to place the decimal point in the product.

4.6 Dividing Whole Numbers

Division helps you determine how many times one number is contained in another number. When dividing whole numbers, you can use organized estimation to determine the quotient.

Example

To determine the quotient using the organized estimation strategy, follow the steps shown.

$$
\left.\begin{array}{r}
7 \\
20 \\
200 \\
5000
\end{array}\right\} 5227
$$

$$
\begin{array}{r}
8\overline{)41{,}816} \\
-40{,}000 \\
\hline
1816 \\
-1600 \\
\hline
216 \\
-160 \\
\hline
56 \\
-56 \\
\hline
\end{array}
$$

- First estimate how many eights are in 41,816. Think: $5000 \times 8 = 40,000$. Therefore, take the difference of 41,816 and 40,000. The difference is 1816.

- Next, estimate how many eights are in 1816. Think: $200 \times 8 = 1600$. Therefore, take the difference of 1816 and 1600. The difference is 216.

- Then, estimate how many eights are in 216. Think: $20 \times 8 = 160$. $30 \times 8 = 240$—that's too much! Therefore, take the difference of 216 and 160. The difference is 56.

- You know that $8 \times 7 = 56$.

- Finally, add the factors to find the quotient.

The quotient is 5227.

You can check your answer by multiplying the quotient and the divisor. If the product is the same as the dividend, the quotient is correct.

$$8 \times 5227 = 41,816$$

4.6 Dividing Whole Numbers with Quotients that Have Remainders

Not all numbers divide evenly into other numbers. When a divisor does not evenly divide into the dividend, the quotient contains a remainder. Remainders can be written as fractions, decimals, or as a whole number. Depending on the situation, the remainder can be ignored because all that needs to be calculated are whole numbers.

Example

It takes 6 screws to assemble a pair of eyeglass frames. An eyeglass manufacturer has 3309 screws and needs to determine how many pairs of eyeglass frames they can create.

$$
\begin{array}{r}
1 \\
50 \\
500 \\
6\overline{)3309} \\
-3000 \\
\hline
309 \\
-300 \\
\hline
9 \\
-6 \\
\hline
3
\end{array}
$$

$$6 \times 551.5 = 3309$$

Using the estimating organization strategy, the company determines that they can create $551\frac{1}{2}$ pairs of eyeglass frames. However, the manufacturer cannot manufacture half a pair of glasses, so they can ignore the remainder.

If the question also asked how many screws were left over after manufacturing the total possible number of eyeglass frames, then the remainder would be important.

4.7 Dividing Decimals

When dividing decimals, first multiply the dividend and the divisor by the power of ten that makes the divisor a whole number. Then divide. Be sure to line up the decimal point in the quotient with the decimal point in the dividend. Estimating the quotient helps to check if the quotient is reasonable.

Example

The estimate of the division expression $15.19 \div 4.9$ to the nearest whole number is shown. Then, the quotient of the division expression is shown.

Estimate: $15.19 \div 4.9 \approx 15 \div 5$

$$= 3$$

Actual quotient:

$$15.19 \div 4.9 = (15.19 \times 10) \div (4.9 \times 10)$$
$$= 151.9 \div 49$$

$$
\begin{array}{r}
3.1 \\
49\overline{)151.9} \\
-147 \\
\hline
49 \\
-49 \\
\hline
0
\end{array}
$$

$15.19 \div 4.9 = 3.1$

Estimating first made it easier to determine that the quotient is reasonable.

5 RATIOS

As one of North America's great natural wonders, the Niagara River plunges over Niagara Falls between New York and Ontario, Canada. The falls are about 170 feet high and over 3600 feet wide.

5

5

5.1 MIXING PAINT
Introduction to Ratios

Learning Goals

In this lesson, you will:

▶ Write ratios as part-to-part and part-to-whole relationships.

▶ Represent ratios using models.

▶ Use models to determine equivalent ratios.

Key Term

▶ ratio

Yellow and blue make green. Red and blue make purple. And yellow and red make orange. But what do you get when you combine all the colors? Well, with paints, what you probably get is a big mess. But when you combine all the visible colors of light, what you get is the color white.

Try it out! Take three flashlights—one covered in blue film, one in red film, and one in green film—and shine them on the wall in a darkened room. Where all the colors overlap, you see white light!

What other combinations of colors do you know about?

Problem 1   Comparing Quantities

The school colors at Riverview Middle School are a shade of bluish green and white. The art teacher, Mr. Raith, knows to get the correct color of bluish green it takes 3 parts blue paint to every 2 parts yellow paint.

There are different ways to think about this relationship and make comparisons. One way is to draw a picture, or model.

From the model, you can make comparisons of the different quantities.

- blue parts to yellow parts
- yellow parts to blue parts
- blue parts to total parts
- yellow parts to total parts

Each comparison is called a *ratio*. A **ratio** is a comparison of two quantities that uses division. The first two comparisons are part-to-part ratios. The last two comparisons are part-to-whole ratios because you are comparing one of the parts (either blue or yellow) to the total number of parts.

Part-to-Part Ratios

In Words	With a Colon	In Fractional Form
2 parts yellow to every 3 parts blue	2 parts yellow : 3 parts blue	$\dfrac{2 \text{ parts yellow}}{3 \text{ parts blue}}$
3 parts blue to every 2 parts yellow	3 parts blue : 2 parts yellow	$\dfrac{3 \text{ parts blue}}{2 \text{ parts yellow}}$

Part-to-Whole Ratios

In Words	With a Colon	In Fractional Form
2 parts yellow to every 5 total parts	2 parts yellow : 5 total parts	$\dfrac{2 \text{ parts yellow}}{5 \text{ total parts}}$
3 parts blue to every 5 total parts	3 parts blue : 5 total parts	$\dfrac{3 \text{ parts blue}}{5 \text{ total parts}}$

Notice that when you write a ratio using the total number of parts, you are also writing a fraction. A fraction is a ratio that shows a part-to-whole relationship.

Ratios

$$\underbrace{\frac{\text{part}}{\text{part}} \quad \underbrace{\frac{\text{part}}{\text{whole}}}}$$

Fraction

1. Suppose Mr. Raith needs 2 parts blue paint and 5 parts red paint to make a purplish paint.

   a. Write all the possible part-to-part ratios using colons and fractional form.

   b. Write all the possible part-to-whole ratios using colons and fractional form.

So you are never in doubt what a ratio represents . . . label all quantities with the units of measure!

5

Problem 2   Muffins to Start Your Morning

The local bakery sells muffins in 6-packs. They sell the muffins in this variety:

    3 blueberry muffins

    2 pumpkin muffins

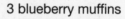   1 bran muffin

1. Write the ratio that expresses each relationship.

   a. blueberry muffins to total muffins   **b.** pumpkin muffins to total muffins

   c. bran muffins to total muffins   **d.** blueberry muffins to pumpkin muffins

   e. bran muffins to pumpkin muffins

   f. blueberry muffins to bran muffins

2. Which ratios are part-to-part ratios and which are part-to-whole ratios?

Don't forget to label each quantity with the unit of measure!

3. Complete the table to show the number of muffins in each variety pack.

Number of Variety Packs	1	3		8	
Number of Blueberry Muffins	3			24	30
Number of Pumpkin Muffins	2		12		20
Number of Bran Muffins	1		6		
Total Number of Muffins	6	18			

4. Analyze the table and describe the relationship between each number of muffins in any given variety pack.

   a. the number of blueberry muffins related to the number of bran muffins

   b. the number of blueberry muffins related to the number of pumpkin muffins

   c. the number of pumpkin muffins related to the number of bran muffins

   d. the number of bran muffins related to the number of blueberry muffins

   e. the number of bran muffins related to the number of pumpkin muffins

   f. the number of pumpkin muffins related to the number of blueberry muffins

   g. the number of blueberry muffins related to the total number of muffins in the variety pack

h. the number of pumpkin muffins related to the total number of muffins in the variety pack

i. the number of bran muffins related to the total number of muffins in the variety pack

5. Which ratios in Question 4 are part-to-part ratios and which are part-to-whole ratios?

6. Each model shows a ratio of muffins to juice boxes.

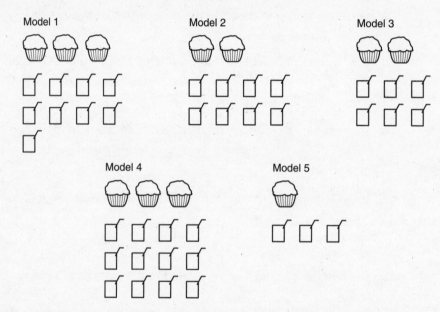

Which models show the same ratio of muffins to juice boxes? Explain your reasoning.

Problem 3 Variety Muffin Packs

Two out of every five muffins are blueberry in one muffin variety pack.

1. Complete the model shown for each question using the ratio given. Then, calculate your answer from your model, and explain your reasoning.

   a. How many muffins are blueberry muffins if there are a total of 25 muffins?

blueberry muffin

   b. How many muffins are blueberry muffins if there are a total of 35 muffins?

   c. How many total muffins are there if 8 muffins are blueberry?

I think I see a pattern? Do you see it?

Be prepared to share your solutions and methods.

5.2 WHAT'S IN A NAME?
Ratio Representations

Learning Goals

In this lesson, you will:

▶ Write comparisons using ratios.

▶ Distinguish between part-to-part and part-to-whole ratios.

▶ Write equivalent ratios.

Did you know that some of the professional teams you root for may have come from another city? Throughout professional sports history, some teams have left their native cities in hopes of finding a better fan base and more money in another city. Sometimes when teams move, they keep their nickname, while at other times, they adopt new nicknames to match their new city and identity. For example, Major League Baseball's Athletics started as a professional baseball team in Philadelphia, then moved to Kansas City, and then Oakland—all the time maintaining their nickname as the A's. However, the National Basketball Association's Supersonics departed from Seattle to reside in Oklahoma City. After the move, this team adopted the nickname of the "Thunder." Can you think of any other teams that have changed location?

5

Problem 1   The Fightin'_____?

Lanterton Middle School is adopting a new nickname. They have narrowed their search to the following two names:

Lynx

Leopards

Each homeroom reported the correct results of the nickname survey for the entire school differently.

- Homeroom 6A: Students who preferred Lynx outnumbered students who preferred Leopards by a ratio of 240 to 160.

- Homeroom 6B: 80 more students preferred Lynx than Leopards.

- Homeroom 7A: Students who preferred Lynx outnumbered students who preferred Leopards by a ratio of 3 to 2.

- Homeroom 7B: 3 out of 5 students preferred Lynx.

1. Describe the meaning of each statement.

2. Which statement gives you the best information about the survey results? Explain your reasoning.

Let's consider the statement:

"3 out of 5 students chose Lynx over Leopards as Lanterton Middle School's new nickname."

You can write this relationship in different ways.

As a part-to-whole ratio (or fraction):

$$\frac{part}{whole} = \frac{3}{5} \frac{\text{students chose Lynx}}{\text{total students}}$$

$$\frac{part}{whole} = \frac{2}{5} \frac{\text{students chose Leopards}}{\text{total students}}$$

As a part-to-part ratio:

$$\frac{part}{part} = \frac{3}{2} \frac{\text{students chose Lynx}}{\text{students chose Leopards}}$$

part:part = 3 students chose Lynx :
           2 students chose Leopards

3. Complete the table by writing each homeroom's statement two different ways. Use the results reported by each homeroom and the fact that 400 total students were surveyed.

Homeroom	Ratio		part / part
	$\dfrac{part}{whole}$		
6A	$\dfrac{\text{Chose Lynx}}{400\ \text{Total Students}},$	$\dfrac{\text{Chose Leopards}}{400\ \text{Total Students}}$	$\dfrac{\text{Lynx}}{\text{Leopards}}$
6B	$\dfrac{\text{Chose Lynx}}{\text{Total Students}},$	$\dfrac{\text{Chose Leopards}}{400\ \text{Total Students}}$	$\dfrac{\text{Lynx}}{\text{Leopards}}$
7A	$\dfrac{\text{Chose Lynx}}{5\ \text{Total Students}},$	$\dfrac{\text{Chose Leopards}}{5\ \text{Total Students}}$	$\dfrac{\text{Lynx}}{\text{Leopards}}$
7B	$\dfrac{\text{Chose Lynx}}{\text{Total Students}},$	$\dfrac{\text{Chose Leopards}}{\text{Total Students}}$	$\dfrac{\text{Lynx}}{\text{Leopards}}$

a. Compare the part-to-whole ratios you wrote for HR 6A and 6B to those for HR 7A and 7B. What do you notice?

b. Compare the part-to-part ratios you wrote for HR 6A and 6B to those for HR 7A and 7B. What do you notice?

Problem 2 Comparing Ratios

1. There are 20 sixth graders and 30 eighth graders in the chess club.

   a. Write the ratio of sixth graders to eighth graders in the chess club.

   i. Write the ratio of sixth graders to the total number of chess club members. Assume that there are no seventh graders in the club.

   ii. Write the ratio of the number of eighth graders in the club to the total number of chess club members. Assume that there are no seventh graders in the club.

   iii. Which is greater: the ratio of sixth graders to the total number of club members, or the ratio of eighth graders to the total number of club members? Explain your reasoning.

b. Write the ratio of eighth grade club members to sixth grade club members.

    i. Write the ratio of the total number of chess club members to the number of eighth grade club members.

    ii. Write the ratio of the total number of chess club members to the number of sixth grade club members.

    iii. Which is greater: the ratio of all chess club members to eighth grade members, or the ratio of all chess club members to sixth grade members? Explain your reasoning.

2. A local mall owner is trying to attract more middle school students on the weekends to increase business from both the students and their parents or guardians. The owner collected the data shown from local middle schools for the question: Which activity should the mall add to increase business?

Types of Activities Preferred by Middle School Students

Activity	6th Graders	7th Graders
Roller Skating	120	60
Arcade Playing	80	120
Watching Movies	40	180
TOTAL	**240**	**360**

Manny said that the ratio of 6th graders who prefer roller skating is the same as the ratio of 7th graders who prefer watching movies. Donnie thought he was wrong because the number of 7th graders who prefer watching movies is larger than the number of 6th graders who prefer roller skating. Who is correct? Explain your reasoning.

3. A survey of the sixth graders with pets revealed that 20 students prefer cats and 10 students prefer dogs.

   a. How would you compare these two statements using part-to-whole ratios?

   b. How would you compare these two statements using part-to-part ratios?

Talk the Talk

There are several ways to compare two quantities and write ratios.

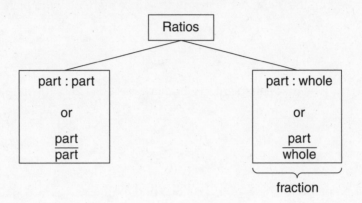

Ratios

part : part

or

$\dfrac{part}{part}$

part : whole

or

$\dfrac{part}{whole}$

fraction

1. Consider the statement: There are 40 sixth grade band members and 160 total sixth graders.

   a. Write a part-to-part ratio using colon notation.

   b. Write a part-to-whole ratio using colon notation.

2. Analyze each statement. Determine whether a part : part or a part : whole relationship exists.

   a. There are 9 girls for every 2 boys in art class.

   Think about the quantities you are comparing.

   b. Three out of every five students in art class will help paint the mural in the library.

   c. There are 3 blueberry muffins to every bran muffin in a variety pack.

d. There are 9 calories of fat in every gram of fat.

e. Of the 30 students in chorus, 14 of them play the piano.

f. The students planted 22 yellow daffodils and 10 white daffodils.

 Be prepared to share your solutions and methods.

5.3

I'D LIKE TO SOLVE THE PUZZLE...

Writing Equivalent Ratios

The 1950s can easily be described as the game show era. Game shows dominated network television, pitting people against each other. Contestants used their intelligence to answer questions to win either money or household appliances. Unfortunately, in 1956, it was discovered that certain game shows had ensured that audience-favored contestants would continue to win by supplying those contestants with the answers ahead of time. Despite this, legislation helped game shows regain their popularity—which exists even to this very day.

Can you think of any game shows where your mathematical knowledge would be helpful?

5

Problem 1   Quiz Bowl

Only one sixth grader will represent Stewart Middle School in the Math Quiz Bowl that airs on television next month. Auditions were held yesterday after school. The results for four students are shown.

Maria

6 problems correct
9 problems incorrect

Tony

4 problems correct
8 problems incorrect

Anita

3 problems correct
7 problems incorrect

Carlo

9 problems correct
15 problems incorrect

1. Write each student's result as a ratio of problems correct to total problems attempted.

2. Which student should represent the sixth grade? Explain your reasoning.

3. List the students in order from the student who had the best results to the student who had the worst results.

4. Explain how Tia's reasoning and Lisa's reasoning are incorrect.

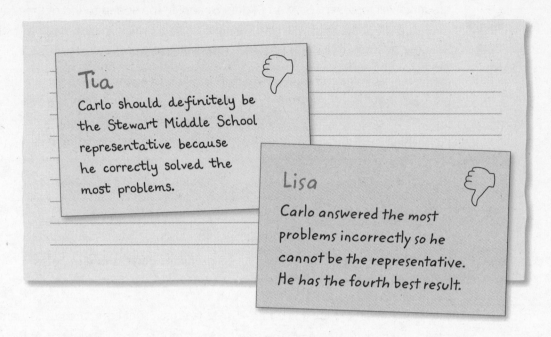

Tia

Carlo should definitely be the Stewart Middle School representative because he correctly solved the most problems.

Lisa

Carlo answered the most problems incorrectly so he cannot be the representative. He has the fourth best result.

5. Predict how many problems each student would solve correctly in a 240-problem Math Quiz Bowl tournament. Use the data from the auditions to formulate your prediction.

5

One of the rounds at the Math Quiz Bowl tournament is a speed round. A team of four students will represent Stewart Middle School in the speed round of the Math Quiz Bowl. One student of the team will be chosen to solve as many problems as possible in 20 minutes. The results from this week's practice are recorded in the table.

Student	Number of Correctly Solved Problems in a Specified Time
Kaye	4 problems correct in 5 minutes
Susan	7 problems correct in 10 minutes
Doug	1 problem correct in 2 minutes
Mako	3 problems correct in 4 minutes

Each quantity in the table is a *rate*. A **rate** is a ratio that compares two quantities that are measured in different units. The rate for each student in this situation is the number of problems solved per amount of time.

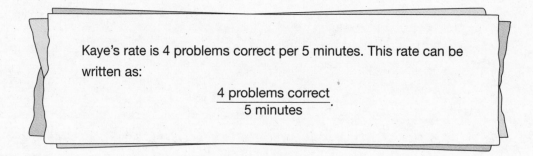

Kaye's rate is 4 problems correct per 5 minutes. This rate can be written as:

$$\frac{4 \text{ problems correct}}{5 \text{ minutes}}.$$

6. Write the rates for the other three team members.

   a. Susan:

   b. Doug:

   c. Mako:

When two ratios or rates are equivalent to each other, you can write them as a proportion. A proportion is an equation that states that two ratios are equal. You can write a proportion by placing an equals sign between the two equivalent ratios.

For example, you know that Kaye got four problems correct per 5 minutes. So, you can predict how many problems she could answer correctly in 20 minutes.

$$\frac{\text{problems correct}}{\text{minutes}} \longrightarrow \overset{\times 4}{\underset{\times 4}{\frac{4}{5} = \frac{\boxed{16}}{20}}}$$

Kaye can probably answer 16 problems correctly in 20 minutes.

When you change a ratio to an equivalent ratio with larger numbers, you are *scaling up* the ratio. **Scaling up** means you multiply the numerator and the denominator by the same factor.

It is important to remember to write the numbers representing the same quantity in both numerators and in both denominators. It doesn't matter which quantity is in the numerator or denominator; it matters that the unit of measure is consistent among the ratios.

Another way you can write equivalent ratios for Kaye correctly solving problems in 20 minutes is this way:

It's important to think about ing up the labels hen writing equal ratios.

$$\frac{\text{minutes}}{\text{problems correct}} \longrightarrow \overset{\times 4}{\underset{\times 4}{\frac{5}{4} = \frac{20}{\boxed{16}}}}$$

7. Use the scaling up method to determine the number of problems the student can probably solve in 20 minutes. Explain the scaling up factor you used to determine the equivalent ratio.

   a. Susan

   b. Doug

   c. Mako

5

The muffin variety packs baked by the Healthy for U Bakery come in a ratio of 2 blueberry muffins to 5 total muffins.

8. Scale up each muffin ratio to determine the unknown quantity.

   a. $\dfrac{2 \text{ blueberry muffins}}{5 \text{ total muffins}} = \dfrac{20 \text{ blueberry muffins}}{? \text{ total muffins}}$

   b. $\dfrac{2 \text{ blueberry muffins}}{5 \text{ total muffins}} = \dfrac{30 \text{ blueberry muffins}}{? \text{ total muffins}}$

c. $\dfrac{2 \text{ blueberry muffins}}{5 \text{ total muffins}} = \dfrac{? \text{ blueberry muffins}}{100 \text{ total muffins}}$

d. $\dfrac{2 \text{ blueberry muffins}}{5 \text{ total muffins}} = \dfrac{50 \text{ blueberry muffins}}{? \text{ total muffins}}$

e. $\dfrac{2 \text{ blueberry muffins}}{5 \text{ total muffins}} = \dfrac{? \text{ blueberry muffins}}{15 \text{ total muffins}}$

f. $\dfrac{2 \text{ blueberry muffins}}{5 \text{ total muffins}} = \dfrac{28 \text{ blueberry muffins}}{? \text{ total muffins}}$

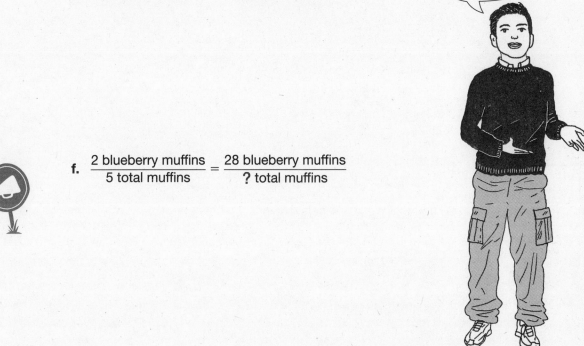

This is just like when we found equivalent fractions!

When you change a ratio to an equivalent ratio with smaller numbers, you are *scaling down* the ratio. **Scaling down** means you divide the numerator and the denominator by the same factor. Scaling down a ratio often makes it easier to understand.

9. Scale down each ratio to determine the unknown quantity.

a. $\dfrac{3 \text{ people}}{9 \text{ pizzas}} = \dfrac{?}{3 \text{ pizzas}}$

b. $\dfrac{2 \text{ hoagies}}{6 \text{ people}} = \dfrac{1 \text{ hoagie}}{?}$

c. $\dfrac{100 \text{ track shirts}}{25 \text{ people}} = \dfrac{?}{1 \text{ person}}$

d. $\dfrac{60 \text{ tracks}}{5 \text{ CDs}} = \dfrac{?}{1 \text{ CD}}$

e. $\dfrac{3 \text{ tickets}}{\$26.25} = \dfrac{1 \text{ ticket}}{?}$

f. $\dfrac{20 \text{ hours of work}}{\$240} = \dfrac{1 \text{ hour of work}}{?}$

g. $\dfrac{12 \text{ hours}}{720 \text{ miles}} = \dfrac{4 \text{ hours}}{?}$

h. $\dfrac{3 \text{ gallons of red paint}}{2 \text{ gallons of yellow paint}} = \dfrac{?}{1 \text{ gallon of yellow paint}}$

Problem 2 Scaling Up and Down

Did you know that chocolate comes from cocoa beans! It's true! It was first invented by the natives of Mexico and Central America!

1. The 6th grade students are making hot chocolate to sell at the Winter Carnival. Each homeroom suggested a different recipe.

The "T" in each recipe stands for Tablespoon!

HR 6A

2 cups milk

3 T cocoa powder

HR 6B

5 cups milk

8 T cocoa powder

HR 6C

3 cups milk

4 T cocoa powder

HR 6D

4 cups milk

7 T cocoa powder

Complete the table and label the last column with a ratio that will help you answer each question.

Recipe	Cups of Milk Per Recipe	T of Cocoa Powder	
6A			
6B			
6C			
6D			

a. Which recipe should the students use if they want to make their hot chocolate have the most chocolate?

b. Which recipe should the students use if they want to make their hot chocolate have the least chocolate?

2. Scale each common measurement up or down to determine the unknown quantity.

   a. $\dfrac{12 \text{ in.}}{1 \text{ ft}} = \dfrac{48 \text{ in.}}{?}$

   b. $\dfrac{3 \text{ ft}}{1 \text{ yd}} = \dfrac{?}{4 \text{ yd}}$

   c. $\dfrac{360 \text{ min}}{6 \text{ hrs}} = \dfrac{?}{1 \text{ hr}}$

   d. $\dfrac{300 \text{ cm}}{3 \text{ m}} = \dfrac{100 \text{ cm}}{?}$

   e. $\dfrac{64 \text{ fl oz}}{8 \text{ cups}} = \dfrac{?}{1 \text{ cup}}$

   f. $\dfrac{16 \text{ c}}{8 \text{ pt}} = \dfrac{?}{1 \text{ pt}}$

   g. $\dfrac{32 \text{ oz}}{2 \text{ lb}} = \dfrac{16 \text{ oz}}{?}$

   h. $\dfrac{1 \text{ km}}{0.6 \text{ mi}} = \dfrac{5 \text{ km}}{?}$

   i. $\dfrac{5280 \text{ ft}}{1 \text{ mi}} = \dfrac{?}{2 \text{ mi}}$

   j. $\dfrac{72 \text{ hours}}{3 \text{ days}} = \dfrac{?}{1 \text{ day}}$

3. Cube-X's marketing team is designing an advertisement for a new video game called X-QUE. The team's notes say, "Gamers prefer X-QUE over last year's games by 4000 out of 5000." Write a more effective advertising statement. Be creative, but don't forget that your statement must be mathematically accurate.

Be prepared to share your solutions and methods.

5.4 THE MOST IMPORTANT MEAL OF THE DAY

Modeling Ratios

Nutrition experts agree that breakfast is the most important meal of the day. However, many people, including many students, skip this meal. In some instances, people have claimed they would rather sleep more in the morning than wake up earlier to eat. With this thought in mind and the invention of preservatives, the breakfast bar was created. These bars pack enough calories to get people moving in the morning without containing caffeine. Why do you think nutrition experts believe breakfast is the most important meal of the day? Do you think a big breakfast in the morning would cause people to be sluggish in the morning?

5

Problem 1 Breakfast before Activity

Kerri and her friends are going hiking. Kerri invites her friends to meet at her house for a quick breakfast before heading out on their hike. Kerri wants to offer muffins to her friends. She knows that one muffin combo has four muffins that can feed four people.

1. Draw a model showing the relationship between the muffin combo and the number of people it will feed.

2. If Kerri invites 6 friends, how many muffin combos will she need? Draw a model to show how many muffin combo(s) she will need, and explain your answer.

3. If Kerri has $2\frac{3}{4}$ muffin combos, how many friends can she feed? Draw a model to show how many friends she can feed, and explain your answer.

How do your models show a relationship between two quantities?

Problem 2 Oh Yes I Am the Muffin Man

In Problem 1, you drew models to determine the relationship between two quantities. You can also use a *double number line* to visualize relationships. A **double number line** is a model that is made up of two number lines used to represent the equivalence of two related numbers. Each interval on the number line has two sets of numbers and maintains the same ratio.

The Muffin Man Bakery offers two types of muffins—corn or cinnamon raisin. It costs the bakery $2.50 to make 3 corn muffins.

> Remember, the ratio has to be maintained when labeling each number line.

The ratio $2.50 : 3 corn muffins is shown on the double number line.

```
                0         2.50
Cost ($)        ├─────────●─────────┼─────────┼─────────┼─────────┼────────▶
                          ┊
Number
of corn         ├─────────●─────────┼─────────┼─────────┼─────────┼────────▶
muffins         0         3
```

You can see other equivalent ratios of *cost : number of corn muffins* by continuing to label each interval.

```
                0         2.50      5.00      7.50
Cost ($)        ├─────────●─────────●─────────●─────────┼─────────┼────────▶
                          ┊         ┊         ┊
Number
of corn         ├─────────●─────────●─────────●─────────┼─────────┼────────▶
muffins         0         3         6         9
```

1. State the two new ratios of cost : number of corn muffins shown on the second double number line.

2. Describe the interval represented on each number line.

3. Use the double number line to determine equivalent ratios. Then, plot the new ratios. Explain your calculations.

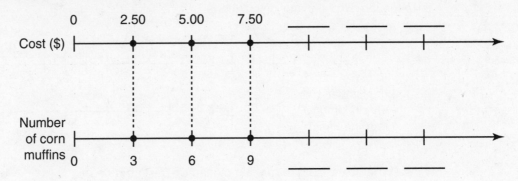

a. What is the cost of making 12 corn muffins?

b. What is the cost of making 15 corn muffins?

c. What is the cost of making 18 corn muffins?

d. Describe any patterns you notice between the cost and the number of corn muffins made.

4. The cost for The Muffin Man Bakery to make 4 cinnamon raisin muffins is $3.20. Complete the double number line to determine equivalent ratios and answer each question. Explain your calculations.

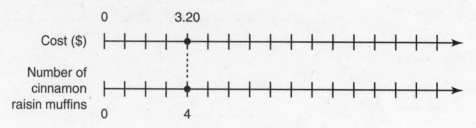

a. What is the cost to make 8 cinnamon raisin muffins?

b. How many cinnamon raisin muffins are made for $12.80?

c. What is the cost of making 12 cinnamon raisin muffins?

5. It takes 1 cup of sugar to make 12 oat bran muffins. Use the double number line to determine equivalent ratios and answer each question. Explain your calculations.

Cups of sugar   0

Number of oat bran muffins   0

a. Plot the given ratio on the double number line.

b. How many oat bran muffins can be made using $\frac{1}{2}$ cup of sugar?

c. How many oat bran muffins can be made using $\frac{2}{3}$ cup of sugar?

d. How many oat bran muffins can be made using $1\frac{1}{2}$ cups of sugar?

e. How many cups of sugar are needed to make 3 muffins?

f. How many cups of sugar are needed to make 15 muffins?

g. How many cups of sugar are needed to make 9 muffins.

6. One pound of bananas costs $0.64. Use the double number lines to determine the cost for each quantity of bananas.

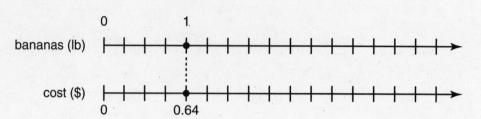

a. $2\frac{1}{2}$ pounds

b. $\frac{1}{2}$ pound

c. 2 pounds

Be prepared to share your solutions and methods.

5.5

A TRIP TO THE MOON
Using Tables to Represent Equivalent Ratios

Learning Goals

In this lesson you will:

▶ Create tables of equivalent ratios.

▶ Use known values in a table to determine equivalent ratios.

A person who weighs 100 pounds on Earth would weigh only about 40 pounds on the planet Mercury and about 91 pounds on Venus. In fact, there are only three planets in our solar system where a 100-pound person would weigh *more* than 100 pounds: Jupiter, Saturn, and Neptune. On Saturn, a 100-pound person would weigh about 106 pounds, on Neptune, about 113 pounds, and on Jupiter, about 236 pounds! On Pluto—which is no longer considered a planet—a 100-pound person would weigh less than 7 pounds.

But what if a 100-pound person could stand on the surface of the Sun? If that were possible, then that person would weigh over 2700 pounds! More than a ton! What causes these differences in weight?

5

Problem 1 Earth Weight : Moon Weight

Gravity is a natural force that attracts objects to each other. Gravity is the pull toward the center of an object like the Earth, a planet, or the moon. Your weight on the Earth is the measure of the amount of gravitational attraction exerted on you by the Earth. The moon has a weaker gravitational force than the Earth.

The ratio of weight on Earth: weight on the moon is approximately 60 lbs : 10 lbs.

You can use ratio tables to show how two quantities are related. Ratio tables are another way to organize information.

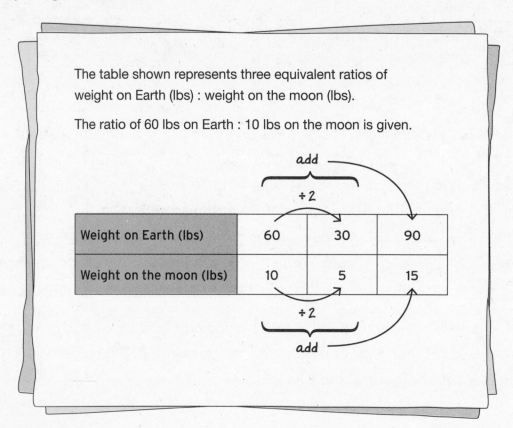

The table shown represents three equivalent ratios of weight on Earth (lbs) : weight on the moon (lbs).

The ratio of 60 lbs on Earth : 10 lbs on the moon is given.

	add	
	÷2	
Weight on Earth (lbs)	60	30	90
Weight on the moon (lbs)	10	5	15
	÷2	
	add	

1. Describe how the second ratio of 30 lbs on Earth : 5 lbs on the moon was calculated.

2. Can you think of a different strategy to determine the ratio of 90 lbs on Earth : 15 lbs on the moon?

Think about how the numbers in the table relate to each other.

3. Howard, Kaye and Carla each determined the weight of a 120-lb person on the moon.

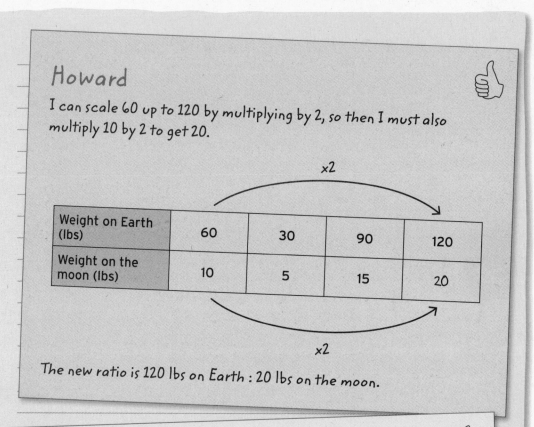

Howard

I can scale 60 up to 120 by multiplying by 2, so then I must also multiply 10 by 2 to get 20.

×2

Weight on Earth (lbs)	60	30	90	120
Weight on the moon (lbs)	10	5	15	20

×2

The new ratio is 120 lbs on Earth : 20 lbs on the moon.

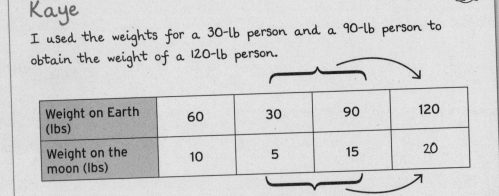

Kaye

I used the weights for a 30-lb person and a 90-lb person to obtain the weight of a 120-lb person.

Weight on Earth (lbs)	60	30	90	120
Weight on the moon (lbs)	10	5	15	20

So that means 120 lbs on Earth : 20 lbs on the moon.

a. Explain Kaye's reasoning.

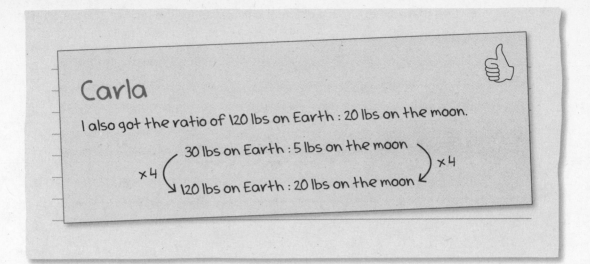

Carla

I also got the ratio of 120 lbs on Earth : 20 lbs on the moon.

30 lbs on Earth : 5 lbs on the moon

×4 ⟨ 120 lbs on Earth : 20 lbs on the moon ⟩ ×4

b. Explain Carla's reasoning.

4. Kaye said, "I see another equivalent ratio when I look at the way Carla showed her work."

30 lbs on Earth : 5 lbs on the moon

120 lbs on Earth : 20 lbs on the moon

150 lbs on Earth : 25 lbs on the moon

Is Kaye correct? Explain her reasoning.

5. Use the table to show a different calculation for the ratio of 150 lbs on Earth : 25 lbs on the moon.

Weight on Earth (lbs)	60	30	90	120	150
Weight on the moon (lbs)	10	5	15	20	25

Problem 2   How Many Pizzas Should I Order?

The 6th-grade pizza party is planned for tomorrow. Tracy is in charge of ordering the pizza for 450 students. The pizza parlor said two pizzas will serve 9 students. Tracy made a ratio table to help her determine how many pizzas to order for 450 students.

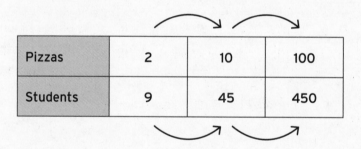

Pizzas	2	10	100
Students	9	45	450

1. She said she should order 100 pizzas. Explain Tracy's method.

2. Complete the table to show the number of pizzas to order given the number of students. Explain your calculations.

Pizzas	2	10	100					
Students	9	45	450	135	270	225	900	1350

3. Use your table of values to answer each question. Explain your calculations.

   a. How many students will 12 pizzas feed?

   b. How many students will 20 pizzas feed?

Think about how to use the ratio of 10 pizzas : 45 students to help you figure out the other pizza amounts.

   c. How many students will 6 pizzas feed?

Problem 3   Mixing More Paint!

Remember, the school colors at Riverview Middle School are a shade of bluish green and white. The art teacher, Mr. Raith, needs to mix different quantities of the green paint for several school projects. It takes 3 parts blue paint to 2 parts yellow paint to create the bluish green color. Carla needs 5 total pints of the bluish green paint, so she used 2 pints of yellow paint and 3 pints of blue paint.

Mr. Raith thought that the art students needed a table to help determine the correct amount of each color of paint for different projects—both large and small.

1. Complete the table with the correct amounts. Explain your reasoning.

Amount of Bluish Green Paint Needed	5 pints	15 pints			
Yellow Paint	2 pints		8 pints		
Blue Paint	3 pints		12 pints	18 pints	1.5 pints

2. Explain what is wrong with Sally's thinking.

Sally

If I want 15 pints of bluish green paint, then I will need to add 10 to the original 5 total parts of bluish green to get 15. So, I should add 10 to each of the other numbers too to get 12 pints of yellow and 13 pints of blue.

Charlie said, "The table is helpful, but it cannot list every amount we might need for every painting project. I think if we multiply $\frac{2}{5}$ times the total amount of bluish green paint we need, we can determine the amount of yellow paint needed. If we multiply $\frac{3}{5}$ times the total amount of bluish green paint we need, we can determine the amount of blue paint needed."

3. What do you think about Charlie's method? Is he correct or incorrect? Explain your reasoning.

Charlene said, "I am thinking about this in a different way. The amount of blue paint is always $1\frac{1}{2}$ times as much as the amount of yellow paint."

4. Is she correct in her thinking? Explain your reasoning.

Clifford said, "My thinking is related to Charlene's. The yellow paint is $\frac{2}{3}$ of the blue paint."

5. Is Clifford correct? Explain your reasoning.

6. How does Clifford's thinking relate to Charlene's thinking?

Problem 4 Yellow and White Daffodils

Each table represents the ratio of yellow daffodils to white daffodils for different garden displays. Complete each ratio table. Explain your calculations.

1.

Yellow daffodils	9	36	45	
White daffodils	15			90

2.

Yellow daffodils	7		28	
White daffodils	6	12		42

3.

Yellow daffodils	32			16
White daffodils		48	6	12

4.

Yellow daffodils	5	1		9
White daffodils		3	30	

5.

Yellow daffodils		105	84	21
White daffodils	20	60		

6.

Yellow daffodils	55	22	77	
White daffodils	25	10		5

 Be prepared to share your solutions and methods.

GRAPHING OUT EQUIVALENCE

Using Graphs to Represent Equivalent Ratios

Learning Goals

In this lesson, you will:

▶ Graph a table of equivalent values.

▶ Read equivalent ratios from graphs.

▶ Use graphs to determine equivalent ratios.

▶ Use graphs to compare different ratios.

A tortoise and a man named Achilles decided to race each other. But before the race began, Achilles was kind enough to offer the tortoise a head start of about 300 feet. The tortoise accepted, saying, "But now, no matter what, I will win the race."

Achilles was startled. "Impossible. I run much faster than you, tortoise."

The tortoise explained, "By the time you reach my starting point 300 feet ahead, I will have run 30 feet. Then, by the time you go 30 more feet to catch up with me, I will have run 3 feet more. By the time you run those extra 3 feet, I will have moved 0.3 foot. It could go on and on like this forever: You run 0.3 foot more to catch up to me, I will be 0.03 foot ahead of you. You run the 0.03 foot required to catch up to me, I will be 0.003 foot ahead of you. Thus, I will certainly win, no matter how fast you run!"

This situation is known as Zeno's second paradox. The tortoise is clearly wrong. But why?

Problem 1   Graphing Equivalent Ratios

Stephanie is driving her car to college at a steady rate of 50 miles per hour. The table shows the ratio *time : distance.*

Time (hrs)	1	2	3	4
Distance (miles)	50	100	150	200

The double number line shown represents the same data.

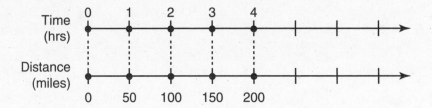

You can also represent equivalent ratios on a coordinate plane.

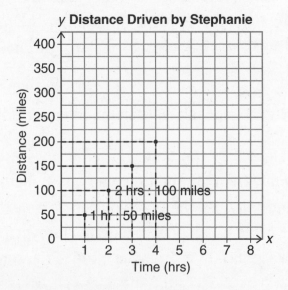

1. Label the remaining ratios on the graph.

You have used several different models and strategies to determine equivalent ratios. You have scaled up and scaled down to determine equivalent ratios. You have also used tables and double number lines. Let's investigate how you can use a graph to determine other equivalent ratios, and see how all the representations are connected.

Let's consider the question: How many miles can Stephanie drive in 6 hours?

You know 4 different equivalent ratios from the original graph. The graph shows how to use the two ratios 2 hrs : 100 miles and 4 hrs : 200 miles to determine the equivalent ratio 6 hrs : 300 miles.

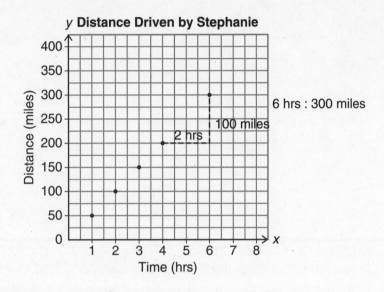

y **Distance Driven by Stephanie**

6 hrs : 300 miles

100 miles

2 hrs

Stephanie can drive 300 miles in 6 hours.

2. Describe how to determine how many miles she can drive in 7 hours given each representation.

   a. using the graph

   b. using the table

   c. using the double number lines

One way to analyze the relationship between equivalent ratios displayed on a graph is to draw a line to connect the points. You can also extend the line to make predictions of other equivalent ratios.

Sometimes when you analyze a graph by drawing a line, all the points on the line make sense. Other times when you draw a line, all the points on the line do not make sense.

A line has an infinite number of points

3. Draw a line through all the points you plotted on your graph. What do you notice?

4. Do all the points on the line you drew make sense in this problem situation? Why or why not?

So, we are comparing time and distance. Do fractional values make sense?

5. How do all the representations—tables, double number lines and graphs—show equivalent ratios. How are they similar? Describe any advantages you see one representation has over the others.

5

Problem 2   Comparing Ticket Costs—and Ratios!

The adult ticket price for admission into the Rollerville Amusement Park is $15.

The table and graph show the ratio *number of adult ticket prices: cost*.

Adult Tickets	1	2	3	4
Cost ($)	15	30	45	60

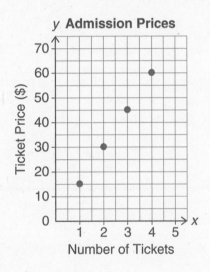

The Rollerville Amusement Park has different charges for students and pre-school age children. Student tickets are $10. Pre-school age children tickets are $5.

1. Complete each table.

Student Tickets	1	2	3	4
Cost ($)				

Pre-School Tickets	1	2	3	4
Cost ($)				

2. Plot each set of equivalent ratios on the previous graph. Use a △ for the student tickets : cost ratios and a □ for pre-school tickets : cost ratios.

3. Draw three separate lines through the points that represent each ratio. What do you notice?

Drawing a line is a way to model equivalent ratios.

4. Do all the points on the line you drew make sense in this problem situation? Why or why not?

5. How can you tell by looking at the three lines which rate *cost to ticket* is the highest?

6. How can you tell by looking at the three lines which rate *cost to ticket* is the lowest?

Problem 3 Picture Day!

Pictures in the school yearbook must be in a constant ratio of *width to length* of 2 to 3.

1. Complete the table showing acceptable measurements for pictures.

Width (cm)	2		6		10	
Length (cm)	3	6		12		18

A constant ratio is a ratio that has a constant value.

2. Label the axes and plot the table values on the graph.

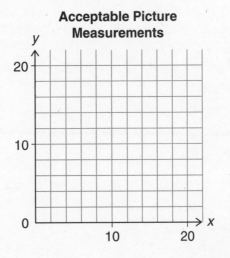

Acceptable Picture Measurements

3. Compare your graphs with the graphs of your classmates. Did everyone label their axes the same? Could you have labeled your axes differently?

Problem 4   Using Graphs to Chart Calorie Loss!

Augie burns 225 calories per 30 minutes of bicycling.

1. Complete the table to chart his calorie expenditure for different amounts of time.

Calories Burned				
Time (mins)	30	10	60	50

2. Plot the table of values on the graph.

Drawing a line may help you see the relationships.

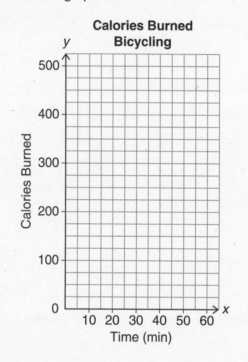

Calories Burned Bicycling

3. Use your graph to answer each question.

   a. How many minutes would Augie have to bike to burn 150 calories?

   b. How many calories can he burn if he bikes for 25 minutes?

4. How was the graph helpful? Were there any limitations when using the graph to determine values?

Problem 5   Mixing Trail Mix

The 6th grade chorus made and sold their own mixture of trail mix at basketball games to raise money for an upcoming trip. During the first basketball game they only sold 1 lb bags for $2.80. They got many requests to sell different sized bags of their trail mix. The group decided to vary the size of the bag, but wanted to make sure that the ratio of *cost : pound* remained the same.

1. Complete the table to display the cost for various pounds of trail mix.

Trail Mix Weight (lbs)	0.25	0.5	0.75	1	1.25	1.5
Cost ($)						

2. Create a graph for your table of values. Be sure to label the axes and name the graph.

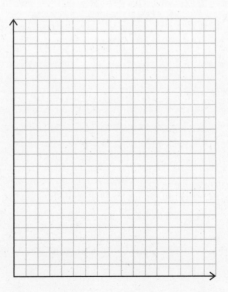

3. How does your graph display equivalent ratios?

4. Compare your graphs with your classmates. Did everyone label their axes the same? Could you have labeled your axes differently?

Talk the Talk

Go back and examine all the graphs in this lesson.

1. What is similar about all of the graphs?

2. What is different about all the graphs?

3. What are the advantages and disadvantages of displaying and interpreting ratios from graphs? Describe how you can use a line to analyze equivalent ratios. What do you have to consider to determine if any point on the line represents an equivalent ratio?

Be prepared to share your solutions and methods.

WATER IS A PRECIOUS RESOURCE
5.7
Using Multiple Ratio Representations to Solve Problems

Learning Goals

In this lesson you will:

▶ Read and interpret ratios from graphs, double number lines, and tables.

▶ Use multiple ratio models to solve problems.

▶ Determine equivalent ratios using multiple representations.

Have you ever noticed the acronym "gpf" written on toilets? This acronym stands for "gallons per flush," which refers to the amount of water used each time you flush the toilet.

Today's toilets use much less water, which saves people money and is friendlier to the environment. Before 1980, a typical toilet used 5 to 7 gallons of water for each flush. Today, about 1 gallon is used per flush. For a typical household, this provides a savings of about 10,000 to 20,000 gallons of water each year.

So today people save a little more money, instead of just throwing it down the toilet!

Problem 1   Using Water for Waste and to Clean

1. The graph shown represents the number of gallons of water used for the number of times a toilet is flushed.

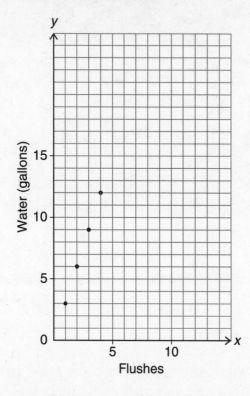

a. Write each point on the graph as the ratio of *gallons of water used : number of flushes*.

b. What do you notice about each ratio?

c. How many gallons of water would be used if the toilet was flushed 8 times? Explain the method you used.

d. How many flushes would occur to use 18 gallons of water? Explain the method you used.

e. Did you use the same method to answer each question? If not, why?

2. The graph shown represents the number of gallons of water used for the number of loads of laundry washed.

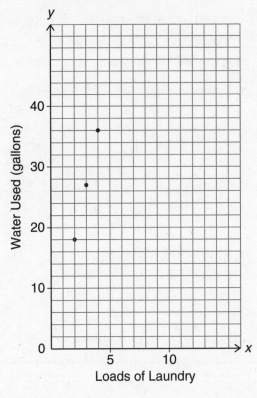

a. Write each point on the graph as the ratio of *gallons of water used : number of loads of laundry*.

b. What do you notice about each ratio?

c. How many gallons of water would be used for 7 loads of laundry? Explain the method you used.

d. How many loads of laundry can be done if 45 gallons of water are used? Explain the method you used.

e. Did you use the same method to answer each question? If not, why?

Problem 2   Determining the Most Efficient Shower Head

Shower heads come in various styles and allow different rates of water to flow. The ratio *gallons of water : time* is given for three different shower head models. Explain your reasoning for each question by using the double number line, or creating a table.

1. The first shower head uses 20 gallons of water for every 5 minutes.

a. How many gallons of water are used in 1 minute?

b. How many gallons of water are used in 15 minutes?

c. How many gallons of water are used in 10 minutes?

d. How many gallons of water are used in 14 minutes?

e. How many gallons of water are used in 22 minutes?

f. Did you use the same method to answer each question? If not, why?

2. A second shower head model uses 25 gallons of water for every 10 minutes.

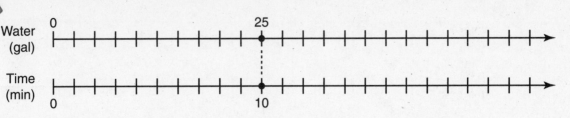

a. How many gallons of water are used in 1 minute?

b. How many gallons of water are used in 15 minutes?

c. How many gallons of water are used in 4 minutes?

d. How many gallons of water are used in 14 minutes?

e. How many gallons of water are used in 22 minutes?

f. Did you use the same method to answer each question? If not, why?

3. A third shower head model uses 8 gallons of water for every 5 minutes.

a. How many gallons of water are used in 1 minute?

b. How many gallons of water are used in 15 minutes?

c. How many gallons of water are used in 10 minutes?

d. How many gallons of water are used in 7 minutes?

e. How many gallons of water are used in 14 minutes?

4. Which of the three shower heads used the least amount of water per minute?

5. Which method or model did you use to answer each? Was one method more efficient than another?

Talk the Talk

Given the ratio 6 red marbles : 9 blue marbles, represent one ratio that is larger than the given and one ratio that is smaller than the given through each model in the graphic organizer provided. Explain how you can use each model to determine the equivalent ratios.

Be prepared to share your solutions and methods.

SCALE UP / SCALE DOWN

TABLE

6 RED MARBLES :
9 BLUE MARBLES

DOUBLE NUMBER LINES

GRAPH

5

5.8 WHAT IS THE BETTER BUY?

Introduction to Unit Rates

Learning Goals

In this lesson, you will:

▶ Use unit rates to solve problems.

▶ Use unit rates to calculate the best buy.

▶ Calculate unit rates.

Key Term

▶ unit rate

Have you ever traveled to another country? If so, you probably had to take your passport with you, and exchange American dollars into foreign currency. Exchange rates are generally between the lowest currency denominations of two countries. So when exchanging American dollars, the exchange rate will reflect how much the U.S. dollar is worth compared to the foreign currency. Some examples of foreign currencies are the euro, the British pound, and the Argentine peso. Can you name other foreign currencies? Do any currencies share a similar name to the U.S. dollar?

5

Problem 1   Using Unit Rates to Determine the Best Buy!

As you learned previously, a rate is a ratio in which the two quantities being compared are measured in different units. A **unit rate** is a comparison of two measurements in which the denominator has a value of one unit. The most common place you may have encountered unit rates is at the supermarket. Unit rates can help you determine which of two or more items is the best buy.

Car manufacturers also use unit rates when they advertise how many miles per gallon their car can travel in the city or on the highway.

Even microwave popcorn producers will boast about how few kernels of popcorn remained unpopped per one bag. They will usually use this unit rate to compare to their rival popcorn producers.

1. Compare the prices for various sizes of popcorn sold at the local movie theater.

Mega Bag	$10.24 for 32 oz
Giant Bag	$6.00 for 24 oz
Medium Bag	$4.48 for 16 oz
Kid's Bag	$2.40 for 8 oz

a. What is the unit rate price per ounce for each bag of popcorn?

b. What size popcorn is the best buy? Explain your reasoning.

2. The local paper published these rates on gas mileage for a few new cars.

"Avalar can travel 480 miles on 10 gallons of gas."

"Sentar can travel 400 miles on 8 gallons of gas."

"Comstar can travel 360 miles on 9 gallons of gas."

Change each to unit rates so that it reports miles per one gallon of gas.

a. Avalar

b. Sentar

c. Comstar

3. How can unit rates help you make decisions about comparisons?

Unit rates are also useful when calculating multiple numbers of an item.

4. Complete each table.

a. Carpet is sold by the square yard. Classroom carpet sells for $10.50 per square yard.

1 yd²	40 yd²	50 yd²	100 yd²
$10.50			

b. Pink Lady apples are sold by the pound. One pound of Pink Lady apples costs $2.99.

1 lb	2 lbs	5 lbs	10 lbs	20 lbs
$2.99				

c. Purchases in your county have a 7 percent sales tax added for every dollar of the purchase price.

$1	$5	$10	$20	$50	$100
$0.07					

d. How did you use each unit rate to complete each table?

Problem 2   Using Unit Rates

The yearbook advisors at Stewart Middle School organize *The Prep* Rally and Run each year to raise money for *The Prep* Yearbook. *The Prep* Rally and Run takes place over the weekend so students can accumulate miles for two days. Each student must find sponsors who will pledge a dollar amount for each mile the student runs.

1. Paul asks for $1 pledges for every mile he runs. He was able to find 35 people to each pledge $1 per mile he runs. Casey asks for $2 pledges for every mile she runs. She was able to find 15 people to each pledge $2 per mile she runs.

a. Complete the rate table for Paul to track his pledges.

Number of Miles Run	1	2	3	4	5	6	7	8	9	10
Money Pledged Per Mile Run (dollars)										
Total Money Raised										

b. Complete the rate table for Casey to track her pledges.

Number of Miles Run	1	2	3	4	5	6	7	8	9	10
Money Pledged Per Mile Run (dollars)										
Total Money Raised										

c. If Paul raises $525 for *The Prep* Rally and Race, how many miles did he run? Explain your reasoning.

d. If Casey raises $420 for *The Prep* Rally and Race, how many miles did she run? Explain your reasoning.

2. In the spring, the gym teachers at Stewart Middle School sponsor a bike-a-thon to raise money for new sporting equipment. Students seek sponsors to pledge a dollar amount for each mile they ride.

a. Paul can ride 5.5 miles per hour. At this rate, how far will he ride in 5 hours?

b. Casey can ride 6.25 miles per hour. At this rate, how far will she ride in 5 hours?

c. If Leticia rides 36.25 miles in 5 hours, what is her rate?

d. Guadalupe rode 38 miles at 8 miles per hour. How long did she ride?

e. Emil got a cramp in his leg after riding 19 miles in 2 hours. What was his rate up until he got a leg cramp?

f. Ichiro was pedaling at 15 miles per hour and could only last for 19.5 miles. How long did he ride?

g. What formula can you use to relate the distance, the rate, and the time?

3. Guests at a dinner play are seated at three tables. Each table is served large, round loaves of bread instead of individual rolls. Each person at the table shares the loaves equally.

> Table 1 has six guests and is served two loaves of bread.
>
> Table 2 has eight guests and is served three loaves of bread.
>
> Table 3 has 10 guests and is served four loaves of bread.

a. At which table does each guest get the most bread?

b. How much bread does each guest at each table get?

4. Katy can run 3 laps in 9 minutes. Sonya can run 2 laps in 7 minutes. Who is the faster runner, or do they run at the same pace?

5. Peter and Paul are making mini-muffins for the school bake sale. Peter makes 5 mini-muffins every 25 minutes. Paul makes 3 mini-muffins every 10 minutes. If they both continue to make mini-muffins at the same rate, which boy will make more muffins, or will they make the same amount?

5

6. On Monday, the school cafeteria sold 4 chocolate milks for every 10 white milks. On Tuesday, the cafeteria sold 1 chocolate milk for every 3 white milks. On which day did the cafeteria sell more chocolate milk, or did it sell the same amount on the two days?

7. The tour bus drove 120 miles in 2 hours and the school bus drove 180 miles in 3 hours. Which bus drove faster, or did the two buses drive at the same speed?

 Be prepared to share your solutions and methods.

5

Chapter 5   Summary

5.1   Introduction to Ratios

A **ratio** is a comparison of two quantities that uses division. There are two types of ratios, part-to-part ratios and part-to-whole ratios. Ratios can be represented in words, with a colon, as a fraction, or with a model.

Example

A department store sells multi-packs of dress socks. Each pack includes 3 pairs of grey socks, 2 pairs of striped socks, and 1 pair of polka dot socks. There are different ways to think about this relationship and make comparisons.

The relationship between the number of pairs of striped socks and the number of pairs of grey socks can be represented in a model as follows.

The relationship between the number of pairs of polka dot socks and the number of pairs of striped socks can be written in words as follows. These ratios are examples of part-to-part ratios.

1 polka dot pair to 2 striped pairs   2 striped pairs to 1 polka dot pair

The relationship between the number of black pairs of socks and the total number of pairs of socks can be written with a colon as follows. These ratios are examples of part-to-whole ratios.

3 grey pairs : 6 total pairs   6 total pairs : 3 grey pairs

The relationship between the number of grey pairs of socks and the number of polka dot pairs of socks can be written in fractional form as follows.

$$\frac{3 \text{ grey pairs}}{1 \text{ polka dot pair}}$$ $$\frac{1 \text{ polka dot pair}}{3 \text{ grey pairs}}$$

Comparing Ratios

To compare two ratios, first write each ratio in fractional form. Then write each ratio in simplest form.

Example

A survey of middle school students shows that 175 out of 250 seventh grade students prefer sports drinks to water. For eighth grade students, the survey shows 160 out of 200 prefer sports drinks to water.

Seventh Grade Students:

$$\frac{175 \text{ prefer sports drinks}}{250 \text{ total students}} = \frac{7}{10}$$

Eighth Grade Students:

$$\frac{160 \text{ prefer sports drinks}}{200 \text{ total students}} = \frac{8}{10}$$

Because $\frac{8}{10} > \frac{7}{10}$, the eighth grade has a higher ratio of students who prefer sports drinks to water.

Writing Rates

A **rate** is a ratio that compares two quantities that are measured in different units.

Example

Shen is taking a timed math quiz. During the 10-minute quiz he answers 24 problems. The rate at which Shen took the quiz is the number of problems answered per amount of time.

Shen's rate is 24 problems per 10 minutes, or $\frac{24 \text{ problems}}{10 \text{ minutes}}$.

5.3 Scaling Up and Scaling Down

When you change a ratio to an equal ratio with larger numbers, you are *scaling up* the ratio. **Scaling up** means you multiply the numerator and the denominator by the same factor. When you change a ratio to an equivalent ratio with smaller numbers, you are *scaling down* the ratio. **Scaling down** means you divide the numerator and the denominator by the same factor.

Example

A variety box of fruit snacks contains 6 packs of orange snacks, 3 packs of cherry snacks, and 3 packs of grape snacks.

The ratio of packs of orange snacks to the total number of packs in a box is $\frac{6 \text{ orange packs}}{12 \text{ total packs}}$.

You can scale up the ratio to determine the number of packs of orange snacks if there are 36 total packs.

$$\frac{6 \text{ orange packs}}{12 \text{ total packs}} = \frac{? \text{ orange packs}}{36 \text{ total packs}}$$

$$\frac{6 \text{ orange packs}}{12 \text{ total packs}} \overset{\times 3}{\underset{\times 3}{\longrightarrow}} \frac{18 \text{ orange packs}}{36 \text{ total packs}}$$

You can scale down the ratio to determine the number of packs of orange snacks if there are 6 total packs.

$$\frac{6 \text{ orange packs}}{12 \text{ total packs}} = \frac{? \text{ orange packs}}{6 \text{ total packs}}$$

$$\frac{6 \text{ orange packs}}{12 \text{ total packs}} \overset{\div 2}{\underset{\div 2}{\longrightarrow}} \frac{3 \text{ orange packs}}{6 \text{ total packs}}$$

5

5.4 Drawing Models to Solve Problems Involving Ratios

You can use any symbols to represent objects in a ratio. You can compare parts to parts, or parts to the whole. Represent simple fractions with parts of a circle or other shape.

Example

One container of soup feeds four adults. To determine how many containers of soup will feed 15 people, you can perform the following steps:

● Draw groups of four people per container until you draw 15 people.

● Because three people form three-fourths of a group, draw only three-fourths of the symbol representing the container.

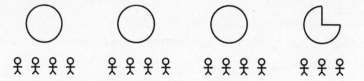

● Count the number of containers.

A total of $3\frac{3}{4}$ containers of soup are needed for 15 people.

5.4 Drawing Double Number Lines to Solve Problems Involving Ratios

A **double number line** is a model that is made up of two number lines used to represent the equivalence of two related numbers. Each interval on the number line has two sets of numbers and maintains the same ratio.

Example

Kelly used 7 balls of yarn to knit 3 sweaters of the same size. You can complete a double number line to determine equivalent ratios and determine how many balls of yarn are needed for 12 sweaters.

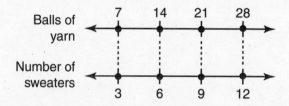

Kelly would need 28 balls of yarn to make 12 sweaters.

5.5 Completing Ratio Tables

A ratio table shows how two quantities are related.

Example

Nina is mixing red paint and yellow paint to make orange paint. The shade of orange Nina wants to make is made by mixing 2 parts red paint to 5 parts yellow paint. You can complete a ratio table to determine the amount of paint Nina needs to make 28 pints of orange paint.

Amount of Orange Paint	7 pints	14 pints	21 pints	28 pints
Red Paint	2 pints	4 pints	6 pints	8 pints
Yellow Paint	5 pints	10 pints	15 pints	20 pints

5.6 Graphing Equivalent Ratios

Equivalent ratios can be represented on a coordinate plane.

Example

Carmen is driving to the beach for a summer vacation. She is traveling at a steady rate of 60 miles per hour. The table shows the ratio *time* : *distance*.

Time (hours)	1	3	5
Distance (miles)	60	180	300

The coordinate plane also shows the ratio *time* : *distance*.

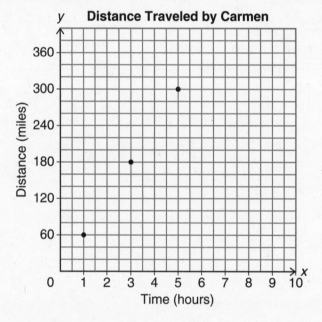

The graph can be used to determine other equivalent ratios. From the graph you can see that Carmen traveled 120 miles after 2 hours.

5.7 Reading and Interpreting Ratios from Graphs

Equivalent ratios can be represented on a coordinate plane.

Example

The graph shows the cost of bananas on sale at a local grocery store.

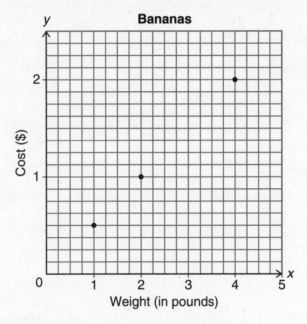

Write each point on the graph as the ratio of *cost : pound*.

$0.50 : 1 pound of bananas

$1.00 : 2 pounds of bananas

$2.00 : 4 pounds of bananas

Eight pounds of bananas would cost $4.00.

$$\frac{\$2.00}{4 \text{ pounds}} = \frac{?}{8 \text{ pounds}}$$

$$\frac{\$2.00}{4 \text{ pounds}} \overset{\times 2}{\underset{\times 2}{\rightrightarrows}} \frac{\$4.00}{8 \text{ pounds}}$$

Unit Rates

A **unit rate** is a comparison of two measurements in which the denominator has a value of one unit.

Example

Pedro is comparing brands of cereal at the grocery store.

Brand A: 20 oz box for $3.49

Brand B: 18 oz box for $2.89

Brand C: 22 oz box for $3.15

The unit rate for Brand A is $\frac{\$3.49}{20 \text{ oz}}$, or approximately $0.17 per ounce.

The unit rate for Brand B is $\frac{\$2.89}{18 \text{ oz}}$, or approximately $0.16 per ounce.

The unit rate for Brand C is $\frac{\$3.15}{22 \text{ oz}}$, or approximately $0.14 per ounce.

Brand C has the lowest unit rate price per ounce and is the best buy.

Nice work! You just finished a tough chapter!

6 PERCENTS

A symphony orchestra can create a wide range of musical sounds. According to the Guinness Book of World Records, the largest orchestral work ever written is Havergal Brian's Symphony #1, which calls for 190 instruments (including a thunder machine and some chains) and a choir of 700 voices!

6

387

6

6.1 PERCENTS CAN MAKE OR BREAK YOU!

Introduction to Percents

What are the latest numbers in the polls? The word poll actually has several meanings. It can be used as another word for *survey*, but *poll* usually refers to the survey used to find out the opinions of voters during an election process. In almost any election, candidates and candidate advisors constantly monitor polls to see what the voters' opinions are about that candidate. What other types of polls have you seen? Where have you seen polls displayed?

Problem 1   They're All Part of the Same Family

What do these statements mean to you?

- There is an 80 percent chance of rain tomorrow.

- You earn 90 percent on a science test.

- Big Sale! 25 percent discount on all regular-priced items.

- Your bill at the Eat and Talk Restaurant is $40. Below the total, the restaurant adds a 20 percent tip.

- The star of the high school basketball team makes 80 percent of his free throws.

- Sales tax is 7 percent in Richmond County.

- Yuma, Arizona, has sunny days 90 percent of the time.

A **percent** is a fraction in which the denominator is 100. Percent is another name for hundredths. The percent symbol "%" means "out of 100." Therefore:

35% means 35 out of 100.

35% as a fraction is $\frac{35}{100}$.

35% as a decimal is 0.35.

35% as a ratio is 35 to 100, or 35 : 100.

You can shade 35 of the 100 squares on the hundredths grid to represent 35%.

So, a percent is a part-to-whole ratio.

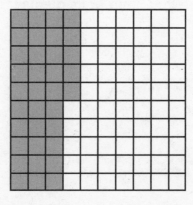

Percents, fractions, and decimals can be used interchangeably.

1. Each hundredths grid represents a whole. Write the shaded part as a fraction, decimal, and percent.

a.

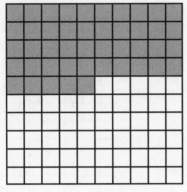

b.

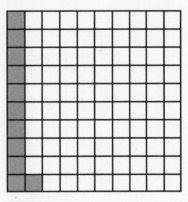

c.

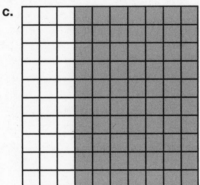

d.

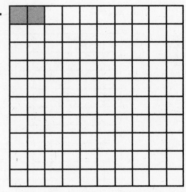

e.

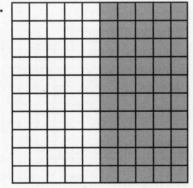

f.

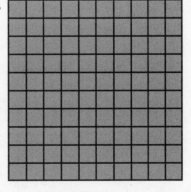

2. Shade the hundredths grids to represent each percent shown. Then, write the equivalent fraction and decimal for each percent.

a. 44%

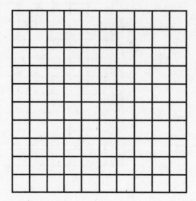

b. 16%

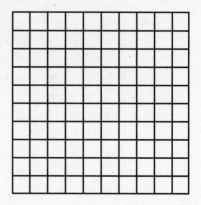

c. 97%

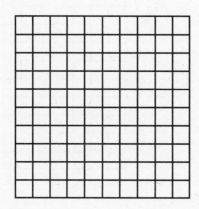

d. 117%

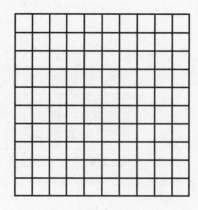 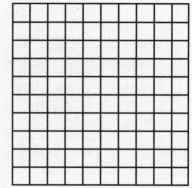

3. Look at the percents and the decimals you wrote for Question 2 to determine a pattern. Use this pattern to describe how you can write any percent as a decimal.

Remember a percent tells you how many hundredths.

4. Write each percent as a decimal.

   a. 12%   **b.** 3%

   c. 80%   **d.** 125%

5. Write each decimal as a percent.

   a. 0.4   **b.** 0.37

   c. 0.7381   **d.** 0.52

When the denominator is a factor of 100, scale up the fraction to write it as a percent. When the denominator is not a factor of 100, you can divide the numerator by the denominator to write the fraction as a decimal, which you can then write as a percent.

6. Write each fraction as a percent. Round your answer to the nearest tenth.

   a. $\frac{4}{5}$ **b.** $\frac{3}{10}$

   c. $\frac{3}{8}$ **d.** $\frac{1}{3}$

Use the scaling up method if the denominator is a factor of 100.

6

7. Label each mark on the number line with a fraction, decimal, and percent. Make sure your fractions are in simplest form.

a.

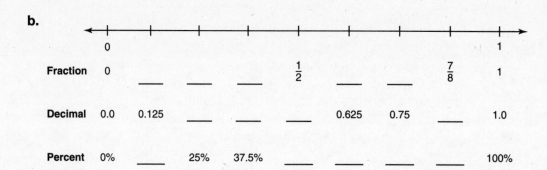

	0		1
Fraction	0	$\frac{1}{3}$	____	1
Decimal	0.0	____	0.6$\overline{6}$	1.0
Percent	0%	____	____	100%

b.

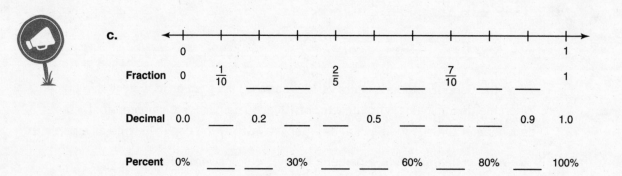

	0				$\frac{1}{2}$			$\frac{7}{8}$	1
Fraction	0	____	____	____	$\frac{1}{2}$	____	____	$\frac{7}{8}$	1
Decimal	0.0	0.125	____	____	____	0.625	0.75	____	1.0
Percent	0%	____	25%	37.5%	____	____	____	____	100%

c.

	0									1
Fraction	0	$\frac{1}{10}$	____	____	$\frac{2}{5}$	____	____	$\frac{7}{10}$	____	____	1
Decimal	0.0	____	0.2	____	____	0.5	____	____	____	0.9	1.0
Percent	0%	____	____	30%	____	____	60%	____	80%	____	100%

Problem 2 Survey Says . . .

1. One hundred sixth-grade students took a survey that asked questions about an upcoming class trip.

   a. Complete the table to represent each survey result as a ratio using colon notation, as a fraction, as a decimal, and as a percent. Make sure your fractions and ratios are in simplest form.

	Ratio	Fraction	Decimal	Percent
How many days should we plan for the trip?				
Stay overnight two nights 60 out of 100 students				
Stay overnight one night 25 out of 100 students				
No overnight stay 15 out of 100 students				
Where should we go?				
Philadelphia 35 out of 100 students				
Washington, D.C. 22 out of 100 students				
New York City 30 out of 100 students				
Atlanta 13 out of 100 students				
How should we get there?				
Bus 25 out of 100 students				
Airplane 75 out of 100 students				
Are you planning on going on the trip?				
Yes 100 out of 100 students				

b. Write a summary of the results of the survey using percents.

2. On Saturday, Melanie won 3 out of 4 of her tennis matches at the Redstone Tournament. On Sunday, she won 1 out of 4 of her matches at the Mesa Tennis Tournament.

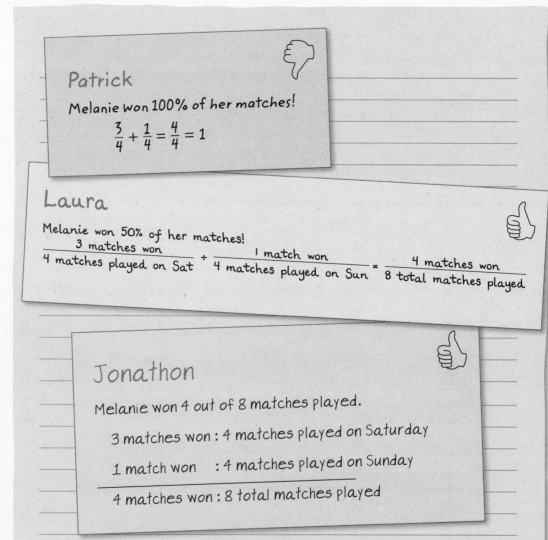

Patrick

Melanie won 100% of her matches!

$$\frac{3}{4} + \frac{1}{4} = \frac{4}{4} = 1$$

Laura

Melanie won 50% of her matches!

$$\frac{3 \text{ matches won}}{4 \text{ matches played on Sat}} + \frac{1 \text{ match won}}{4 \text{ matches played on Sun}} = \frac{4 \text{ matches won}}{8 \text{ total matches played}}$$

Jonathon

Melanie won 4 out of 8 matches played.

3 matches won : 4 matches played on Saturday

1 match won : 4 matches played on Sunday

4 matches won : 8 total matches played

a. What is wrong with Patrick's reasoning?

b. How did Laura make her reasoning explicit?

c. What is the same about Laura's and Jonathon's reasoning? What is different?

d. What ratio of matches did Melanie win?

Problem 3   Do You Think You Know Your Percents?

It's time to play The Percentage Match Game. In this game, you will use your knowledge of percents, fractions, and decimals, and your memory.

Rules of the Game:

- Cut out the cards shown.

- Deal all the cards face down in an array.

- The first player chooses any card in the array. That player then turns over another card to see if it is an equivalent match. If the two cards are an equivalent match, then the two matched cards are put into the player's pile. The first player then picks again and repeats the process until a match is not found.

- If the first player does not have an equivalent match, it is the second player's turn. The same process for picking and matching cards described is now followed by the second player.

- The game continues until all the cards have been paired with an equivalent match.

- Both players then count the number of equivalent matches each player has, and receive 5 points for each equivalent match. The player with the most points wins!

6

$\frac{3}{5}$	$\frac{3}{10}$	$\frac{6}{10}$	30%
0.6	$\frac{1}{3}$	60%	33%
$\frac{1}{8}$	$\frac{2}{6}$	12.5%	$0.\overline{3}$
$\frac{1}{10}$	$\frac{1}{2}$	1%	50%
0.1	$\frac{2}{3}$	10%	$66.6\overline{6}\%$
$\frac{1}{5}$	$\frac{3}{4}$	$\frac{2}{10}$	$\frac{6}{8}$
$\frac{1}{4}$	0.75	$\frac{2}{8}$	75%

6

Talk the Talk

Percents, fractions, and decimals can be used interchangeably. The chart shows some common equivalent fractions, decimals, and percents.

	Common Equivalent Fractions, Decimals, and Percents								
Fraction	$\frac{1}{5}$	$\frac{1}{4}$	$\frac{1}{3}$	$\frac{2}{5}$	$\frac{1}{2}$	$\frac{3}{5}$	$\frac{2}{3}$	$\frac{3}{4}$	$\frac{4}{5}$
Decimal	0.2	0.25	$0.33\overline{3}$	0.4	0.5	0.6	$0.66\overline{6}$	0.75	0.8
Percent	20%	25%	$33\frac{1}{3}\%$	40%	50%	60%	$66\frac{2}{3}\%$	75%	80%

1. How are percents similar to decimals? How are percents and decimals different?

2. How are percents similar to fractions? How are percents and fractions different?

3. How are percents similar to ratios? How are percents and ratios different?

Be prepared to share your solutions and methods.

6

6.2 WACKY WEATHER!
Estimating Percents

Learning Goals

In this lesson, you will:

▶ Estimate percents as fractions and decimals.

▶ Write fractions as percents.

▶ Identify equivalent forms of fractions, decimals, and percents.

▶ Order fractions, decimals, and percents.

Key Term

▶ benchmark percents·

What do you think the following statement means?

"Tomorrow, there will be a 30 percent chance of rain."

Although this statement seems simple enough, a study showed that its meaning can vary dramatically from person to person. There appears to be three different interpretations of the statement: (1) It will rain 30 percent of the time during the day; (2) only 30 percent of the forecasted area will have rain, while the remaining areas will be dry; or (3) there is a 30 in 100, or 3 in 10, chance that it will actually rain. What is common with all of these interpretations is that they are all estimates, but that is where the similarities stop.

So, what do you think "30 percent chance of rain" means?

6

Problem 1   How Much Juice Does It Have?

1. What does the saying, "I gave it 100 percent!" mean?

When you estimate with percents, it is easier to work with those you are familiar with. You know that 100% means one, or the whole, and 50% means half.

A laptop computer uses an icon of a battery on the toolbar to show how much power is left in the battery. When you glance at the icon, you can get a good estimate of how much battery life remains before you need to recharge the battery.

2. Estimate how much battery power remains by writing the percent under each battery icon.

a.
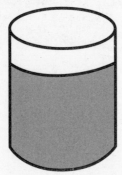

b.
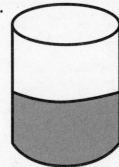

c.
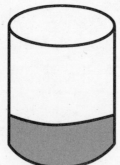

d.
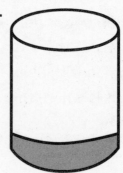

6

e.

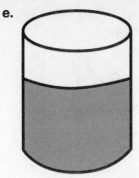

f.

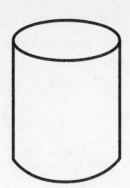

3. Estimate the shaded part of each circle shown, and write it as a percent.

a.

b.

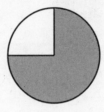

c.

d.

e.

f.

6

4. Estimate the shaded part of each model, and write it as a fraction, a decimal, and a percent. Make sure your fraction is in simplest form.

a.

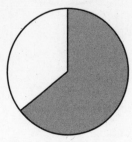

b.

c.

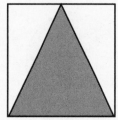

d.

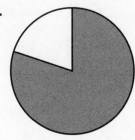

e.

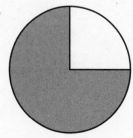

f.

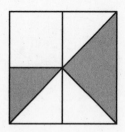

Can I determine the percent shown if the shading isn't all together and the parts are not all the same size?

Sure you can! Think about how you can evenly divide the model to determine the percent shaded!

Problem 2   Benchmark Percents

1. Use your calculator to determine the percent of each number.

   a. 1% of 28 =   **b.** 10% of 28 =

   c. 1% of 234 =   **d.** 10% of 234 =

   e. 1% of 0.85 =   **f.** 10% of 0.85 =

   g. 1% of 5.86 =   **h.** 10% of 5.86 =

   i. 1% of 98.72 =   **j.** 10% of 98.72 =

   k. 1% of 1085.2 =   **l.** 10% of 1085.2 =

   m. What patterns do you notice?

2. Write a rule to calculate 1% of any number.

3. Write a rule to calculate 10% of any number.

A **benchmark percent** is a percent that is commonly used, such as 1%, 5%, 10%, 25%, 50%, and 100%. You can use benchmark percents to calculate any whole percent of a number.

4. State each relationship.

   a. How is 50% related to 100%?

Remember, you worked with the benchmark fractions of 0, $\frac{1}{2}$, and 1.

   b. How is 25% related to 100%? How is 25% related to 50%?

   c. How is 10% related to 100%? How is 10% related to 50%?

   d. How is 5% related to 10%?

   e. How is 1% related to 10%? How is 1% related to 5%?

5. Try these percents mentally. Calculate the value of each using your knowledge of benchmark percents.

   a. 100% of $300   **b.** 1% of $300

   c. 50% of $300   **d.** 25% of $300

   e. 10% of $300   **f.** 5% of $300

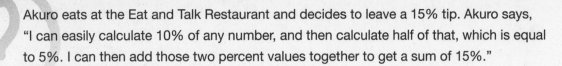

Akuro eats at the Eat and Talk Restaurant and decides to leave a 15% tip. Akuro says, "I can easily calculate 10% of any number, and then calculate half of that, which is equal to 5%. I can then add those two percent values together to get a sum of 15%."

6. Do you think Akuro's method is reasonable? How much should she leave for a tip of 15% on $16.00?

7. What is 15% of each restaurant check total? Explain how you calculated your answer. Round to the nearest hundredth if necessary.

  a. $24.00

  b. $32.56

  c. $47.00

You can determine any whole percent of a number in your head by using 10%, 5%, and 1%.

8. How can you use 10%, 5%, and/or 1% to determine each percent given? Explain your reasoning.

    a. How can you calculate 18% of a number?

    b. How can you calculate 25% of a number?

    c. How can you calculate 37% of a number?

9. Estimate each using 1%, 5%, and 10%.

   a. 27% of 84

   b. 43% of 116

   c. 98% of 389

   d. 77% of 1400

Hmmmm. . . . if we are estimating, will we all get the same answer? If we have different estimates, did we follow different steps?

   e. 12% of 1248

10. About 12% of the United States population is left-handed. Estimate how many left-handed students are in a class of:

    a. 100 students.

    b. 200 students.

    c. 150 students.

So, if 12 percent of the U.S. population is left-handed, what percent of the population might be right-handed?

Problem 3 Ordering Fractions, Decimals, and Percents

1. Order these numbers from greatest to least using what you have learned about fractions, decimals, and percents. Cut out the cards to help you order the numbers.

$33\frac{1}{3}\%$	$\frac{1}{4}$	$\frac{13}{50}$	78%
0.0666...	0.1%	$\frac{3}{4}$	$\frac{50}{75}$
0.098	0.51	$\frac{3}{5}$	80%
0.98	1.0	27%	$\frac{198}{200}$

6

Talk the Talk

The rules for ways to calculate common equivalent fractions, decimals, and percents are shown.

	Fraction	Decimal	Percent
Percent	Write the percent as a fraction with a denominator of 100. Simplify. $28\% = \dfrac{28}{100} = \dfrac{7}{25}$	Write the percent as a fraction with a denominator of 100. Write the fraction as a decimal. $42\% = \dfrac{42}{100} = 0.42$ OR Move the decimal point two places to the left and remove the percent sign. $38\% = 0.38$	
Fraction		Write the fraction as an equivalent fraction with a denominator of 10, 100, 1000 . . . Then, write it as a decimal. $\dfrac{7}{20} = \dfrac{35}{100} = 0.35$ OR Divide the numerator by the denominator. $\dfrac{2}{9} = 2 \div 9 = 0.22\overline{2}\ldots$	Write an equivalent fraction with a denominator of 100. Write the fraction as a percent. $\dfrac{3}{5} = \dfrac{60}{100} = 60\%$ OR Use division to write the fraction as a decimal, and then a percent. $\dfrac{5}{8} = 5 \div 8 = 0.625 = 62.5\%$
Decimal	Write the decimal as a fraction with a denominator of 10, 100, 1000 . . . Simplify. $0.28 = \dfrac{28}{100} = \dfrac{7}{25}$		Write the decimal as a fraction. Then, write the fraction as a percent. $0.08 = \dfrac{8}{100} = 8\%$ OR Write the decimal as a fraction. Then, write the equivalent fraction with a denominator of 100. Then, write the fraction as a percent. $0.4 = \dfrac{4}{10} = \dfrac{40}{100} = 40\%$ OR Move the decimal point two places to the right and add the % sign. $0.08 = 8\%$

6

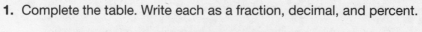

1. Complete the table. Write each as a fraction, decimal, and percent.

Fraction	Decimal	Percent
		3%
	1.5	
$\frac{13}{20}$		
$\frac{2}{3}$		

Be prepared to share your solutions and methods.

6

IT'S ALL IN THE FOLLOW-THROUGH

6.3

Determining the Percent of a Number

Learning Goals

In this lesson, you will:

▶ Determine the percent of a number.

▶ Use double number lines.

Did you know that a professional basketball player can shoot thousands of shots over his or her career? Think about it! Basketball players routinely shoot thousands upon thousands of shots during practices, scrimmages, drills, and the actual games. In fact, one basketball player shot 28,307 shots during career games, making 15,837 of them. This doesn't even include the shots made during practices! How would you calculate this player's shots-made percentage?

Problem 1   There's More than One Way . . .

Mr. Goodwin, the sixth grade math teacher, asked the class to determine 25% of 44. Five different student responses are shown.

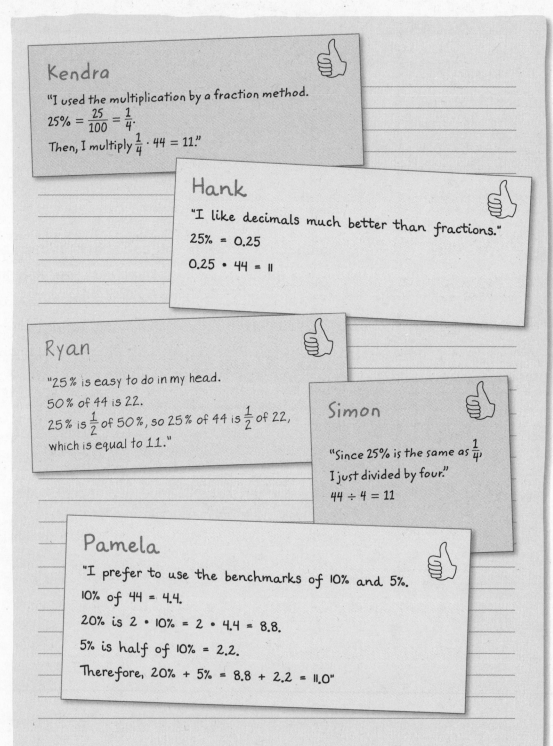

Kendra

"I used the multiplication by a fraction method.

$25\% = \frac{25}{100} = \frac{1}{4}$.

Then, I multiply $\frac{1}{4} \cdot 44 = 11$."

Hank

"I like decimals much better than fractions."

$25\% = 0.25$

$0.25 \cdot 44 = 11$

Ryan

"25% is easy to do in my head.

50% of 44 is 22.

25% is $\frac{1}{2}$ of 50%, so 25% of 44 is $\frac{1}{2}$ of 22, which is equal to 11."

Simon

"Since 25% is the same as $\frac{1}{4}$, I just divided by four."

$44 \div 4 = 11$

Pamela

"I prefer to use the benchmarks of 10% and 5%.

10% of 44 = 4.4.

20% is 2 • 10% = 2 • 4.4 = 8.8.

5% is half of 10% = 2.2.

Therefore, 20% + 5% = 8.8 + 2.2 = 11.0"

1. Discuss each student method used.

   a. When is Kendra's method most efficient to use?

   A more efficient method is one that requires fewer steps to determine an answer.

   b. When is Ryan's method most efficient to use?

   c. When is Simon's method most efficient to use?

   d. When is Pamela's method most efficient to use?

2. Which method(s) can be used in any situation?

6

Ellen said, "All the methods are correct, and everyone got the correct answer, but what if Mr. Goodwin gave us the problem 32% of 732?"

- Kendra said, "My fraction method is not as easy this time."

$$\frac{\overset{8}{\cancel{32}}}{\underset{25}{\cancel{100}}} \cdot \frac{732}{1} = \frac{5856}{25} = 234.24$$

- Hank said,
  "32% = 0.32
  0.32 · 732 = 234.24
  My method is not that different."

- Ryan said, "I can still estimate, but my answer will be close, not exact. 32% is close to $\frac{1}{3}$ and $\frac{1}{3}$ of 732 is 244."

- Simon said, "I don't have an easy fraction to use for 32%, so my method only works for certain percents."

- Pamela said, "I can still use my method."
  32% = 10% + 10% + 10% + 1% + 1%
  10% of 732 = 73.2
  73.2 · 3 = 219.6
  1% of 732 = 7.32
  7.32 · 2 = 14.64
  219.6 + 14.64 = 234.24

3. Which method do you prefer with this problem? Discuss with your partner and explain your thinking.

4. Determine the percent for each by using your preferred method.

a. 7% of 80

b. 15% of 55

c. 12% of 320

d. 8% of 300

e. 75% of 240

f. 37% of 120

g. 60% of 232

h. 150% of 27

i. 12.5% of 64

5. You are the coach of the Gators' basketball team. The Gators are playing the Crocs. The game is tied 64 to 64 with time running out. Just before the buzzer sounds, the Crocs' coach illegally steps out onto the floor while play is taking place. This results in a penalty—and a free throw shot for the Gators! You have to pick a Gators' player to shoot the free throw. If the player makes the shot, the Gators win!

You can choose one of four players to shoot the free throws. During the past few games,

- Natalie made 17 out of 25 free throws.
- Angela made 15 out of 20 free throws.
- Casey made 7 out of 10 free throws.
- Erin made 37 out of 50 free throws.

You want to select the player who is most likely to make the shot. Which player should you choose? Use mathematical reasoning and the data on the players' performance in the last few games to explain your choice.

Problem 2   Giving Back to the Community

 This school year, students are asked to volunteer for a service project to help in the community. The results of the questionnaire that was given to the sixth-grade students are shown in the table. Three hundred students returned the questionnaire, with each student choosing one service project.

Working at the . . .	Boys	Girls
Food Bank	42	48
Soup Kitchen	40	48
Senior Center	28	94

1. Explain each statement mathematically using your knowledge of fractions, decimals, and percents.

   a. 30% of the students prefer working at the Food Bank.

   b. About 30% of the students prefer working at the Soup Kitchen.

   c. About 40% of the students prefer working at the Senior Center.

6

d. About 50% of the girls prefer working at the Senior Center.

e. About 25% of the boys prefer working at the Senior Center, and about 25% of the girls prefer working at the Soup Kitchen.

f. The boys prefer working at the Food Bank over the girls.

g. The boys prefer working at the Soup Kitchen over the girls.

h. The ratio of boys who prefer *not* working at the Soup Kitchen to total boys is 7 to 11.

6

Problem 3 Percent Problems

Karla is in charge of designing a way to keep a running total of the money raised by her homeroom for the Food Bank project. As of today, her homeroom has raised $240, which is 60% of their goal.

Karla decided to use a double number line to record the money raised and the percent of the goal raised.

A double number line is a graph that has two number lines with the same intervals indicated with tick marks. Each number line represents different data value. However, the data values are related to each other.

In the graph shown, the bottom number line represents the percent of the homeroom goal. The top number line represents the amount of money raised.

Karla's homeroom has raised $240, which is 60% of the goal.

1. Which way of reporting is more informative: the amount of money raised, or the percent of money raised? Explain your thinking.

2. Create double number lines to represent the goals of the other sixth-grade homerooms using the information from the table. Write the equivalent dollar amount for each percent on the double numbers lines.

Homeroom	Goal (dollars)
6B	240
6C	360
6D	480
6E	120
6F	280

a. Homeroom 6B

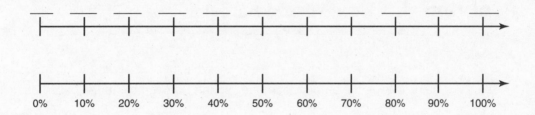

b. Homeroom 6C

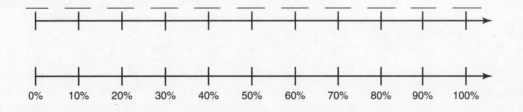

c. Homeroom 6D

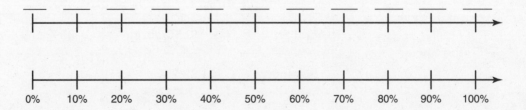

d. Homeroom 6E

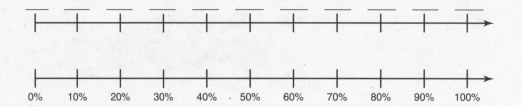

e. Homeroom 6F

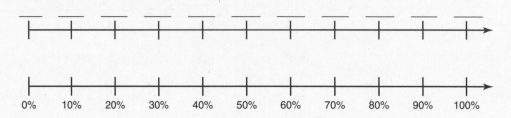

Problem 4 Wow! What a Bargain!

Everyone loves a bargain. When you have a lot of shopping to do, every discount or sale helps reduce the amount of money spent. Sometimes, this is called bargain shopping.

Back to School Sale		
Item	**Regular Price**	**Now**
Notebook	$2.95	25% off
Pencils	$1.20/dozen	15% off
Pens	$0.99	12% off
Markers	$4.95/dozen	30% off
Erasers	$1.50/dozen	20% off
Scissors	$2.25	10% off
Yearly Planners	$7.92	30% off

1. The school supplies you need for the upcoming school year include:

- 2 notebooks
- 2 pens
- 1 dozen pencils
- 1 yearly planner

a. How much is your total, *not* including the discounts?

Wait ... can I have $2.2125? Should I round that before I solve or can I round after?

b. How much is your total, including the discounts?

c. Tax in your county is 7%. How much tax will you pay on the discounted total?

d. How much will you spend, including tax?

2. Your brother's school supplies for the upcoming school year include:

- 2 dozen pencils
- 1 dozen markers
- 1 dozen erasers
- 1 pair of scissors

a. How much is his total, including the discounts?

b. How much tax will he pay on his total?

c. What is his total cost?

6

The newspaper has a coupon for 30% off the price of planners. Kendra has two strategies for calculating the discounted price. She said that to determine the price of a planner, she could calculate 30% of $7.92 and then subtract that amount from the original price—a two-step process.

Two-step method:

30% of $7.92

$0.30 \cdot \$7.92 = \$2.38$

$\$7.92 - \$2.38 = \$5.54$

Kendra can also calculate the new price in one step.

Kendra can determine 70% of $7.92, since she is receiving a 30% discount. With the discount, she is actually paying 70% of the cost of the item. Kendra can do one calculation that gives her the final discounted price.

One-step method:

70% of $7.92

$0.70 \cdot \$7.92 = \$5.54$

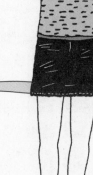

I wonder if there are ever any advantages to using the two-step process—maybe if the discount is not easily divisible by a whole number?

3. What do you think about Kendra's methods? Which method do you prefer? Explain your reasoning.

4. If you receive a 10% discount, what percent of the original price will you pay?

5. If you receive a 25% discount, what percent of the original price will you pay?

6. If you receive a 48% discount, what percent of the original price will you pay?

Problem 5   Who's Correct?

1. An in-store flyer has a coupon for an extra 10% off the sale price of yearly planners.

> Extra **10% off**
> the sale price
> of planners!

- Patricia says, "The price will be $4.75, which is 40% off, because the price is currently 30% off, and I will get an additional 10% off with the coupon. 40% off of $7.92 is $4.75."

- Karla says, "The price is $4.99 because the 30% discount is calculated first, which makes the price $5.54. Then, the coupon will give you an extra 10% off the sale price, which will make the price $4.99."

Who is correct? Explain your reasoning.

6

2.

Jake

"There is a big sale at Music Box. Everything is 50% off and there is a coupon in the newspaper that says to take an additional 50% off the sale price. We better hurry. Everything is free!"

You doubt that Music Box could be giving everything away for free. Explain to Jake what is wrong with his reasoning. Be sure he understands exactly what percent he will be paying.

3. Allen thought that if Kendra's method worked for calculating a discount, it could probably work for calculating the tax and other percentages that get added onto a base price. If an item costs $10.50 plus 7% tax, what is the total cost of the item. He calculated the total cost using a two-step method first.

Two-step method:
7% of $10.50
$0.07 \cdot \$10.50 = \$0.74$ tax
$\$10.50 + \$0.74 = \$11.24$

Allen thought that if he was paying the base price plus 7% tax, it is like paying 100% + 7% or 107%.

One-step method:
107% of $10.50
$1.07 \cdot \$10.50 = \$11.24$

What do you think about Allen's one-step method? Explain your reasoning.

4. What percent can you use to represent paying an 8% tax?

5. What percent can you use to represent paying a 25% surcharge?

6. What percent can you use to represent adding a 15% tip?

7. What is more helpful to know, $2.00 off or $20% off?

Problem 6　Target Heart Rate

It is important to maintain the proper pacing during exercise. The maximum heart rate for a person is calculated by subtracting a person's age (in years) from 220, which represents the *maximum* number of heart beats per minute for a person. A heart rate should stay within the 50% to 85% range of the maximum number of heart beats per minute.

1. Complete the chart shown using the information about healthy heart rates.

Age (years)	Maximum Heart Rate (beats per minute)	Target Heart Rate Zone (beats per minute)
20	200	100–170
25	195	98–166
30	190	95–162
35		
40		
45		
50		
55		
60		
65		
70		

Be prepared to share your solutions and methods.

6.4

MI MI MI MI MI MI MI!
Determining the Part, Whole, or Percent of Percent Problems

Learning Goals

In this lesson, you will:

▶ Determine the percent given the part and the whole.

▶ Determine the whole given a part and the percent.

▶ Determine the part given the whole and the percent.

Have you ever seen a choir sing? Most choirs have four voice parts: basses, tenors, altos, and sopranos. Women generally sing the alto and soprano parts because those parts are higher in pitch. Men generally sing the tenor and bass parts because those parts are lower in pitch.

What do you think the choir might sound like if there were more sopranos than tenors? What do you think the choir might sound like if there were more basses than altos? Do you think most choirs strive to have an even amount of people sing various parts?

Problem 1   What Percent Is It?

Previously, you have learned how to determine the percent of a number. You can use your knowledge of percents to determine the whole of a group or the percent of the whole that a certain number represents.

1. This picture shows triangles.

    a. If the picture shown is 30% of the triangles, draw 100% of the triangles.

    b. What percent is 1 triangle?

2. Analyze the rectangle shown.

If the rectangle shown is 25% of another rectangle:

    a. Draw 50% of the other rectangle.

    b. Draw 75% of the other rectangle.

    c. Draw 100% of the other rectangle.

3. The figure shown represents 75% of the whole figure.

   a. Draw 25% of the figure.

   b. Draw 100% of the figure.

4. The rectangle shown represents 150%.

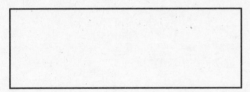

   a. On the rectangle, shade 50% of the rectangle.

   b. What is the percent of the rectangle that is not shaded?

5. The figure shown represents 700%.

Draw 100%.

6. The figure shown represents 160%.

x   x   x   x
x   x   x   x
x   x   x   x
x   x   x   x

a. Draw 10%

b. Draw 100%

Problem 2   Determining Parts, Wholes, and Percents

Percent problems involve three quantities: the part, the whole, and the percent. If you know two of the quantities, you can determine the third.

Previously, you calculated the price of a notebook after the 25% discount. The notebook cost $2.95 and the discount was 25%. You calculated either 25% of $2.95 and subtracted the difference from the total, or you calculated 75% of $2.95.

The whole usually comes after the word "of" in percent problems. The percent is generally indicated in percent problems.

Let's investigate a situation that involves determining the percent if you know the part and the whole.

In the middle school chorus, 34 of the 50 students are girls. What percent of the chorus is girls?

Holly used a double number line to think about this problem.

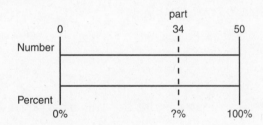

Then, she wrote equivalent fractions.

$$\frac{part}{whole} \qquad \overset{\times 2}{\frac{34}{50} = \frac{?}{100}}$$
$$\underset{\times 2}{}$$
$$= \frac{68}{100} = 68\%$$

Holly determined that by doubling 50, she could calculate the percent. Since $50 \times 2 = 100$, she calculated the correct denominator for a percent. Then, she multiplied the numerator by the same factor, 2, which is $34 \times 2 = 68$.

When calculating percents, you may want to avoid simplifying fractions. Instead, determine an equivalent fraction with a denominator of 100.

1. The middle school band has 25 students.

   a. Twelve students play brass instruments. What percent of band members play brass instruments?

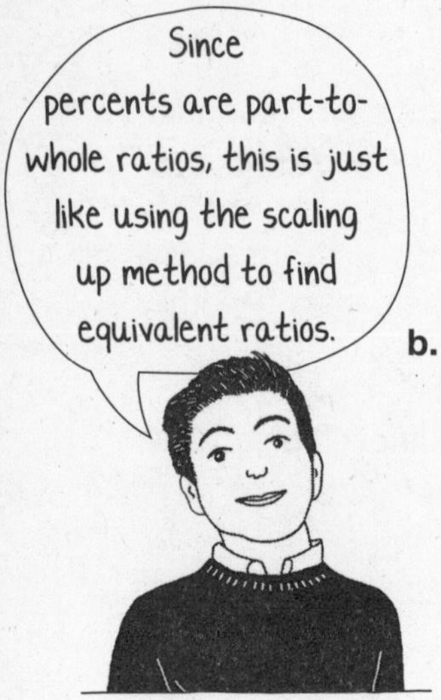
Since percents are part-to-whole ratios, this is just like using the scaling up method to find equivalent ratios.

   b. Eight students play the drums. What percent of band members play the drums?

   c. Five students play woodwinds. What percent of band members play woodwinds?

You can write an equivalent fraction with a denominator of 100 by doubling, tripling, or quadrupling the original denominator. However, some denominators are not a factor of 100. When this occurs, you can simply divide the numerator by the denominator to calculate the decimal equivalent of the fraction. Then, you can multiply the decimal by 100 to determine the percent.

2. Jasmine is a piano and organ teacher. Of the 36 students she teaches, 19 take piano lessons. What percent of her students take piano lessons?

3. The seventh-grade marching band has 40 members. First, calculate the percent for each type of instrument (brass, woodwinds, percussion). Then, calculate the percent of each instrument in the band.

Band Section	Number of Students	Percent
Brass Instruments	**23**	
Cornet	8	
Trumpet	9	
Tuba	6	
Woodwinds	**10**	
Clarinet	7	
Flute	2	
Saxophone	1	
Percussion	**7**	
Bass Drum	4	
Cymbals	3	
Total	**40**	**100**

The sixth-grade class was asked the question, "How do you spend most of your time on computers?"

The results of this survey are shown:

Activity Done While Spending Time on Computers	Number of Students
Email – Instant Messaging	88
Homework	70
Games	30
Movies/DVDs/TV	24
Other Internet Activities	38

4. What percent of the sixth-grade class preferred each activity? Round your answers to the nearest whole percent.

Carlos is told that 65% of the students, or 78 students, prefer pizza for lunch according to a recent survey. He wants to know how many students were surveyed. He drew the double number line shown to visualize the problem.

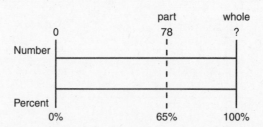

He then wrote the equivalent fractions and determined that 120 students were surveyed.

$$\frac{part}{whole} \qquad \frac{78}{?} = \frac{65}{100}$$

$$\frac{65}{100} = \frac{13}{20} = \frac{78}{?}$$

$$\frac{78}{120} = \frac{13}{20}$$

5. How did Carlos determine the total number? Explain Carlos' calculations.

6. Determine the whole in each situation. Explain your reasoning.

   a. Your friends ate at a restaurant and left a $2.40 tip. They left a 15% tip. What was the cost of their bill?

   b. The best player on your school basketball team makes 60% of her free throws. If she scored 90 points with free throw shots, which are worth one point each, how many free throws did she attempt?

   c. Sandy made a 30% deposit on a computer. She gave the clerk $168. What is the price of the computer?

   d. You got a quiz back and your teacher wrote +16, and 80% at the top. How many points was the quiz worth?

Talk the Talk

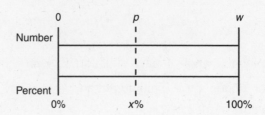

Given the percent equation, *p* represents the part, *w* represents the whole, and $\frac{x}{100}$ represents the percent.

1. Calculate a part given the percent and the whole.

   25% of 48 is what number?

2. Calculate a percent given the part and the whole.

   12 is what percent of 48?

3. Calculate a whole given the percent and the part.

25% of what number is 12?

 Be prepared to share your solutions and methods.

6

6

6.5 PRACTICAL PERCENTS PRACTICE!
Using Percents in Real-World Situations

Learning Goals

In this lesson, you will:

▶ Calculate the percent increase and decrease.

▶ Calculate the discount of a base price.

▶ Calculate additional discount on sales price.

▶ Calculate gratuity on a bill.

▶ Calculate sales tax.

Key Terms

▶ commission

▶ gratuity

Many people who eat at restaurants leave a tip for the waiter at the end of their meal. This is a little extra money—usually 15% or 20% of the cost of the meal—that people give directly to the server for waiting on them.

In 2007, however, a waitress at a pizza place in Angola, Indiana, got much much more than a 20% tip. The family that she waited on every Friday—who ordered the same thing on every visit—left their 20-year-old waitress, Jessica Osborne, a tip of $10,000!

Can you estimate what percent *that* tip amounted to? Do you think the $10,000 tip is greater or less than 100% of the bill?

6

Problem 1   Using Percents

1. Determine the value for each using your knowledge of percents. Round your answer to the nearest tenth, if necessary.

   a. What is 25% of 60?

   b. 15 is what percent of 50?

   c. 45 is what percent of 60?

   d. What number is 20% of 80?

   e. 36 is 40% of what number?

   f. What is 15% of 40?

   g. 27 is what percent of 90?

Problem 2   How Much are You Going to Save?

Kala and Keisha are shopping for new basketball shoes. They notice a flyer that reads:

> Take an additional
> **40% off**
> the sales-tag price
> of all merchandise!

Kala finds a pair of shoes she likes and in her size, but the additional sale price tag has been removed. The original price is $120, and the original sale price is 25% off. Kala says, "I think I can determine the final cost of the shoes. Since the shoes were already reduced 25% and are being reduced again by 40%, then the shoes must be 65% off!"

Keisha disagrees. She says, "You cannot just add the discounts together. You have to read the flyer more closely. First, you must calculate the sale price after the 25% discount. Then, once you know the sale price, then you can reduce the sale price by 40%. That's the way you can determine the price after the additional 40% off."

1. What would the sale price be if you used Kala's method?

2. What would the sale price be if you used Keisha's method?

3. Who is correct in their reasoning? Explain how you determined your answer.

4. Kala's brother said that the shoes would have been cheaper if the store had taken 40% off first, and then taken an additional 25% off the sale price. Is he correct? Explain your reasoning.

5. You need a graphing calculator for math class. You saw the same graphing calculator at 3 different stores. On the day before school starts, you decide to do some comparative shopping for the calculator. All three stores are having a Back-to-School Sale, and as luck has it, all three stores have the graphing calculator you want on sale.

All Things Math has the price of the graphing calculator down 30%, but if you show your student ID card, you receive an additional 25% off the original price.

Rational Numbers for Rational Math has the price of the graphing calculator marked down 25%, but if you come between 10:00 am and 1:00 pm, you can get an additional 30% off the sale price.

Pi, Protractors, and Percents has the price of the graphing calculator marked down 50%.

Which store has the best price of the calculator? Explain how you determined your answer.

Problem 3 Is This for Here? Or to Go?

A year ago, Isosceles Triangle Restaurants (ITR) decided to offer curbside dining as another option for potential diners to eat. Now, restaurant executives are determining whether they should continue the curbside option. In the past year, ITR had 2,650,000 diners. The diners are listed in the following fashion:

- 636,000 ate in the restaurant
- 1,590,000 used the drive-thru window
- 424,000 used curbside dining

1. What percent of customers used the drive-thru windows?

2. What percent of customers ate in the restaurant?

3. What percent used curbside dining?

Out of the 2,650,000 customers, 75% ordered beef, and the other 25% ordered chicken.

4. Determine the number of customers that ordered beef using the information given. Explain how you determined your answer.

6

5. Determine the number of customers that ordered chicken. Explain your reasoning.

Problem 4   I Got the Sale! Now, What's My Cut?

Sales **commission** is an amount or percent of an item that is paid to employees or companies that sell merchandise in stores, or by calling customers. The commission is meant to motivate sales people to sell more. A commission may be paid in addition to a salary, or in place of a salary. Commissions are typically paid in the business of real estate, marketing, automobile sales—and even in textbook sales!

1. An automobile saleswoman earns 12% on all of her sales. Last month, she sold 3 cars for a total sales amount of $28,950. What is her commission?

2. A real estate agent earns 6% of the selling price of each house he sells. If he sells a home for $250,000, how much of a commission will he make?

3. If a car salesman made $2450 last month from a 12% commission, what is the total sales amount of all the cars that he sold?

4. A real estate agent made $7500 on a $150,000 home sale. What was the percent of her commission?

Problem 5 When Black Equals Green!

Many experts have determined that the day after Thanksgiving is the busiest shopping day of the year in the United States. Nicknamed Black Friday, this day is seen by many stores and retail outlets as a huge opportunity to make a lot of money on the sales of merchandise. To lure customers to the big sales, some stores open at midnight on Black Friday and sometimes offer discounts of over 50% off the original price.

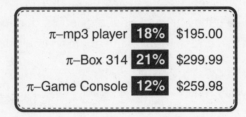

π–mp3 player **18%** $195.00

π–Box 314 **21%** $299.99

π–Game Console **12%** $259.98

1. Analyze the Black Friday Sales Flyer shown.

   a. Determine the sale price of the π-mp3 player. How much will a customer save from the discount?

   b. Determine the sale price of the π-Box 314.

   c. Determine the sale price of the π-Game Console.

2. During a Black Friday sale, Alberto paid $158.00 for new smart cell phone that was reduced by 30%. What was the original price of the smart phone?

3. Kalisha paid $243.19 for a flat-screen television that was originally $319.99. What percent discount did she receive?

While stores offer sale prices on items, they also tend to *mark up* the products they sell. Typically, stores buy items from a wholesaler or distributor, and then they increase the price when they sell the items to consumers. The increase in price provides money for the operation of the store and the salaries of people who work in the store.

A store may have a rule that the price of a certain type of item needs to be increased by a certain percentage to determine how much to sell it for. This percentage is called the markup.

4. Oh! Shiny! Jewelry Store marks up all of their jewelry by a percent that allows for a profit even if they have to offer a discount during the holiday season. Analyze the table shown and determine the appropriate values to complete the table.

Jewelry Item	Markup Percent	Original Cost (dollars)	Customer Price (dollars)
Necklace	100	119	
Earrings	200		234
Bracelet		324	810
Watch	125	85	
Cuff links		63	252
Ring	250		938

Problem 6   No Taxation Without Calculation

1. The table shown lists 20 states and the different sales tax added to every dollar of a purchase as of February 2010. Complete the table by determining the tax amount added to each purchase amount. If necessary, round your answer to the nearest penny.

State	Sales Tax (percent)	Tax on $10.00 (dollars)	Tax on $100.00 (dollars)	Tax on $1000.00 (dollars)
Indiana	7			
California	8.25			
Florida	6			
Arizona	5.6			
Kansas	5.3			
Alabama	4			
Missouri	4.225			
Minnesota	6.875			
Oklahoma	4.5			
Utah	4.7			
Colorado	2.9			
Maine	5			
Illinois	5.25			
North Carolina	5.75			
Nebraska	5.5			

Problem 7 Thanks for the Service!

In many service-oriented occupations, employees work for an hourly wage, plus a tip that is left by a customer to show appreciation for good service. A tip, also called a **gratuity**, for wait staff in a restaurant is generally a percent of the total amount of the bill. In the United States, the typical gratuity for good service ranges between 15% to 20%. Sometimes, if a party is more than six people, the restaurant will automatically add a gratuity charge to the bill.

1. Darlene works at a restaurant during the dinner shift. At her restaurant, the gratuity is automatically added to the bill. The gratuity is 18% of the total bill. If Darlene is hoping to earn $125.00 in tips, what will the total cost of dinners need to be?

2. Rajan is a dog groomer at a local pet store. He receives a 15% tip of the total from the dog owners. If he hopes to make $54 this weekend, how much money must be spent on dog baths? Show how you determined your answer.

3. If each dog bath and grooming costs $12.00, how many dog baths and grooming must he do to receive $54 in tips?

Be prepared to share your solutions and methods.

Chapter 6 Summary

Key Terms

▶ percent (6.1)

▶ benchmark percents (6.2)

▶ commission (6.5)

▶ gratuity (6.5)

6.1 Introducing Percents

A percent is a fraction with a denominator of 100. It means the same thing as hundredths. The percent symbol, "%," means "out of 100." Percents, fractions, and decimals are often used interchangeably.

Example

The shaded part of the hundredths grid is shown as a fraction, decimal, and percent.

Fraction: $\frac{35}{100}$

Decimal: 0.35

Percent: 35%

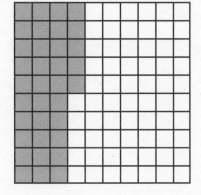

Your brain only takes up about 2% of your body weight. However, it is working so hard that it requires 20% of the oxygen you breathe. So breathe deep and feed your brain!

6

6.2 Estimating Percents with Models

A whole is the same as 100%.

Example

The estimate of the shaded part of the circle is 60%.

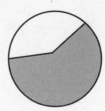

6.2 Estimating Percents Using Benchmarks

A benchmark percent is a commonly used percent, such as 1%, 5%, 10%, 25%, 50%, and 100%. Benchmark percents can help calculate the percent of any number.

Example

Benchmark percents are used to calculate 35% of 6500 as shown.

10% of 6500 is 650.
30% of 6500 is 3(650) = 1950.
Half of 10% is 5%, so 5% of 6500 is half of 650, or 325.
35% of 6500 is 1950 + 325 = 2275.

So, 35% of 6500 is 2275.

6.3 Determining the Percent of a Number

To determine the percent of a number, convert the percent to a decimal, and then multiply.

Example

What is 38% of 1200?

38% of 1200 = 0.38 × 1200

= 456

So, 456 is 38% of 1200.

6

6.4 Determining Parts, Wholes, and Percents

A percent problem involves three quantities: the part, the whole, and the percent. If you know two of the quantities, you can determine the third. Given the percent equation, $\frac{x}{100} = \frac{p}{w}$, p represents the part, w represents the whole, and $\frac{x}{100}$ represents the percent.

Examples

a. 16 is what percent of 25?

$$\frac{x}{100} = \frac{p}{w}$$

$$\frac{x}{100} \overset{\times 4}{\underset{\times 4}{=}} \frac{16}{25}$$

$$x = 64$$

So, 16 is 64% of 25.

b. 72% of what number is 54?

$$\frac{x}{100} = \frac{p}{w}$$

$$\frac{72}{100} = \frac{54}{w}$$

$$\frac{18}{25} \overset{\times 3}{\underset{\times 3}{=}} \frac{54}{w}$$

$$75 = w$$

So, 72% of 75 is 54.

6.5 Calculating the Sale Price

To calculate a sale price, you can multiply the percent off by the base price to determine the discount. Then, subtract the discount from the base price.

Example

Felipe bought a pair of jeans on sale. The jeans were originally priced at $33 but were on sale for 40% off.

base price: $33
percent off: 0.40

discount: $33 × 0.40 = $13.20

sale price: $33 − $13.20 = $19.80

Felipe paid $19.80 for the jeans on sale.

6

6.5 Calculating Commission

Sales commission is a percent of a total sale paid to the salesperson. To determine a commission, multiply the percent by the total sale.

Example

A makeup salesperson had total sales of $1400 in one month. The salesperson earns 5% commission.

$1400 × 0.05 = $70

So, the salesperson earned $70 in commission.

6.5 Calculating Sales Tax and Tips

A sales tax is an amount added to each dollar of a purchase. A tip, also called a gratuity, is a percent of the total amount of a bill that is often given to a waiter. You can use percents to calculate sales tax and tip amounts.

Mr. Clark's restaurant bill, without tax, was $55.79. He must pay an 8% sales tax.

$55.79 × 1.08 = $60.25

His total bill, after sales tax, is $60.25

Mr. Clark leaves a 20% tip on top of the total bill.

$60.25 × 1.20 = $72.30

So he pays $72.30 altogether.

INTRODUCTION TO EXPRESSIONS

USA

"T minus 3, 2, 1 . . ." Most of us see the final seconds before launch, but a countdown for a typical space shuttle mission begins about 43 hours before launch. The shuttle goes through a number of inspections and systems testing. At T – 6 hours, the shuttle begins fueling, and this process takes nearly three hours.

7

7.1 THERE'S A REASON BEHIND THE RHYME

Order of Operations

Learning Goals

In this lesson, you will:

▶ Evaluate numerical expressions with addition, subtraction, multiplication, and division.

▶ Evaluate numerical expressions involving exponents and parentheses.

▶ Justify the order of operations used to simplify numerical expressions.

Key Terms

▶ conventions
▶ numerical expression
▶ evaluate
▶ operations
▶ parentheses
▶ order of operations

Have you ever wondered why in some states cars can turn right on red? Or why in England and Ireland cars drive on the left side of the road? Why are all books written in English printed horizontally from left to right and from front to back? Did you know that traditional Chinese, Japanese, and Korean texts are written vertically from right to left? Rules like these, which are called **conventions**, are usually developed over time and are followed so that everyone knows what to do. Many conventions deal with the order in which something is done. For example, you usually eat your salad before your meal, and the meal before your dessert. What other conventions do you know? Do you know of any mathematical conventions?

7

Problem 1   There's a Reason for the Rules

In mathematics, people follow rules to clarify the order of how to solve problems. Part of these rules include *numerical expressions* and strategies for calculating values. A **numerical expression** is a mathematical phrase containing numbers. To **evaluate** a numerical expression means to calculate an expression to get a single value. Many times, numerical expressions have *operations* that tell you what to do with each value. The **operations** in an expression are addition, subtraction, multiplication, and division.

For example, consider the numerical expression $8 - 7 + 4 - 3$.

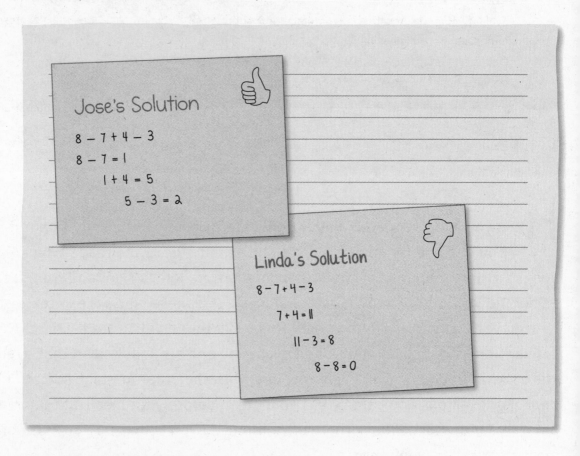

Jose's Solution

$8 - 7 + 4 - 3$
$8 - 7 = 1$
  $1 + 4 = 5$
    $5 - 3 = 2$

Linda's Solution

$8 - 7 + 4 - 3$
  $7 + 4 = 11$
    $11 - 3 = 8$
      $8 - 8 = 0$

1. What does Jose's solution tell you about how to add and subtract in a numerical expression?

When you need to add and subtract in a numerical expression, you must perform the operations from left to right.

If you're adding and subtracting in a numerical expression, you solve it in the same order that you read: from left to right.

2. Consider the numerical expression
   6 + 4 • 3.
   What operations are represented in this expression?

3. The numerical expression 6 + 4 • 3 was evaluated in two different ways, resulting in different values.

Solution A	Solution B
6 + 4 • 3	6 + 4 • 3
= 10 • 3	= 6 + 12
= 30	= 18

a. Describe the strategy used in Solution A. What operation was performed first?

b. Describe the strategy used in Solution B. What operation was performed first?

As with adding and subtracting in a numerical expression, there is a certain order to perform the operations when using addition and multiplication. To determine which solution is correct, think about what the expression really means.
Remember, multiplication is repeated addition.

c. Rewrite 6 + 4 • 3 using only one operation.

d. Evaluate your new expression.

e. Is Solution A or Solution B correct? Cross out the incorrect solution. Explain what you discovered by evaluating your new expression.

7

4. Rewrite each numerical expression to represent only addition, and then evaluate each expression.

    a. $2 + 8 \bullet 3$ **b.** $4 + 2 \bullet 5 + 3 \bullet 2$

5. Write a rule that states the order in which you should perform addition and multiplication when evaluating a numerical expression.

6. Consider the numerical expression $8 \bullet 2 \div 4 \bullet 3$. What operations are represented in this expression?

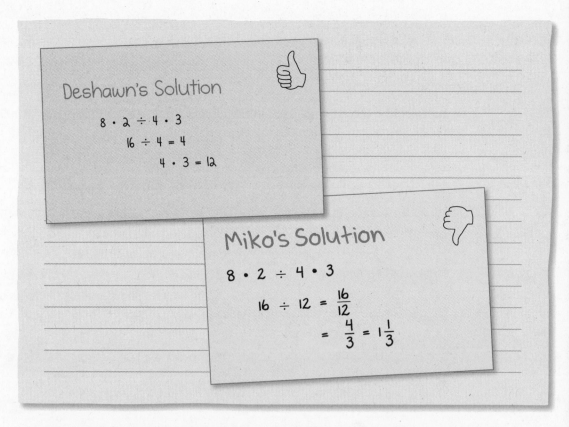

7. What does Deshawn's solution tell you about how to multiply and divide in a numerical expression?

7

Just like addition and subtraction, when you have multiplication and division in a numerical expression, you must multiply and divide from left to right.

8. Consider the numerical expression 8 + 12 ÷ 4.
   What operations are represented in this expression?

9. The numerical expression 8 + 12 ÷ 4 was evaluated in two different ways, resulting in different values.

Solution A	**Solution B**
8 + 12 ÷ 4	8 + 12 ÷ 4
= 20 ÷ 4	= 8 + 3
= 5	= 11

   a. Describe the strategy used in Solution A. What operation was performed first?

   b. Describe the strategy used in Solution B. What operation was performed first?

   To determine which solution is correct, think about what the expression really means. Remember, division is repeated subtraction.

   c. Explain what 12 ÷ 4 means as repeated subtraction.

   d. Is Solution A or Solution B correct? Cross out the incorrect solution.

10. Write a rule that states the order in which you should perform addition and division when evaluating a numerical expression.

11. Evaluate each numerical expression.

    a. $12 - 8 \div 2 =$ **b.** $3 \bullet 2 - 6 \div 3 =$

    c. $12 \bullet 5 - 8 =$ **d.** $40 - 28 + 2 \bullet 5 =$

    e. $12 \div 4 \div 2 =$ **f.** $28 \div 7 \bullet 2 =$

Problem 2   What about Exponents and Parentheses?

1. Consider the numerical expression $9 + 2^3$.

    a. What does 2^3 mean? What operation is being used?

    b. Evaluate the expression. Use the rules you wrote to help you calculate your answer. Then, explain the order in which you evaluated the expression.

2. Consider the numerical expression $2 \bullet 5^2$.

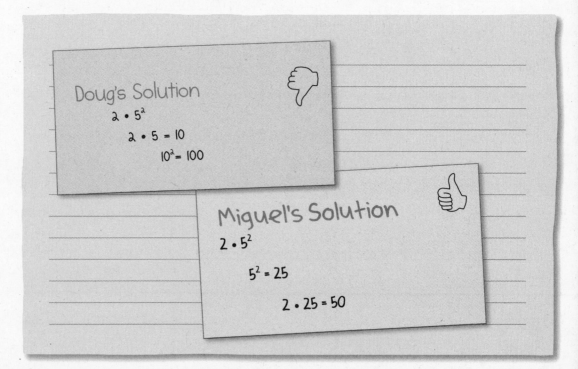

Doug's Solution

$2 \bullet 5^2$

$2 \bullet 5 = 10$

$10^2 = 100$

Miguel's Solution

$2 \bullet 5^2$

$5^2 = 25$

$2 \bullet 25 = 50$

3. What does Miguel's solution tell you about how to solve a numerical expression with both multiplication and exponents?

Previously, you learned that it did not matter which order you multiplied factors. However, when there are exponents and multiplication in a numerical expression, perform the exponent operation first, and then multiply.

4. Evaluate each numerical expression.

a. $4 \cdot 7^2 =$

b. $12 + 8^2 =$

c. $3^2 - 6 \div 3 =$

d. $12 + 25 \div 5^2 =$

e. $10 \div 2 - 3 + 2^4 =$

f. $12^2 - 48 \div 2 =$

g. $28 \div 2^2 - 36 \div 3^2 =$

h. $168 \div 2^3 + 3^3 - 20$

Parentheses are symbols used to group numbers and operations, and are used to change the normal order in which you perform operations.

For example, you know that $6 + 4 \cdot 3 = 18$ because you multiply first, and then add. What if you wanted to add first, and then multiply?

5. If parentheses were added to create the new expression $(6 + 4) \cdot 3$, would the solution change? If so, what is the new value of the expression? Explain your reasoning.

6. Consider the numerical expression $(3 + 5)^2$.

This numerical expression was evaluated in two different ways, resulting in different values.

Solution A

$(3 + 5)^2$

$= 8^2$

$= 64$

Solution B

$(3 + 5)^2$

$= 9 + 25$

$= 34$

Determine which solution is correct. State the reasons why one solution is correct and the error that was made in the other solution. Cross out the incorrect solution.

7. Let's consider another numerical expression containing parentheses $3 \bullet (7 - 2)$.

Solution A

$3 \bullet (7 - 2)$

$= 21 - 2$

$= 19$

Solution B

$3 \bullet (7 - 2)$

$= 3(5)$

$= 15$

Determine which solution is correct. State the reasons why one solution is correct and the error that was made in the other solution. Cross out the incorrect solution.

Parentheses group numbers and operations together. Parentheses change the order of how you should perform operations. Any operations in parentheses must be performed first before any other operations in a numerical expression.

8. Evaluate each numerical expression.

    a. $(3 + 5)^2$

    b. $12 + (25 \div 5)^2$

    c. $10 \div (5 - 3) + 2^2$

    d. $(12^2 - 48) \div 2$

    e. $(28 \div (2^2 + 3)) + 3^2$

    f. $((5 + 2 \bullet 2)^2 \div 3) - 20$

Talk the Talk

There is an *order of operations,* a particular order in which operations are performed when evaluating any numerical expression. The **Order of Operations** is a set of rules that ensures the same result every time an expression is evaluated.

Order of Operations Rules

1. Evaluate expressions inside parentheses or grouping symbols such as ( ) or [ ].
2. Evaluate exponents.
3. Multiply and divide from left to right.
4. Add and subtract from left to right.

Keep in mind that multiplication and division are of equal importance and evaluated in order from left to right, as well as addition and subtraction.

We should use "Please Excuse My Dear Aunt Sally" to remember Parentheses, Exponents, Multiplication, Division, Addition, and Subtraction, right?

The mnemonic may help you remember the order. The important thing is to understand **WHY** the order of operations works.

I like "Pink Elephants Must Dance Around Snakes" better. Is that OK?

1. Each numerical expression has been evaluated correctly and incorrectly. First, state how the order of operations rules were used correctly to evaluate the expression, and then determine the error that was made in the second calculation.

a. $4 + 3^2$

$= 4 + 9$

$= 13$

$4 + 3^2$

$= 7^2$

$= 49$

b. $10 \div 4 + 1$

$= \dfrac{10}{4} + 1$

$= \dfrac{5}{2} + 1$

$= \dfrac{7}{2}$

$10 \div 4 + 1$

$10 \div 5$

$= 2$

c. $6 + 15 \div 3$

$= 6 + 5$

$= 11$

$6 + 15 \div 3$

$= 21 \div 3$

$= 7$

d. $(2 + 6)^2$

$= (8)^2$

$= 64$

$(2 + 6)^2$

$= 4 + 36$

$= 40$

e. $2(10 - 1) - 3 \cdot 2$
    $= 2(9) - 3 \cdot 2$
    $= 18 - 6$
    $= 12$

$2(10 - 1) - 3 \cdot 2$
$= 2(9) - 3 \cdot 2$
$= 18 - 3 \cdot 2$
$= 15 \cdot 2$
$= 30$

f. $3(4 + 2)$
    $= 3(6)$
    $= 18$

$3(4 + 2)$
$= 12 + 2$
$= 14$

Be prepared to share your solutions and methods.

GETTING TO THE ROOT OF IT

7.2

Exploring Squares, Cubes, and Roots

Learning Goals

In this lesson, you will:

▶ Determine the square of a number.

▶ Calculate the square root of a number.

▶ Determine the cube of a number.

▶ Calculate the cube root of a number.

Key Terms

▶ square of a number
▶ perfect squares
▶ square root
▶ radical

▶ radicand
▶ perfect cube
▶ cube of a number
▶ cube root
▶ index

You've probably gone to a park before. Do you ever wonder how a park is designed? Ever wondered why some parks have sports fields, while others have swings, slides, and jungle gyms? Well, you would need to ask a landscape architect.

Landscape architects are people who design outdoor and public places. Landscape architects can design parks, school grounds, office parks, public centers like youth or senior centers, and other buildings and parkways. In many places, a landscape architect is involved in the planning as well. In fact, in Ontario, Canada, and Santa Barbara, California, all designs that involve public places must have a landscape architect review and approve the designs before building can begin. How do you think landscape architects use mathematics when they are working?

7

Problem 1   Landscaping by Linda

 Linda is a landscape architect who specializes in designing backyard patio floors. She has a large collection of different square tiles that she uses to layout her patio floor designs. When she consults with a possible client, she always takes graph or grid paper to demonstrate her designs.

1. Why do you think Linda takes graph paper when she consults with possible clients?

Linda needs to make a square patio out of 169 blue square tiles. She needs to determine how many different sized square patios she can create with 169 tiles. Linda starts with the designs shown.

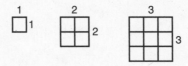

2. What is the area of each square patio design? Complete the table.

Dimensions of Square Patio Design	Area (square units)

3. Describe the different ways you can determine the area of each square.

The area of a square is calculated by multiplying the length of the side by itself. The formula $A = s \times s$ can be written as $A = s^2$.

To calculate the **square of a number** you multiply the number by itself 2 times.

In Question 2, you calculated the area for the first three square patio designs:

$$1^2 = 1,\ 2^2 = 4, \text{ and } 3^2 = 9.$$

The 1, 4, and 9 are called **perfect squares** because each is the square of a whole number. For instance, 9 is a perfect square because 3 is a whole number and $3 \times 3 = 9$. Another way you can write this mathematical sentence is $3^2 = 9$.

4. Complete the grid by continuing to create squares with side lengths of 4 through 15. Use a straightedge to connect the side lengths together, and then write the mathematical sentence using exponents to represent each perfect square.

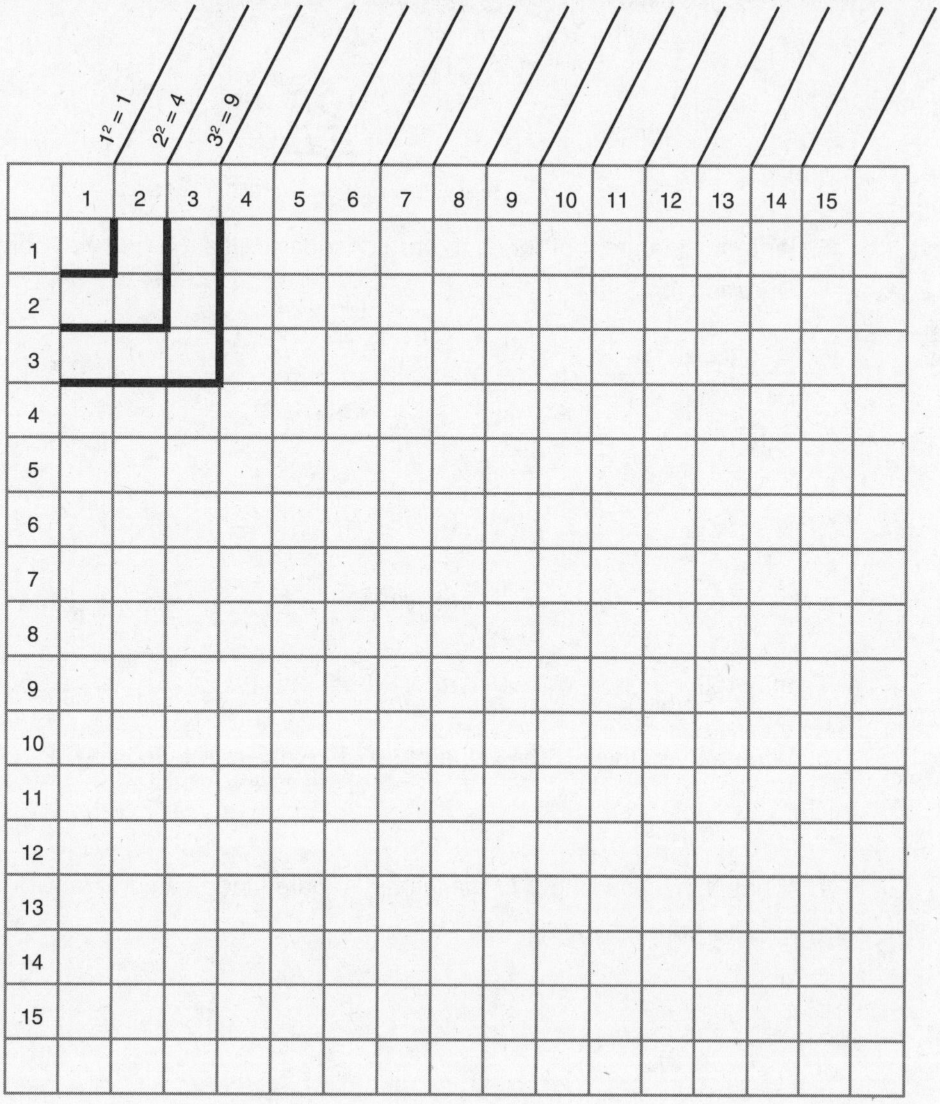

If you know the area of a square, you can work backwards to calculate the length of the side of the square.

For example, to determine the length of a side of a square that has an area of 81, you need to calculate what number multiplied by itself will equal 81. Since $9 \times 9 = 81$, the side length of the square is 9, and 9 is called the *square root* of 81.

A **square root** is one of two equal factors of a given number. Every positive number has two square roots: a positive square root and a negative square root.

For instance, 5 is the square root of 25 because $5 \times 5 = 25$. The symbol, $\sqrt{}$, is called a **radical** and it is used to indicate square roots. The **radicand** is the quantity under a radical sign.

This is read as "the square root of 25," or as "radical 25."

5. Write the square root for each perfect square. Use the grid you completed in Question 4.

    a. $\sqrt{1} = $ _____   **b.** $\sqrt{4} = $ _____   **c.** $\sqrt{9} = $ _____

    d. $\sqrt{16} = $ _____   **e.** $\sqrt{25} = $ _____   **f.** $\sqrt{36} = $ _____

    g. $\sqrt{49} = $ _____   **h.** $\sqrt{64} = $ _____   **i.** $\sqrt{81} = $ _____

    j. $\sqrt{100} = $ _____   **k.** $\sqrt{121} = $ _____   **l.** $\sqrt{144} = $ _____

    m. $\sqrt{169} = $ _____   **n.** $\sqrt{196} = $ _____   **o.** $\sqrt{225} = $ _____

6. What do you think is the value of $\sqrt{0}$? Explain your reasoning.

7. What is the side length of the largest square Linda can create with 169 squares? Explain your reasoning.

8. Do you think the square root of a number will always be a whole number? If not, provide an example of a square root that is not a whole number.

The square root of most numbers is not an integer. You can *estimate* the square root of a number that is not a perfect square. Begin by determining the two perfect squares closest to the radicand so that one perfect square is less than the radicand, and one perfect square is greater than the radicand. Then, use trial and error to determine the best estimate for the square root of the number.

> It might be helpful to use the grid you created in Question 4 to identify the perfect squares.

To estimate $\sqrt{10}$ to the nearest tenth, identify the closest perfect square less than 10 and the closest perfect square greater than 10.

The closest perfect square less than 10:	The square root you are estimating:	The closest perfect square greater than 10:
9	$\sqrt{10}$	16

You know:

$\sqrt{9} = 3$ $\sqrt{16} = 4$

This means the estimate of $\sqrt{10}$ is between 3 and 4.

Next, choose decimals between 3 and 4, and calculate the square of each number to determine which one is the best estimate.

Consider: $(3.1)(3.1) = 9.61$

$(3.2)(3.2) = 10.24$

So, $\sqrt{10} \approx 3.1$

The symbol $\approx$ means approximately equal to.

> So, the $\sqrt{10}$ is between $\sqrt{9}$ and $\sqrt{16}$. Why can't I say it's between $\sqrt{1}$ and $\sqrt{25}$?

9. Identify the two closest perfect squares, one greater than the radicand and one less than the radicand. Use the grid you completed in Question 4.

   a. $\sqrt{8}$

   b. $\sqrt{45}$

   c. $\sqrt{70}$

   d. $\sqrt{91}$

10. Estimate the location of each square root in Question 9 on the number line. Then, plot and label a point for your estimate.

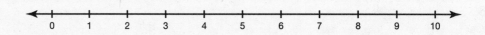

11. Estimate each radical in Question 9 to the nearest tenth. Explain your reasoning.

   a. $\sqrt{8}$

   b. $\sqrt{45}$

   c. $\sqrt{70}$

   d. $\sqrt{91}$

7

12. Linda's customer wants a square patio that has an area of 70 square meters.

   a. What is the side length of the patio? Represent the side length in radical form.

   b. Estimate the side length to the nearest tenth.

Problem 2   Making Cubes

1. Use unit cubes to build a cube with side lengths of:
   - 1 unit.
   - 2 units.
   - 3 units.

2. Complete the table.

Dimensions of Cube	Number of Unit Cubes
$4 \times 4 \times 4$	

The volume of a cube is calculated by multiplying the length of the cube by the width of the cube by the height of the cube; the formula $V = s \times s \times s$ can be written as $V = s^3$.

In Question 1, you calculated the volume of 3 cubes whose side lengths were the first 3 counting numbers, $1^3 = 1$, $2^3 = 8$, and $3^3 = 27$. The numbers 1, 8, and 27 are called *perfect cubes.* A **perfect cube** is the cube of a whole number. For example, 64 is a perfect cube since 4 is a whole number and $4 \times 4 \times 4 = 64$. To calculate the **cube of a number** you multiply the number by itself 3 times.

3. Calculate the cubes of the first 10 whole numbers.

   a. $1^3 =$ b. $2^3 =$

   c. $3^3 =$ d. $4^3 =$

   e. $5^3 =$ f. $6^3 =$

   g. $7^3 =$ h. $8^3 =$

   i. $9^3 =$ j. $10^3 =$

If you know the volume of a cube, you can work backwards to calculate the side lengths of the cube. For example, to determine the side lengths of a cube that has a volume of 125, you need to calculate what number multiplied by itself 3 times will equal 125. Since $5 \times 5 \times 5 = 125$, a side length of the cube is 5, and 5 is called the *cube root* of 125. A **cube root** is one of 3 equal factors of a number. As with the square root, the cube root also uses a radical symbol but has a 3 as an *index*: $\sqrt[3]{1}$. The **index** is the number placed above and to the left of the radical to indicate what root is being calculated.

4. Write the cube root for each perfect cube.

   a. $\sqrt[3]{1} =$ b. $\sqrt[3]{8} =$

   c. $\sqrt[3]{27} =$ d. $\sqrt[3]{64} =$

   e. $\sqrt[3]{125} =$ f. $\sqrt[3]{216} =$

   g. $\sqrt[3]{343} =$ h. $\sqrt[3]{512} =$

   i. $\sqrt[3]{729} =$ j. $\sqrt[3]{1000} =$

5. What is the side length of the largest cube you can create with 729 cubes?

6. Will the cube root of a number always be a whole number? If not, provide an example of a cube root that is not an integer.

Most numbers do not have whole numbers for their cube root. Let's estimate the cube root of a number using the same method used to estimate the square root of a number.

To estimate $\sqrt[3]{33}$ to the nearest tenth, first identify the two perfect cubes closest to the radicand. One of the perfect cubes must be less than the radicand, and the other must be greater than the radicand. Then, use trial and error to determine the best estimate for the cube root.

The closest perfect cube less than 33:	The cube root you are estimating:	The closest perfect cube greater than 33:
27	$\sqrt[3]{33}$	64

You know:

$\sqrt[3]{27} = 3$ $\qquad\qquad\qquad\qquad\qquad\qquad\qquad$ $\sqrt[3]{64} = 4$

This means the estimate of $\sqrt[3]{33}$ is between 3 and 4.

Next, choose decimals between 3 and 4, and calculate the cube of each decimal to determine which one is the best estimate.

Consider: $(3.2)(3.2)(3.2) = 32.768$

$\qquad\qquad$ $(3.3)(3.3)(3.3) = 35.937$

So, $\sqrt[3]{33} \approx 3.2$.

7. Identify the two closest perfect cubes, one greater than the radicand and one less than the radicand. Then, estimate each cube root to the nearest tenth.

a. $\sqrt[3]{100}$

Remember, the radicand is under the $\sqrt{}$.

b. $\sqrt[3]{175}$

c. $\sqrt[3]{256}$

Be prepared to share your solutions and methods.

7.3 THINGS THAT VARY

Understanding Variables

Learning Goals

In this lesson, you will:

▶ Analyze problem situations.

▶ Solve problems.

▶ Define variables.

▶ Write algebraic expressions.

▶ Evaluate algebraic expressions.

▶ Write equations.

Key Terms

▶ variable

▶ algebraic expression

▶ equation

First step: pull up next to the front car. Don't forget to signal! Second step: turn the steering wheel toward the curb. Make sure to look in the rear-view mirror and back up slowly. Third step: don't crunch the car next to you. Once the car is clear, turn the steering wheel the other way to make the car parallel to the curb. Make sure not to hit anything behind the car! When the car is in the space, turn off the engine. The perfect parallel park! But that's the easy part. The hard part of parallel parking is figuring out whether the car will fit in the space in the first place. In 2009, mathematician Simon Blackburn at the University of London wrote a formula for a car company that could be used to determine exactly how much space a car needs for the perfect parallel park.

Why do you think a car company is interested in having this formula? Do you think that cars of the future will be able to park themselves? What numbers do you think should be used in the formula to make a self-parking car work?

7

Problem 1   Shipping Charges

1. The flat rate to ship a small box with dimensions of
$8\frac{5}{8}'' \times 5\frac{3}{8}'' \times 1\frac{5}{8}''$ is $4.95.

   a. What is the cost to ship 6 small boxes? Write a numeric expression to help you calculate the cost.

   b. What is the cost to ship 12 small boxes? Write a numeric expression to help you calculate the cost.

   c. What is the cost to ship 17 small boxes? Write a numeric expression to help you calculate the cost.

   d. Write a sentence to describe how you can determine the cost to ship any number of the small boxes.

2. What quantity or quantities changed in each part of Question 1?

3. What quantity or quantities remained the same in each part of Question 1.

In Question 1 there was one quantity that changed or "varied." In mathematics, one of the most powerful concepts is to use a symbol, often a letter, to represent a quantity that varies. The use of letters or symbols, called **variables,** helps you write expressions to understand problem situations. Whenever you perform the same mathematical process over and over, you can write an *algebraic expression* to represent the situation. An **algebraic expression** is a mathematical phrase involving at least one variable, and sometimes numbers and operation symbols.

Let's consider the situation from Question 1.

To write an algebraic expression that represents the shipping charges for any number of small boxes, think about each of the number sentences you wrote in parts (a) through (c).

n doesn't make sense to me. Can I use b for box or s for small box?

| The flat rate, $4.95, stayed the same. | 4.95(6)
4.95(12)
4.95(17) | The number of small boxes changed each time. |

To write an algebraic expression:

- Select a variable, say n for "number of," and assign it to the changing quantity.

  Let n = the number of small boxes.

- Replace the given value of the number of small boxes in the numerical expression with the variable n.

  4.95(n) or 4.95n

4. Use the algebraic expression, 4.95n, to calculate the cost to ship:

   a. 20 small boxes.

   b. 100 boxes.

   c. 252 boxes.

5. The business manager has reviewed expenses for the last three weeks. Determine the number of small boxes that were shipped given the total cost of the shipping receipt.

    a. How many small boxes were shipped if the total cost was $19.80?

    b. How many small boxes were shipped if the total cost was $69.30?

    c. How many small boxes were shipped if the total cost was $103.95?

    d. Write a sentence to describe how to calculate the number of small boxes that were shipped given the total cost of the shipping receipt.

6. What quantity or quantities changed each part of Question 5?

7. What quantity or quantities remained the same?

To help you calculate the costs of an unknown quantity, you can write an *equation*. An **equation** is a mathematical sentence that contains an equal sign. An equation can contain numbers, variables, or both in the same mathematical sentence.

8. Write an equation to describe this situation. Let *n* represent the number of small boxes, and let *c* represent the total shipping cost in dollars.

9. Myra is fulfilling orders and will need to request the correct amount of money for postage from the business manager. Determine if Myra has requested the correct amount of money to ship the small boxes for each order.

a. Myra requests $39.60 from the business manager to ship eight small boxes. Does Myra have the correct amount of money? Explain your reasoning.

b. Myra requests $168.30 from the business manager to ship 35 small boxes. Does Myra have the correct amount of money? Explain your reasoning.

Problem 2   Planning an Event

1. The Social Club is planning an event to kick off the annual charity drive. The Social Club has 15 total members. Each member is responsible for sending out an equal number of invitations for the upcoming event.

a. How many invitations will each club member send if 75 people are invited to the event?

b. How many invitations will each club member send if 225 people are invited to the event?

c. How many invitations will each club member send if 375 people are invited to the event?

d. Write a sentence to describe how you can determine the number of invitations each club member will send.

e. What quantity or quantities changed? What quantity or quantities remained the same?

f. Write an algebraic expression that represents the number of invitations each club member will send. Let *p* represent the number of people invited to the event.

2. Use your expression to determine the number of invitations that each member will send if the club invites:

a. 600 people.

b. 900 people.

3. Determine the total number of people invited to the annual charity drive if each club member sends out a specific number of invitations.

   a. Each club member will send out 9 invitations. How many total people are invited?

   b. Each club member will send out 17 invitations. How many total people are invited?

   c. Each club member will send out 31 invitations. How many total people are invited?

   d. Write a sentence to describe how to calculate the total number of people invited to the event given the number of invitations sent out by each club member.

4. Write an equation to describe this situation. Let p represent the total number of people invited to the annual charity drive, and let n represent the number of invitations sent out by each club member.

Problem 3   Redeeming a Gift Card

1. Marilyn received a $25 gift card from the president of the Social Club for all of her hard work in organizing the social event. Complete the table to determine the price Marilyn will pay for each item if she uses her gift card.

Item	Original Price of the Item	Value of Gift Card	Marilyn's Price After Using Her Gift Card
Shoes	$79.99		
Concert ticket	$28.50		
Video game	$49.99		

2. What quantity or quantities changed? What quantity or quantities remained the same?

3. Write a sentence to describe how you calculated Marilyn's cost for each item if Marilyn uses her gift card.

4. Write an algebraic expression to determine the price Marilyn will pay for any item after using her $25 gift card. Let p represent the original price of the item.

5. Use your expression to determine Marilyn's price if the original price is:

    a. $55.

    b. $114.

6. Complete the table to determine the original price of each item.

Item	Original Price of the Item	Value of Gift Card	Marilyn's Price After Using Her Gift Card
Bike		$25	$84.00
Jeans		$25	$7.50
Fish for her aquarium		$25	$17.35

7. Write a sentence to describe how you calculated the original price of each item.

8. Write an equation to describe this problem situation. Let *p* represent the original price of the item, and let *m* represent the price Marilyn will pay for the item.

Talk the Talk

1. Describe an algebraic expression in your own words.

2. Name an advantage for writing an algebraic expression.

Be prepared to share your solutions and methods.

7.4 WHAT'S MY NUMBER?
Writing Algebraic Expressions

Learning Goals

In this lesson, you will:

▶ Write expressions.

▶ Write algebraic expressions to determine values for real world situations.

▶ Determine the parts of an algebraic expression.

Key Terms

▶ numerical coefficient

▶ constant

▶ evaluate an algebraic expression

What can you learn from a person's facial expressions? Well, some expressions are easy to identify. If someone smiles, it generally means that they are happy. A frown generally means someone is sad or disappointed. But can facial expressions help determine if someone is telling the truth? In fact, there is a science that is dedicated to studying the shifting of someone's eyes, the slight pause in a person's speech, and other facial expressions or body language to determine if someone is telling the truth or telling a lie. What other moods or feelings can you interpret through facial expressions? What can numerical expressions tell you about mathematics?

7

Problem 1   Writing Expressions

1. A school lunch costs $1.85. Use your calculator to determine how much money is collected for each situation. Write the numerical expression you typed in your calculator for each.

   a. Fifty-five students purchase a school lunch.

   b. One hundred twenty-three students purchase a school lunch.

   c. Two thousand thirteen students purchase a school lunch.

   d. One thousand five hundred twelve students purchase a school lunch.

2. Write a sentence to describe how you can determine the amount of money collected for any number of school lunches purchased.

3. Write an algebraic expression that represents the total amount of money collected. Let *n* represent the number of school lunches purchased.

4. The cost to rent a skating rink is $215 for a two-hour party. The cost will be shared equally among all the people who attend the party. Use your calculator to determine how much each person will pay if:

a. 25 people attend?

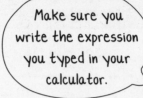

Make sure you write the expression you typed in your calculator.

b. 43 people attend?

c. 81 people attend?

d. 108 people attend?

5. Write a sentence to describe how you can determine how much each person will pay to attend the party.

6. Write an algebraic expression that represents how much each person will pay to attend the skate party. Let *p* represent the number of people attending.

7. Jimmy has three 300-minute international calling cards. Complete the table to determine how many minutes remain on each card after each call.

Number of Minutes on the Calling Card	Duration of Call	Number of Minutes Remaining on Calling Card
300 minutes	33 minutes	
300 minutes	57 minutes	
300 minutes	1 hour and 17 minutes	

8. Write a sentence to describe how you calculated the number of minutes remaining on the calling card.

9. Write an algebraic expression to determine how many minutes remain after each call. Let *c* represent the duration of the call in minutes.

10. Write an algebraic expression that represents each situation.

   a. A pencil costs $0.17. How much will you spend if you buy *p* pencils?

   b. You can run a mile in 7 minutes 30 seconds. How long will it take you to run *m* miles assuming you run at a constant rate of speed?

   c. You have 4 bins. You want to have the same amount of snacks in each. If you have *s* snacks, how many snacks will be in each bin?

   d. You have a sheet of 250 stickers that you want to share equally with your friends. If you have *f* friends, how many stickers will each friend receive?

7

11. Write an algebraic expression that represents each word expression.

    a. 6 times a number, *n*   **b.** 5 more than *c*

    c. *h* minus 7   **d.** *x* plus 1 more

    e. 3 times *y*   **f.** *m* less than 9

You have written many different algebraic expressions, each requiring one of these operations:

- multiplication
- addition
- division
- subtraction

12. Consider each of the algebraic expressions shown.

Example 1:   Example 2:   Example 3:

  $3.45n$ $\dfrac{n}{7}$ $n + 12$

    a. Write a sentence to describe each example.

A number, or quantity, that is multiplied by a variable in an algebraic expression is called the **numerical coefficient**. If the variable does not have a coefficient, then the numerical coefficient is understood to be 1. A number, or quantity, that does not change its value is called a **constant**.

    b. State the numerical coefficients in each example.

    c. State the constants in each example.

7

13. Write the meaning of each algebraic expression in two ways.

a. $6t + 3$

b. $2 - 4s$

c. $b - 5$

d. $3x - y$

e. $10 + r$

f. $10r$

Problem 2 Evaluations

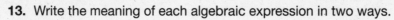

To **evaluate an algebraic expression** means to determine the value of the expression. When you evaluate an algebraic expression, you should substitute the given values for the variables, and then simplify the expression using the Order of Operations.

1. Write the meaning of each algebraic expression. Then, evaluate the algebraic expression for the given values.

a. $3x - 4$, if $x = 10$

b. $11 - s$, if $s = 2$

c. $10 - z$, if $z = 8$

d. $5 - \dfrac{y}{4}$, if $y = 2$

e. $7 + 5a$, if $a = 20$ **f.** $\frac{b}{4}$, if $b = 8$

2. Complete each table.

a.

h	$3h - 2$
2	
$\frac{7}{3}$	
5.1	
$\frac{5}{6}$	

b.

m	$1 + m$
0	
$\frac{2}{3}$	
4	
1.7	

c.

z	$\frac{2z}{3} + 1$
1	
2	
5	
11	

 Be prepared to share your solutions and methods.

7

7

DIFFERENT WAYS
Multiple Representations of Algebraic Expressions

Learning Goal

In this lesson, you will:

▶ Use verbal descriptions, diagrams, algebraic expressions, tables, and graphs to represent problem situations.

Key Term

▶ multiple representations

The value of a baseball card in 1920 may have been a few cents. The same card today may have a value of over $10,000. A house in Ohio may have a value of $150,000. The same house on the beach in South Carolina, Georgia, or California could have a value of over $1,000,000. At one grocery store, a box of cereal may have a value of $2.38, but at another grocery store, the same box may sell for $2.69. Why do the same items sometimes have different values? How do we determine the value of things? How do we determine value in mathematics?

Problem 1 Searching for Patterns

1. Calculate the perimeter of each shape. Each square is one unit by one unit.

   a. Shape 1 Shape 2 Shape 3

   b. Draw and label the next three shapes following the pattern from Question 1, part (a).

   Shape 4   Shape 5   Shape 6

2. Calculate the perimeter of each shape you drew. Complete the table with your calculations.

Shape Number	Perimeter (units)
1	
2	
3	

3. Calculate the perimeter of the seventh shape using the table. Explain how the table helped you determine the perimeter of the seventh shape.

4. Calculate the perimeter of the twentieth shape. Explain how you calculated your answer.

20th shape? What happened to shapes 8 through 19? Do I have to draw all those shapes?

5. Write an algebraic expression that describes the relationship between the shape number and the perimeter. Define your variable.

6. If the pattern continues, what shape has a perimeter of 500 units? Explain how you determined your answer.

7

7. Use your table from Question 2 to plot the points on the graph.

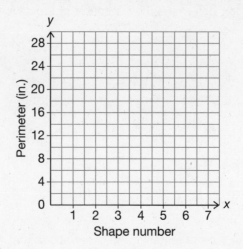

8. Would it make sense to connect the points on this graph? Explain why or why not.

This problem situation was represented in several ways:

- a diagram of figures
- a table of values
- a verbal description
- an algebraic expression, and
- a graph.

These are often called **multiple representations** of a problem situation.

Problem 2   Using Tables of Values

1. The table shows the cost of a particular item.

Number of items	Cost (dollars)
1	6
8	48
16	96
5	30

a. Describe how the cost is related to the number of items.

b. Define a variable for the number of items.

c. Write an algebra expression to represent the cost.

d. Use the expression to calculate the cost of 12 items, and then enter the values in the table.

2. Use your table to construct a graph. Be sure to label the axes.

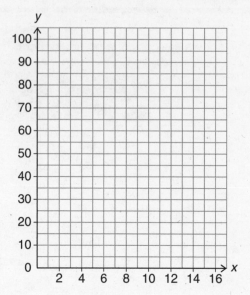

3. Would it make sense to connect the points on this graph? Explain why or why not.

Problem 3   Using Verbal Descriptions

1. A water tank holds 100 gallons of water. The tank is leaking at the rate of two gallons a minute. Determine how many gallons of water will be left in the tank if the leak continues for:

   a. one minute.

   b. 10 minutes.

   c. 34 minutes.

   d. 25 minutes.

2. Describe how you calculated each answer.

3. Define a variable for the quantity that changes. Then, write an algebraic expression for the amount of water in the tank.

4. How long will it take for the tank to be empty? Explain your reasoning.

5. Complete the table.

Number of Minutes the Tank is Leaking	Gallons of Water Remaining in the Tank
1	
10	
25	
34	
50	

6. Use your table to construct a graph. Be sure to label the axes.

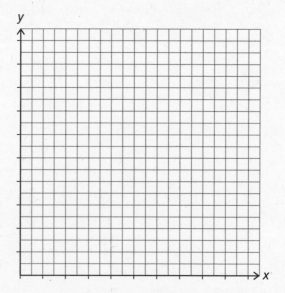

7. Would it make sense to connect the points on this graph? Explain why or why not.

Problem 4 Using Graphs

This graph shows the distance a car is away from home in miles versus the time in minutes.

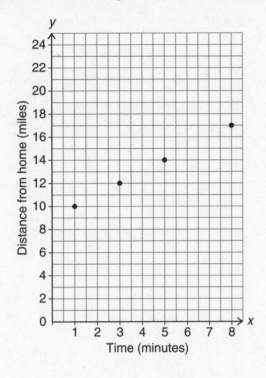

1. Complete the table using the points from the graph.

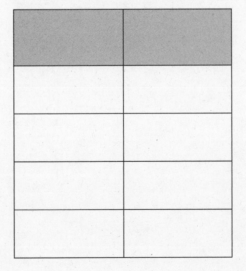

2. Define a variable for the time in minutes, and then write an expression for the distance from the home.

3. Use the expression to calculate the distance the car is from home after 20 minutes.

4. Would it make sense to connect the points on this graph? Explain why or why not.

 Be prepared to share your solutions and methods.

7.6

THERE'S MORE THAN ONE WAY

Using Multiple Representations of Problems

Learning Goal

In this lesson, you will:

▶ Use multiple representations to analyze and solve problems.

Global positioning systems, or simply GPS, are a technology that has made people with map phobias more comfortable with directions.

Today's GPS systems not only give directions on how to get to a location, but can also calculate the time it should take to get there. GPS also offers multiple ways of getting to the same location, and, just in case drivers want to avoid traffic, most GPS systems can determine what the traffic might be along the way. Have you ever looked up directions to get to a specific location?

7

Problem 1   Areas of Squares

Earlier, you determined that the area of a square is calculated by multiplying the length of its side by itself. You are now are going to investigate this situation using a variety of methods.

1. Draw a series of 5 squares. Start with the side length of 1 unit and increase the side length by 1 unit for each new square drawn.

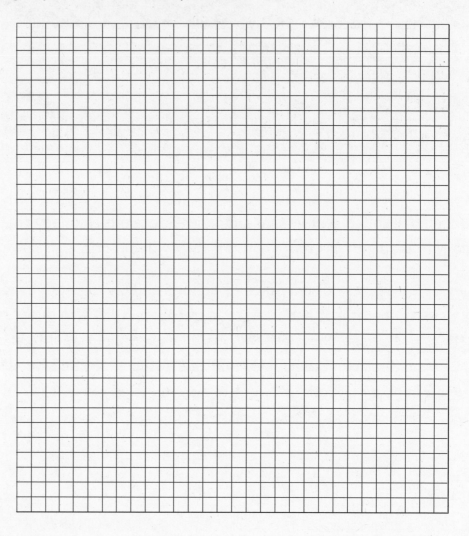

2. Use your drawings to answer each.

   a. Explain why the area of a square with a side length of s units will have an area of s^2 unit squares.

   b. Determine how many unit squares must be added to the first square to get the second square, added to the second square to get the third square, added to the third square to get the fourth square, etc.

   c. How many unit squares would you have to add to the fifth square to get the next square? Explain your reasoning.

   d. What number would you have to add to the 150th square to get the 151st square? Explain how you could determine this.

3. Complete the table, which represents the areas of the squares.

Side of the Square (units)	Area of the Square (square units)
1	
2	
3	
4	
5	
6	
7	
8	
9	
10	

4. Use your table to answer each.

    a. Determine the number of square units that must be added to the area of the first square to get the area of the second square, the number of square units that are added to the second square to get the third square, etc.

    b. How many square units would you have to add to the fifth square to get the next square? Explain your reasoning.

    c. How is this number that you add each time related to the side length of the square in the first column of your table?

5. Using the information from Question 4, what number would you have to add to the 150th square to get the 151st?

Useful to me might not be useful to you ... I guess it just depends on the situation.

6. Was the table or the drawing more useful in answering the question about the formula for the area of a square?

7. Was the table or the drawing more useful in answering the question about the number that must be added to the 150th square to get the 151st square?

8. Use your table to plot the points on the graph.

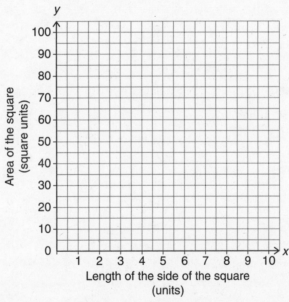

9. Connect the points with a smooth curve. Why does this make sense in this problem situation?

7

10. Consider a square with an area of 70 square units. Use your graph to estimate the side length of the square.

11. Estimate the side length of the square that would have an area of 45 square units.

12. Estimate the area of the square whose side length is $5\frac{1}{2}$ units.

13. How did the graph help you answer these questions? Would a drawing or a table have been more useful? Explain your reasoning.

14. Define a variable for the side length of the square and write an expression for the area of a square.

15. Use this expression to calculate the areas of squares with side lengths of:

    a. 175 units.

    b. 1120 units.

16. What advantage(s), if any, does the expression provide that the drawing, table, or graph does not?

Problem 2   Comparing Strategies Using Different Representations

When you were estimating the side length of the square given the area in Problem 1 Question 10, you were also determining the square root of a number. You wrote the formula for the area of a square as $A = s^2$, where A represents the area of the square and s represents the side length of the square. This formula can also be written as $s = \sqrt{A}$, which can be used to determine the side length of a square if you are given the area of the square.

In Lesson 7.2, you estimated $\sqrt{70}$ using a different strategy. You first identified the two closest perfect squares, one greater than and one less than the radicand. Because $8^2 = 64$ and $9^2 = 81$, you knew that $\sqrt{70}$ was between 8 and 9. Then, using estimation and multiplication you determined a value for $\sqrt{70}$. In Question 10, you estimated $\sqrt{70}$ using the graph.

1. Compare your estimate of $\sqrt{70}$ from Lesson 7.2 to your answer from Question 10. Are they the same?

2. Estimate $\sqrt{95}$. Use the strategy from Lesson 7.2 or the graph from Question 8. Explain your choice in strategy.

7

3. Estimate $\sqrt{200}$. Use the strategy from Lesson 7.2 or the graph from Question 8. Explain your choice in strategy.

4. What are the advantages of using each strategy to estimate a square root?

Talk the Talk

Multiple representations—including drawings or diagrams, verbal descriptions, tables, and graphs—can be useful in analyzing and solving problems.

Complete the graphic organizer describing the advantages of each representation.

- Verbal Description
- Algebraic Expression
- Table
- Graph

Be prepared to share your solutions and methods.

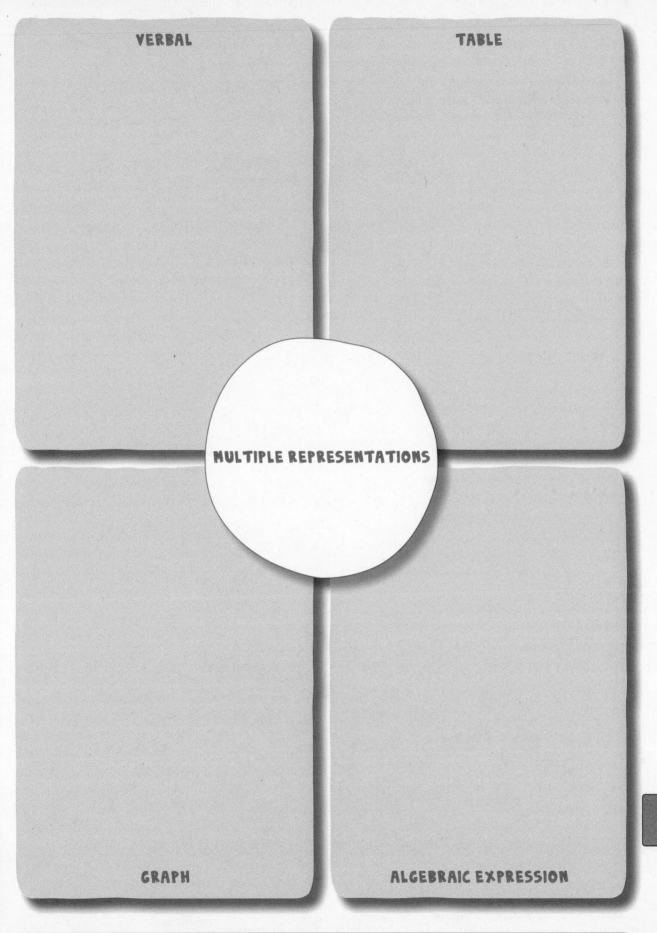

VERBAL

TABLE

MULTIPLE REPRESENTATIONS

GRAPH

ALGEBRAIC EXPRESSION

7

Key Terms

- conventions (7.1)
- numerical expression (7.1)
- evaluate (7.1)
- operations (7.1)
- parentheses (7.1)
- order of operations (7.1)
- square of a number (7.2)
- perfect squares (7.2)
- square root (7.2)
- radical (7.2)
- radicand (7.2)
- perfect cube (7.2)
- cube of a number (7.2)
- cube root (7.2)
- index (7.2)
- variable (7.3)
- algebraic expression (7.3)
- equation (7.3)
- numerical coefficient (7.4)
- constant (7.4)
- evaluate an algebraic expression (7.4)
- multiple representations (7.5)

7.1 Evaluating Numerical Expressions with Addition, Subtraction, Multiplication, and Division

Any time you use mathematical operations, they must be performed in a certain order. In general, operations are performed from left to right. Multiplication and division should be performed before addition and subtraction.

Example

Consider the numerical expression $3 + 2 \cdot 4 - 18 \div 9$. Evaluate the expression by first performing multiplication or division from left to right and then performing addition and subtraction from left to right.

$$3 + 2 \cdot 4 - 18 \div 9$$
$$= 3 + 8 - 2$$
$$= 11 - 2$$
$$= 9$$

Are you thinking something right now? Probably. Humans are thought to think about 7×10^4 thoughts each day. How many is that? Let me think about it . . .

7

7.1

Evaluating Numerical Expressions Involving Exponents and Parentheses

Because exponents are repeated multiplication, they are to be performed before addition and subtraction, and they are also to be performed before multiplication and division. Parentheses are used to group numbers and operations to change the normal order in which you perform operations. Expressions inside parentheses should be performed before other operations.

Example

Consider the numerical expression $5 \bullet 3^2 + 4 \div 2 \bullet (7 - 4)$. Evaluate the expression by first performing operations inside parentheses, then evaluating exponents, and finally performing multiplication, division, addition, and subtraction from left to right.

$5 \bullet 3^2 + 4 \div 2 \bullet (7 - 4)$
$= 5 \bullet 9 + 4 \div 2 \bullet 3$
$= 45 + 2 \bullet 3$
$= 45 + 6$
$= 51$

7.1

Using the Order of Operations to Simplify and Evaluate Numerical Expressions

The Order of Operations is a set of rules that ensures the same result every time an expression is evaluated.

Order of Operations Rules

1. Evaluate expressions inside parentheses or grouping symbols such as ( ) or [ ].

2. Evaluate exponents.

3. Multiply and divide from left to right.

4. Add and subtract from left to right.

Example

The Order of Operations were not followed in Solution A. The same expression has been solved correctly using the Order of Operations in Solution B.

Solution A	Solution B
$8 + 16 \div 4$	$8 + 16 \div 4$
$= 24 \div 4$	$= 8 + 4$
$= 6$	$= 12$

7.2 Determining the Square of a Number

Calculate the square of a number by multiplying the number by itself. A number is a perfect square if it is the square of a whole number.

Example

The number 16 is a perfect square because 4 is a whole number and $4 \times 4 = 16$. Another way to write this mathematical sentence is $4^2 = 16$.

7.2 Calculating Square Roots

A square root is one of two equal factors of a nonnegative number. Every positive number has two square roots, a positive square root (called the principal square root) and a negative square root. To determine a square root that is not a whole number, identify the two closest perfect squares, one greater than and one less than the radicand. Then, estimate the square root to the nearest tenth.

Example

Estimate $\sqrt{23}$ to the nearest tenth.

Twenty-three is between the two perfect squares 16 and 25. This means that $\sqrt{23}$ is between 4 and 5, but closer to 5.

Because $4.7^2 = 22.09$ and $4.8^2 = 23.04$, $\sqrt{23}$ is approximately 4.8.

7.2 Determining the Cube of a Number

Calculate the cube of a number by multiplying the number by itself three times. A number is a perfect cube if it is the cube of a whole number.

Example

The number 27 is a perfect cube because 3 is a whole number and $3 \times 3 \times 3 = 27$. Another way to write this mathematical sentence is $3^3 = 27$.

7.2 Calculating the Cube Root

A cube root is one of three equal factors of a number. To determine a cube root that is not a whole number, identify the two closest perfect cubes, one greater than and one less than the radicand. Then, estimate the cube root to the nearest tenth.

Example

Estimate $\sqrt[3]{35}$ to the nearest tenth.

Thirty-five is between the two perfect cubes 27 and 64. This means that $\sqrt[3]{35}$ is between 3 and 4 but closer to 3.

Because $3.2^3 = 32.77$ and $3.3^3 = 35.94$, $\sqrt[3]{35}$ is approximately 3.3.

7.3 Analyzing and Solving Problems

Determine the important information in the problem situation and identify the quantity that stays the same and the quantity that changes. Write a numeric expression to help solve the problem.

Example

It costs $0.35 for one color copy, so it costs $0.35(25), or $8.75, for 25 color copies and $0.35(50), or $17.50, for 50 color copies. The cost per copy remains the same, but the number of copies changes.

7.3 Writing Algebraic Expressions and Equations

Whenever you perform the same mathematical process over and over, you can write an algebraic expression to represent the situation. The use of letters, called variables, can be used to represent quantities in a problem situation that changes. To write an algebraic expression, assign a variable to the quantity that changes and determine the operation needed to solve the problem. To go further, define the solution as a variable and set it equal to the algebraic expression. An equation is a mathematical sentence that contains an equal sign and may contain numbers, variables, or both.

Example

You buy s songs online for $0.99 each.

The expression $0.99s$ can be used to represent this situation.

To write an equation for the problem situation, set the expression equal to the solution, or the total cost t: $0.99s = t$.

7.3 Using Algebraic Expressions

An algebraic expression can be used to calculate the solution to a problem situation. Replace the variable with a given value to create a numerical expression and solve.

Example

One party table can seat 8 guests. Use the algebraic expression $\frac{g}{8}$, where g represents the total number of party guests, to determine the number of tables needed for a party with 112 guests.

Replace the variable, g, with the number of guests, 112, to create a numerical expression and solve.

$$\frac{112}{8} = 14$$

7.4 Writing Algebraic Expressions

Whenever you perform the same mathematical process over and over, you can write a mathematical phrase, called an algebraic expression, to represent the situation. An algebraic expression is a mathematical phrase involving at least one variable and sometimes numbers and operation symbols. Recall that a variable is a letter or symbol that is used to represent quantities.

Example

Three brothers were given m amount of money to divide equally among them. The algebraic expression that represents how much each brother will get is shown.

$$\frac{m}{3}$$

7.4 Describing Algebraic Expressions

A number, or quantity, that is multiplied by a variable in an algebraic expression is called the numerical coefficient. If the variable does not have a coefficient, then the coefficient is understood to be 1. A number, or quantity, that does not change its value is called a constant.

Example

$35 + x$

Thirty-five plus any number, x. The numerical coefficient is 1, and the constant is 35.

7

7.4 Evaluating Algebraic Expressions

To evaluate an algebraic expression means to determine its value. Substitute the given values for the variables, and then simplify using the Order of Operations rules.

Example

The meaning of the algebraic expression $27 - s$ is shown. Then, the evaluation of the expression is shown when $s = 12$.

Meaning: 27 minus s.

Evaluate: $27 - 12 \rightarrow$ Subtract $27 - 12$ which is a difference of 15.

$27 - 12 = 15$

7.5 Multiple Representations of a Problem Situation

A problem situation can be represented in several ways including a diagram of figures, a table of values, a verbal description, an algebraic expression, and a graph.

Example

Describe the area of the shape. The problem situation is represented as:

A diagram

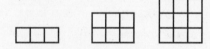

A verbal description

A row of three squares is added in each figure.

So, the area of the shape is equal to the shape number times 3.

A table of values

Shape Number	Area of Shape
1	3
2	6
3	9
4	12
5	15

An algebraic expression

- Let s represent the shape number.
  The area is 3s.

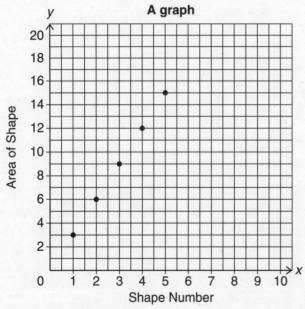

A graph

Using Multiple Representations to Analyze and Solve Problems

Multiple representations—including verbal descriptions, algebraic expression, tables, and graphs—can be useful in analyzing and solving problems. Verbal descriptions can help determine quantities that change and that remain the same. Tables can organize data in numerical order. Graphs provide a quick look at data and can help estimate the value of an unknown quantity. An algebraic expression allows for the exact calculation of unknown quantities.

Example

The volume of a cube can be determined using the algebraic equation s^3, where s is the side length. For side lengths that are not whole numbers, a graph can provide a quick estimation of s for a given volume.

The volume of a cube with a side length of 3.5 is about 40.

Calculate s^3 where s is 3.5: $(3.5)^3 = 42.88$.

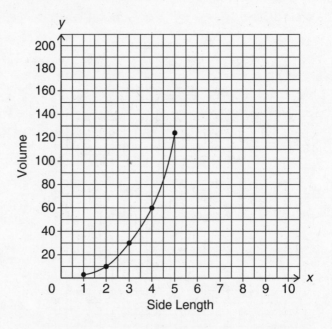

8 ALGEBRAIC EXPRESSIONS

8

Bowling is a popular sport among people all over the world. In the United States, the most popular form of bowling is ten-pin bowling. Other forms of bowling include five-pin bowling, nine-pin skittles, and duckpin bowling, to name a few.

8

8.1 THE PARTS OF CARS YOU DON'T SEE!

Relationships between Quantities

Learning Goals

In this lesson, you will:

► Predict the next term in a sequence.

► Write numerical and algebraic expressions.

Key Terms

► sequence

► term

Have you ever wondered how many parts make up a car? Sure, you can see some parts of a car like the tires, the steering wheel, and the windshield. But what about the other parts you cannot see like the brakes or the fuel filter. Actually, it is estimated that there are roughly 17,000 to 20,000 parts in an average car.

Can you think of some car parts that you cannot see? Do you think it is helpful for car manufacturers to know how many parts are needed for each vehicle they make?

Problem 1   Building Trains

Josh likes building trains out of train parts. Each train car needs four wheels. Josh begins by building a train with one car, then two cars, and finally three cars as shown.

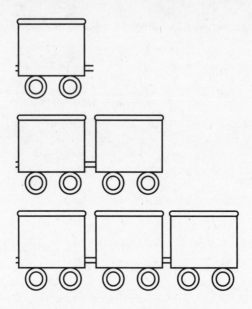

1. Describe how many total wheels Josh will need to build a train with 4 cars. How many total wheels will he need to build a train with 5 cars?

A **sequence** is a pattern involving an ordered arrangement of numbers, geometric figures, letters, or other objects. The number of train cars and the number of wheels needed form sequences of numbers.

2. Write two sequences using Josh's train cars.

   Number of cars:

   Number of wheels:

Each number of cars in the first sequence and each number of wheels in the second sequence form the *terms,* or members, of the sequence. A **term** is a number, a variable, or a product of numbers and variables. The first term is the first object or number in the sequence. The second term is the second object or number in the sequence, and so on.

3. What is the first term in the second sequence?

4. What is the fifth term in the first sequence?

5. What are the two quantities that change in Josh's train-building situation?

6. Explain how you would determine the number of wheels needed to make a train with 6 cars, 7 cars, and 8 cars.

7. Describe in your own words how to calculate the number of wheels needed if the train has any number of cars.

8. Write an algebraic expression to represent the number of wheels needed to build a train with an unknown number of cars.

9. Josh would like to add more trains to his collection. The cost of each car is $8.

    a. Write a sequence that represents the cost of buying 1 car, 2 cars, 3 cars, 4 cars, and 5 cars.

    b. Describe the mathematical process that is being repeated to determine the total cost for a set of cars.

    c. What are the variable quantities, or the quantities that are changing, in this situation? Include the units that are used to measure these quantities.

    d. What quantity remains constant? Include the units that are used to measure this quantity.

    e. Which variable quantity depends on the other variable quantity?

    f. Write an algebraic expression for the total cost, in dollars, for a train set with *n* cars. Rewrite the first five terms of the sequence.

10. Write an algebraic expression to represent each sequence.

    a. 2, 4, 6, 8,...

    b. 1, 3, 5, 7,...

    c. 3, 5, 7, 9,...

    d. 2, 4, 8, 16,...

    e. 101, 102, 103, 104,...

Problem 2   Parts of Algebraic Expressions

As you learned previously, an algebraic expression contains at least one variable and sometimes numbers and operations. A term of an algebraic expression is a number, variable, or product of numbers and variables.

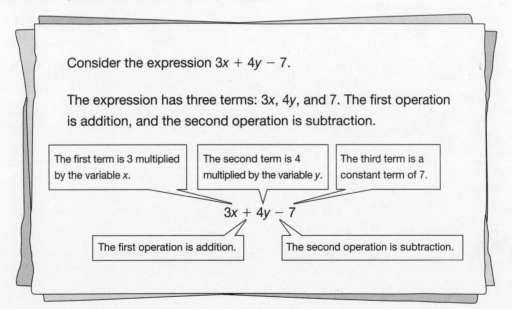

Consider the expression $3x + 4y - 7$.

The expression has three terms: $3x$, $4y$, and 7. The first operation is addition, and the second operation is subtraction.

| The first term is 3 multiplied by the variable x. | The second term is 4 multiplied by the variable y. | The third term is a constant term of 7. |

$$3x + 4y - 7$$

The first operation is addition.

The second operation is subtraction.

1. Let's consider two algebraic expressions:

$8 + 5x$ and $8 - 5x$

   a. Identify the number of terms in each algebraic expression.

   b. Identify the operation in each algebraic expression.

   c. Identify the terms in each algebraic expression.

   d. What is the same in both expressions?

   e. What is different in the expressions?

2. Identify the number of terms, and then the terms themselves for each algebraic expression.

   a. $4 - 3x$

   b. $4a - 9 + 3a$

   c. $7b - 9x + 3a - 12$

3. Write an algebraic expression that represents each situation.

    a. Diego drove at a constant rate of 60 miles per hour. How many miles did he drive in t hours?

    b. The cost of a school lunch is $1.60. How much money was collected if n students bought lunch?

    c. Jackie has 12 cookies. She wants to share them equally among her friends. How many cookies does each friend receive if she shares with f friends?

    d. Donald has $145 in his savings account. How much is left in his account if he withdraws d dollars?

    e. The cost to rent a storage unit is $125. The cost will be shared equally among a number of people, p, who are storing their belongings. How much will each person pay?

    f. Chairs cost $35 and sofas cost $75. How much would it cost to purchase x chairs and y sofas?

    g. Used paperback books cost $6.25 each with a shipping and handling cost of $8.75. What is the cost of x books?

4. Write an algebraic expression that represents each word expression.

   a. the quotient of a number, *n*, divided by 7

   b. three more than a number, *n*

   c. one-fourth of a number, *n*

   d. fourteen less than three times a number, *n*

   e. six times a number, *n*, subtracted from 21

   f. three more than a number, *n*, added to 21

   g. one-fourth of a number, *n*, minus 6

   h. Ten times the square of a number, *w*, divided by 12.

5. Construct an algebraic expression for each description.

   a. There are 2 terms. The first term is a constant added to the second term, which is a product of a number and a variable.

   b. There are 4 terms. The first term is a quotient of a variable divided by 11. This is added to a second term, which is a constant. The third term is a second variable multiplied by three-fourths. The third term is subtracted from the first 2 terms. The last term is a different constant added to the other 3 terms.

   c. The cube of a variable subtracted from a constant and then added to the square of the same variable.

   d. A number multiplied by the square of a variable minus a number multiplied by the same variable minus a constant.

 Be prepared to share your solutions and methods.

8.2 TILE WORK
Simplifying Algebraic Expressions

Learning Goals

In this lesson, you will:

▶ Use the Associative and Commutative Properties of Addition and Multiplication to simplify expressions.

▶ Use the Order of Operations.

▶ Use algebra tiles to simplify algebraic expressions.

Key Terms

▶ Commutative Property of Addition

▶ Commutative Property of Multiplication

▶ Associative Property of Addition

▶ Associative Property of Multiplication

▶ simplify

▶ like terms

If you type your papers, you probably use a word processing program. If you blog, you probably use some type of text program. If you surf the net, you use a browser. What do these and many other computer programs have in common? They all use programming.

Computer programming is the ability of writing directions so that the computer can perform the task. Just think about it: every drop-down menu you select, every mouse click on an icon, even when you close out a program requires directions for the computer to perform the task you want.

As with any directions, the *order* of the directions is important. Just imagine the confusion that might happen if scrolling on a drop-down menu closed out a program. This is why computer programmers must be very careful *how* they instruct computers to do tasks.

Can you think of other directions that people or machines do to perform tasks? Is the order of the directions important?

Problem 1   Going Bowling

1. You and your friends are going bowling. It costs $2.50 to rent shoes, and it costs $3.50 to bowl one game.

   a. How much will it cost you to rent shoes and bowl 1 game?

   b. How much will it cost you to rent shoes and bowl 2 games?

   c. How much will it cost you to rent shoes and bowl 3 games?

2. Describe how you calculated the total cost for each situation.

3. What are the variable quantities in this problem?

4. What are the constant quantities in this problem?

5. What variable quantity depends on the other variable quantity?

6. Write an algebraic expression to determine the total cost to rent shoes and bowl games. Let *g* represent the unknown number of games bowled.

There are several ways to write an algebraic expression to represent the total cost to rent shoes and bowl games.

Let *g* represent the number of games bowled.

Expression 1	Expression 2	Expression 3	Expression 4
$2.50 + 3.50g$	$2.50 + g(3.50)$	$3.50g + 2.50$	$g(3.50) + 2.50$

These expressions are equivalent because they express the same relationship.

The *Commutative Properties of Addition* and *Multiplication* state that the order in which you add or multiply two or more numbers does not affect the sum or product.

The **Commutative Property of Addition** states that changing the order of two or more terms in an addition problem does not change the sum.
For any numbers *a* and *b*, $a + b = b + a$.

The **Commutative Property of Multiplication** states that changing the order of two or more factors in a multiplication problem does not change the product.
For any numbers *a* and *b*, $a \times b = b \times a$.

Expressions 1 and 3 demonstrate the Commutative Property of Addition.
These expressions are equivalent, even though the order of the terms is reversed.

Expressions 1 and 2 demonstrate the Commutative Property of Multiplication.
These expressions are equivalent, even though the factors in the second terms are reversed.

7. Given the four expressions shown:

   a. state one other example of the Commutative Property of Addition.

   b. state one other example of the Commutative Property of Multiplication.

When determining the total cost to rent shoes and bowl games, you used the Order of Operations. Recall that these rules ensure that the order in which numbers and operations are combined is the same for everyone. You should remember that when evaluating any expression, you must use the Order of Operations.

8. Evaluate each numerical expression using the Order of Operations. Show all your work.

a. $22 - 4(3)$

b. $9(3) + 4(5)$

c. $60 - 3^2$

d. $(8 - 5)2 + 5^2$

e. $7(12) - 2(3 + 2)$

f. $(10 - 6) + 2^2$

Problem 2 More Properties

1. Evaluate each numerical expression using the Order of Operations.

(4 + 17) + 3	4 + (17 + 3)
(19 + 42) + 8	19 + (42 + 8)
(16 × 5)2	16(5 × 2)
(12 × 25)4	12(25 × 4)

2. Compare the two expressions in each row. What do you notice?

3. How do the expressions in the first column compare to those in the second column?

The **Associative Property of Addition** states that changing the grouping of the terms in an addition problem does not change the sum. For any numbers a, b, and c, $(a + b) + c = a + (b + c)$.

The **Associative Property of Multiplication** states that changing the grouping of the factors in a multiplication problem does not change the product. For any numbers a, b, and c, $(a \times b) \times c = a \times (b \times c)$.

The Commutative and Associative Properties of Addition and Multiplication are very powerful properties. For any expression involving *only* addition, they allow you to change the order of addends and to add parentheses whenever you want. For any expression involving *only* multiplication, you can also change the order of the factors and include parentheses whenever you want.

Benjamin and Corinne are both trying to determine this sum.

$$22 + 17 + 3 + 8$$

Their methods are shown.

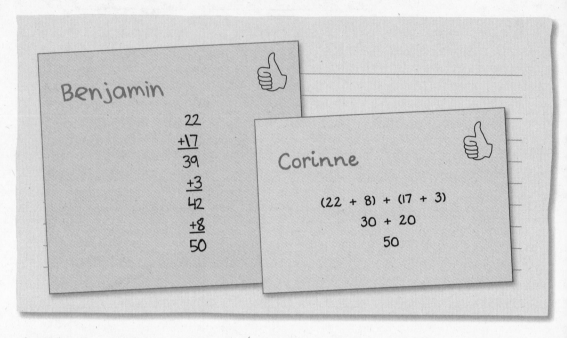

Benjamin

$$
\begin{array}{r}
22 \\
+17 \\
\hline
39 \\
+3 \\
\hline
42 \\
+8 \\
\hline
50
\end{array}
$$

Corinne

$$(22 + 8) + (17 + 3)$$
$$30 + 20$$
$$50$$

4. Describe the differences between the methods Benjamin and Corinne used to calculate the sum.

5. Determine each sum by writing an equivalent numerical expression using the Commutative and Associative Properties.

   a. 5 + 7 + 5

   b. 5 + 13 + 2

   c. 2 + 21 + 8 + 9

   d. 4 + 3 + 6 + 5

Use the properties to look for number combinations that make it simpler to add like Corinne did.

Problem 3 Simplifying Algebraic Expressions

The Commutative and Associative Properties can help you *simplify* algebraic expressions. To **simplify** an expression is to use the rules of arithmetic and algebra to rewrite that expression with fewer terms. An expression is in simplest form if it contains the fewest terms possible, and if all *like terms* have been combined.

In an algebraic expression, **like terms** are two or more terms that have the same variable raised to the same power. The numerical coefficients of like terms can be different.

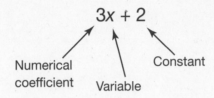

Let's use algebra tiles to explore simplifying algebraic expressions.

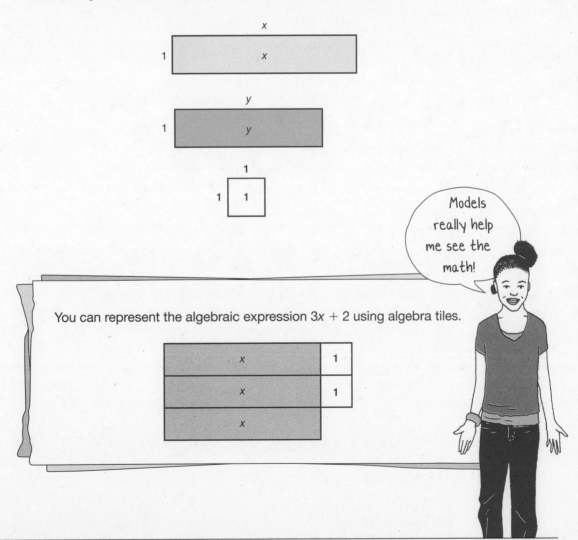

1. Represent each algebraic expression using algebra tiles. Then, sketch the model below each algebraic expression.

a. $3x + 2$

b. $2x + 1$

c. $4y + 3$

d. $5x$

e. 4

f. $2x + 3y$

2. Use your models from Question 1 to write each algebraic expression in simplest form by combining like terms.

    a. $(3x + 2) + (2x + 1)$

When I combine like terms using my models I just regroup all the same tiles together.

    b. $(3x + 2) + (4y + 3)$

    c. $(2x + 1) + (4y + 3)$

    d. $(4y + 3) + 4$

    e. $(3x + 2) + 5x$

    f. $(4y + 3) + 5x$

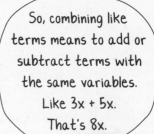

So, combining like terms means to add or subtract terms with the same variables. Like 3x + 5x. That's 8x.

3. Simplify each algebraic expression.

    a. $2x + 3x + 4x$ **b.** $\left(\frac{3}{4}x + 2\right) + \frac{3}{4}x$

    c. $(16.2x + 4.1) + (10.4x - 2)$ **d.** $(8x + 17y) + (11x - 8y)$

    e. $55x + 65y + 75$ **f.** $(2x + 5) + (3y + 2)$

    g. $(3y + 2) + (4y + 2)$ **h.** $(x + 1) + (3y + 2) + (4y + 2)$

Talk the Talk

1. How do you know when an algebraic expression is in simplest form?

2. How do you know when a numerical expression is in simplest form?

Be prepared to share your solutions and methods.

8.3 BLUEPRINTS TO FLOOR PLANS TO COMPUTERS

Using the Distributive Property to Simplify Algebraic Expressions

8

Learning Goals

In this lesson, you will:

▶ Simplify algebraic expressions using the Distributive Property.

▶ Write algebraic expressions using the Distributive Property.

▶ Model the Distributive Property using algebra tiles.

Key Terms

▶ Distributive Property of Multiplication over Addition

▶ Distributive Property of Multiplication over Subtraction

▶ Distributive Property of Division over Addition

▶ Distributive Property of Division over Subtraction

Do you ever wonder how your school was built? Or have you wondered how your house or apartment building was constructed? Before the actual construction takes place, architects plan what the building will look like, what materials will be needed, and how the new structure will interact with other buildings in the area. In certain cities, there are special requirements so that a building can withstand damage from an earthquake or a hurricane and still remain standing.

Not very long ago, the blueprint was the backbone of the building process. Architects and draftspersons would create the floor plan for buildings, malls, homes, apartment buildings—well, almost any building you can think of. However, as more work is being done on computers, people are no longer using paper blueprints—do you think people will no longer plan buildings as well?

Problem 1 Installing Carpet

8

The Lewis family just bought a new house. They will install new carpet in two adjacent rooms before they move in.

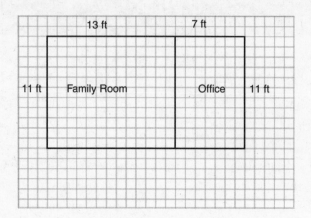

1. How would you calculate the total area of the rooms?

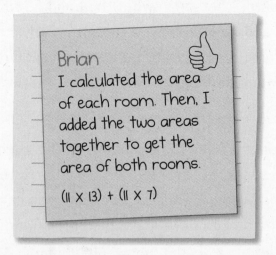

Brian

I calculated the area of each room. Then, I added the two areas together to get the area of both rooms.

(11 × 13) + (11 × 7)

2. Calculate the area using Brian's expression.

Sara 👍

I multiplied the width
by the total length
of both rooms to find
the total area of both
rooms.

11 (13 + 7)

3. Calculate the area using Sara's expression.

4. What do you notice about your results using each expression? What does that tell
you about the two expressions Brian and Sara wrote?

The two expressions, $(11 \times 13) + (11 \times 7)$ and $11 (13 + 7)$, are equal because of the
Distributive Property of Multiplication over Addition.

The **Distributive Property of Multiplication over Addition** states that for any real
numbers a, b, and c, $a \cdot (b + c) = a \cdot b + a \cdot c$.

There is also the **Distributive Property of Multiplication over Subtraction**, which states
that if a, b, and c are any real numbers, then $a \cdot (b - c) = a \cdot b - a \cdot c$.

Problem 2   Algebra Tiles

Let's use algebra tiles to explore rewriting algebraic expressions with the Distributive Property.

x
x

1   1

1
1

> When you are speaking about an algebraic expression use the words "the quantity." For example (x + 3) in words would be "the quantity x plus three."

Consider the expression $5(x + 1)$. This expression has two factors: 5 and the quantity $(x + 1)$. You can use the Distributive Property to rewrite this expression. In this case, multiply the 5 by each term of the quantity $(x + 1)$. The model using algebra tiles is shown.

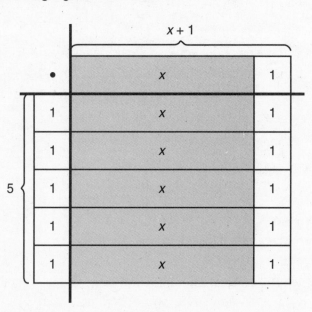

$$5(x + 1) = 5x + 5$$

> This model appears to be just like adding the quantity x + 1 five times!

1. Create and sketch a model of each expression using your algebra tiles. Then, rewrite the expression using the Distributive Property.

   a. $3(x + 2)$

   b. $4(2x + 1)$

   c. $2(x + 3)$

8

d. $(3x + 1)2$

2. Rewrite each expression using the Distributive Property. Then, simplify if possible.

a. $2(x + 4)$

b. $\frac{2}{3}(6x + 12)$

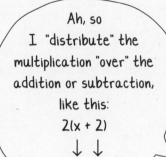

Ah, so I "distribute" the multiplication "over" the addition or subtraction, like this:

$2(x + 2)$
↓ ↓
$2x + 4$

c. $2(x + 5) + 4(x + 7)$

d. $5x + 2(3x - 7)$

e. $2(y + 5) + 2(x + 5)$

f. $\frac{1}{2}(4x + 2) + 8x$

Problem 3 Splitting an Expression Equally

So far in this lesson, you multiplied expressions together using the Distributive Property of Multiplication over Addition and the Distributive Property of Multiplication over Subtraction. Now let's think about how to divide expressions.

How do you think the Distributive Property will play a part in dividing expressions? Let's find out.

1. Represent $4x + 8$ using your algebra tiles.

   a. Sketch the model you create.

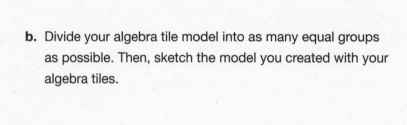

   b. Divide your algebra tile model into as many equal groups as possible. Then, sketch the model you created with your algebra tiles.

c. How many equal groups did you create?

d. Write an expression to represent each group from your sketches in part (b).

e. Verify you created equal groups by multiplying your expression from part (d) by the number of equal groups from part (c). The product you calculate should equal $4x + 8$.

Let's consider the division expression from Question 1. You can rewrite it using the Distributive Property of Division over Addition.

$$\frac{4x + 8}{4} = \frac{4x}{4} + \frac{8}{4}$$

$$= 1x + 2$$

$$= x + 2$$

When you rewrite the expression, you have to divide the denominator into both terms in the numerator.

The model you created in Question 1 is an example that shows that the Distributive Property holds true for division over addition.

2. Represent $2x + 6y + 4$ using your algebra tiles.

   a. Sketch the model you created. Be careful to not combine unlike terms using the same type of algebra tiles.

   b. Divide your algebra tile model into equal groups. Then, sketch the model you created with your algebra tiles.

   c. How many equal groups did you create?

   d. Write an expression to represent each group from part (b).

   e. Verify that you created equal groups by multiplying your expression from part (d) by the number of equal groups from part (c). The product should equal $2x + 6y + 4$.

The **Distributive Property of Division over Addition** states that if a, b, and c are real numbers and $c \neq 0$, then $\frac{a + b}{c} = \frac{a}{c} + \frac{b}{c}$.

3. Rewrite the division expression from Question 2 using the Distributive Property of Division over Addition. Then, simplify the expression.

Remember that you must divide the denominator into all the terms in the numerator.

$$\frac{2x + 6y + 4}{2}$$

4. Represent $6 + 3(x + 1)$ using your algebra tiles.

   a. Sketch the model you created.

   b. Divide your algebra tile model into equal groups. Then, sketch the model you created with your algebra tiles.

   c. How many equal groups did you create?

   d. Write an expression to represent each group from part (b).

   e. Verify that you created equal groups by multiplying your expression from part (d) by the number of equal groups from part (c). The product you calculate should equal $6 + 3(x + 1)$.

The expression in Question 4 can be simplified using the Distributive Property of Division over Addition in two ways.

5. Analyze each correct method. Explain the reasoning used in each.

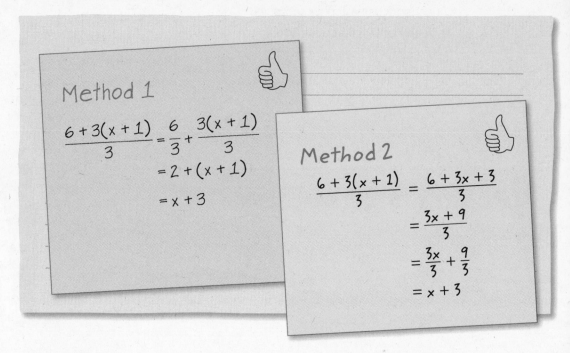

Method 1

$$\frac{6 + 3(x + 1)}{3} = \frac{6}{3} + \frac{3(x + 1)}{3}$$
$$= 2 + (x + 1)$$
$$= x + 3$$

Method 2

$$\frac{6 + 3(x + 1)}{3} = \frac{6 + 3x + 3}{3}$$
$$= \frac{3x + 9}{3}$$
$$= \frac{3x}{3} + \frac{9}{3}$$
$$= x + 3$$

Reasoning:

Reasoning:

The Distributive Property also holds true for division over subtraction.

The **Distributive Property of Division over Subtraction** states that if a, b, and c are real numbers and $c \neq 0$, then $\frac{a - b}{c} = \frac{a}{c} - \frac{b}{c}$.

For example: $\frac{2x - 5}{2} = \frac{2x}{2} - \frac{5}{2}$
$$= x - \frac{5}{2}$$

6. Simplify each expression using a Distributive Property. Then, state which Distributive Property you used.

a. $\dfrac{3x - 7}{3}$

b. $\dfrac{6 + 2(x + 4)}{2}$

c. $\dfrac{32 + 4x}{4}$

d. $\dfrac{2x + 7}{2}$

e. $\dfrac{3(x + 1) + 12}{3}$

Be prepared to share your solutions and methods.

8

ARE THEY SAYING THE SAME THING?

Multiple Representations of Equivalent Expressions

8.4

8

So, what makes a park a national park? There are different ideas on what a national park is, but many experts agree that a National Park is a government-owned plot of natural land. This land is set aside for animal safety, and people can use the land for recreation.

The first national park established was California's Yosemite (pronounced yo - SEM - ih - tee) National Park. The park exists because of two conservationists: John Muir and President Theodore Roosevelt. Both men were pioneers in land conservation. Do you think land conservation is still taking place? Do you think conservation has changed since the time of Roosevelt and Muir?

Problem 1   Off to Camp!

Harley and Jerome belong to a Youth Outdoors Club. Each member needs to raise money to pay for camp by selling tins of popcorn. Each popcorn tin sold earns the member $4 toward the trip. Harley and Jerome have each sold 5 popcorn tins. Club chairperson Ms. Diani, asked all members to think about how much money they could earn toward their trip if they continue to sell more popcorn tins.

Harley and Jerome decide to let p represent the number of additional tins of popcorn to be sold. Harley expressed his potential earnings by the expression $4(p + 5)$. Jerome expressed his potential earnings by the expression $4p + 20$.

1. Describe the meaning of each person's expression in terms of the problem situation. Include a description for the units of each number or variable in the expression.

There are many ways to determine if Harley and Jerome's expressions both accurately describe this situation. Two algebraic expressions are **equivalent expressions** if, when any values are substituted for variables, the results are equal. You can verify that two expressions are equivalent by using properties to simplify the expressions to the same expression, or by graphing them to show that the graphs are the same. Tables can be useful to show that expressions are not equivalent or whether they may be equivalent.

Let's explore each possibility.

2. State the property that verifies that Harley and Jerome's expressions are equivalent.

3. Use the table to answer the questions.

   a. Complete the table shown for each additional number of tins sold.

Number of Additional Popcorn Tins Sold	Harley's Expression $4(p + 5)$	Jerome's Expression $4p + 20$
3		
7		
15		
25		

   b. What can you determine based on the values in the table?

   c. What would you need to do to verify the two expressions are equivalent?

You can use a graphing calculator to determine if two expressions are equivalent. The graphing calculator will create a graph for each expression. Follow the steps.

Step 1: Press $\boxed{Y=}$ and enter what is shown.

$$y_1 = 4(x + 5)$$

$$y_2 = 4x + 20$$

To distinguish between the graphs of y_1 and y_2, move your cursor to the left of y_2 until the \ flashes. Press $\boxed{\textbf{ENTER}}$ one time to select \.

Step 2: Press $\boxed{\textbf{WINDOW}}$ to set the bounds and intervals for the graph.

Xmin = 0, Xmax = 50, and Xscl = 10,

Ymin = 0, Ymax = 100, and Yscl = 10.

Step 3: Press $\boxed{\textbf{GRAPH}}$.

4. Sketch both graphs on the coordinate plane shown.

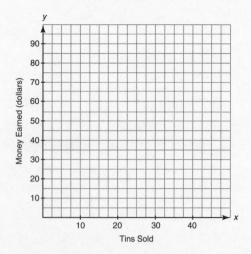

5. How does the graph verify that the two expressions are equivalent?

Problem 2   Equal or Not?

1. Choose three different values for *x* and complete each table.

   a. Do the two expressions appear to be equivalent? Explain your reasoning.

x	$\frac{2}{3}(x + 7)$	$\frac{2}{3}x + \frac{7}{3}$

   b. Do the two expressions appear to be equivalent? Explain your reasoning.

Wow... to know for sure if two expressions were equivalent using a table, I would have to substitute every known value!

But you might only need one value to see if they are not equivalent.

x	$\frac{1}{2}(x + 9)$	$\frac{x}{2} + \frac{9}{2}$

2. Determine if the two expressions are equivalent. Graph each expression using a graphing calculator and sketch the graph in the coordinate plane shown. Press WINDOW to set the bounds: Xmin = 0, Xmax = 10, Xscl = 1, Ymin = 0, Ymax = 10, and Yscl = 1.

a. Are the two expressions equivalent? Explain your reasoning.

$2(x + 2) + 3x$

$5x + 4$

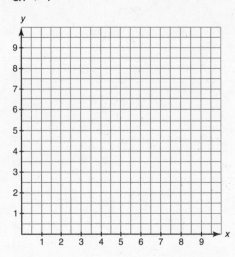

Don't forget to put arrows on each end of your line. The arrows show that the line goes on forever.

b. Are the two expressions equivalent? Explain your reasoning.

$\frac{1}{2}x + 5$

$\frac{1}{2}(x + 5)$

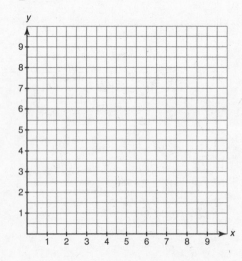

Problem 3   Writing Expressions

1. A local restaurant is busiest over lunch and has three cooks who work at this time. The cooks divide the incoming orders among themselves. So far today, the cooks have prepared 21 meals total.

   a. If 18 additional orders come in, how many meals will each cook prepare? Write an expression, and show your calculations.

   b. If 42 additional orders come in, how many meals will each cook prepare? Write an expression, and show your calculations.

   c. Write an expression to represent the unknown number of meals each cook prepares. Let m represent the number of additional orders.

2. Christopher is selling oatmeal energy bars to raise money for his baseball team. The team receives $1.25 for each oatmeal energy bar sold. He has already sold 25 oatmeal energy bars.

   a. If Christopher sells 10 more energy bars, how much money will he raise for the baseball team? Write an expression, and show your calculations.

   b. If Christopher sells 45 more energy bars, how much money will he raise for the baseball team? Write an expression, and show your calculations.

   c. Write an expression to represent the unknown amount of money Christopher will raise for his baseball team. Let c represent the number of additional energy bars sold.

3. The Music-For-All Club is offering a special deal to all new members. You can join the club at no cost and receive 10 free CDs. However, you must also agree to purchase at least 12 more CDs within the first year at the club's special price of $11.99 per CD.

a. What will 20 CDs from the club cost? Show your calculations.

b. What will 25 CDs from the club cost? Show your calculations.

c. Write an expression to represent the total cost of an unknown number of CDs. Let *m* represent the number of CDs you will get from the club.

4. Four friends decide to start a summer business doing yard work in their neighborhood. They will split all their earnings evenly. They have two lawnmowers, but they need to buy gas, rakes, trash bags, and a pair of pruners. They spend $100 buying supplies to get started.

a. How much profit will each friend receive if they earn $350 the first week? Show your calculations.

b. How much profit will each friend receive if they earn $475 the first week? Show your calculations.

c. Write an expression that represents the unknown profit for each friend. Let *d* represent the amount of money earned.

Problem 4   Number Magic

1. Try this number riddle with a partner. Follow the steps.

   Step 1: Pick a number between 1 and 30.

   Step 2: Add 9 to your number.

   Step 3: Multiply the sum by 3.

   Step 4: Subtract 6 from the product.

   Step 5: Divide the difference by 3.

   Step 6: Subtract your original number.

2. What is your answer? Compare your answer to your partner's answer. What do you notice?

3. Why do you think you will always end with the same number?

Let's use the properties of real numbers to investigate why this riddle works.

4. What quantity is changing in this riddle?

5. Let *n* represent the original number. Write and simplify an expression for each step.

Talk the Talk

 Complete the graphic organizers by stating each rule using variables and providing an example.

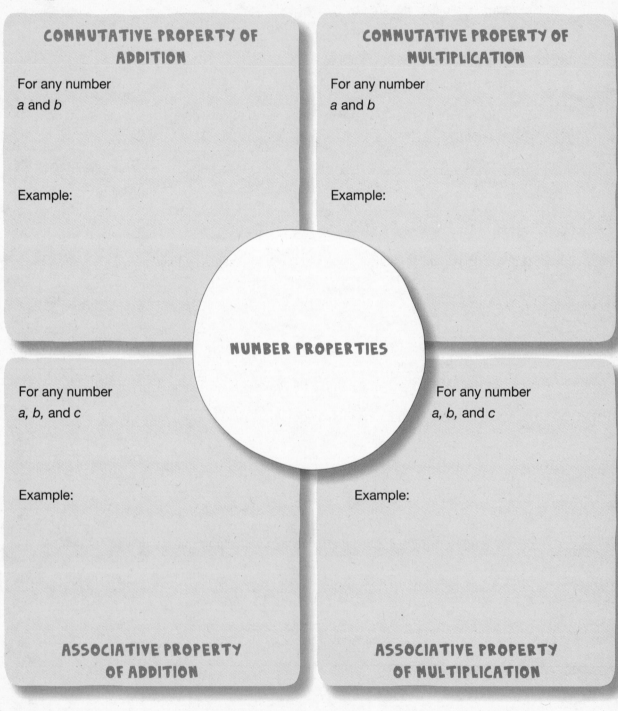

COMMUTATIVE PROPERTY OF ADDITION

For any number
a and *b*

Example:

COMMUTATIVE PROPERTY OF MULTIPLICATION

For any number
a and *b*

Example:

NUMBER PROPERTIES

For any number
a, *b*, and *c*

Example:

ASSOCIATIVE PROPERTY OF ADDITION

For any number
a, *b*, and *c*

Example:

ASSOCIATIVE PROPERTY OF MULTIPLICATION

MULTIPLICATION OVER ADDITION

For any number
a, *b*, and *c*

Example:

MULTIPLICATION OVER SUBTRACTION

For any number
a, *b*, and *c*

Example:

DISTRIBUTIVE PROPERTIES

For any number
a, *b*, and *c*

Example:

DIVISION OVER ADDITION

For any number
a, *b*, and *c*

Example:

DIVISION OVER SUBTRACTION

 Be prepared to share your solutions and methods.

8

8.5

LIKE AND UNLIKE
Combining Like Terms

Learning Goals

In this lesson, you will:

▶ Develop models for algebraic terms.

▶ Use models to combine like terms in algebraic expressions.

▶ Combine like terms in algebraic expressions.

Using categories to classify people, places, and other objects is often very useful. For example, the population of the United States is sometimes divided into rural, urban, and suburban. What does each of the categories mean and why are they useful? What are some other categories that are used to describe the population in the United States?

Problem 1 Like and Unlike

You will use the algebra tiles shown to model algebraic expressions.

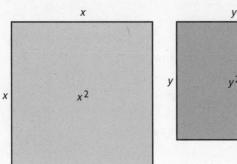

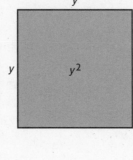

We have used some of these tiles before.

1. What are the dimensions of each of the tiles?

a.

b.

c.

d.

e.

2. Represent each algebraic expression using algebra tiles and the operations symbols. Then sketch your model.

a. $3x^2 + x + 2$

The first expression has 3 terms and 2 operations so I will have 3 groups of algebra tiles separated by 2 addition signs.

b. $2 + x^2 + y^2 + 1$

c. $3x + x + 2y$

d. $5x + 1 + y^2 + 3$

e. $2x + 3 + 3x + x^2$

3. Which of the expressions in parts (a)–(e) have different terms with identical tiles?

4. Rearrange the tiles in Question 2, part (c) so that there are only two terms.

   a. Sketch your new model. Include the operation symbol.

   b. Write the algebraic expression represented.

   c. Could you rearrange the tiles so there was only one term? Explain your reasoning.

   d. What are the terms that can be combined called?

5. Rearrange the tiles in Question 2 part (b) to reduce the number of terms to the fewest possible.

   a. Sketch your new model. Include the operation symbol.

   b. Write the algebraic expression represented.

   c. Could you rearrange the tiles so there was only one term? Explain your reasoning.

6. Rearrange the tiles in Question 2 part (d) to reduce the number of terms to the fewest possible.

    a. Sketch your new model. Include the operation symbol.

    b. Write the algebraic expression represented.

    c. Could you rearrange the tiles so there are fewer terms? Explain your reasoning.

7. Rearrange the tiles in Question 2 part (e) to reduce the number of terms to the fewest possible.

    a. Sketch your new model. Include the operation symbol.

    b. Write the algebraic expression represented.

    c. Could you rearrange the tiles so there are fewer terms? Explain your reasoning.

8. The algebraic expression $2(3x + 2) - 3$ is represented with algebra tiles and the operations symbols.

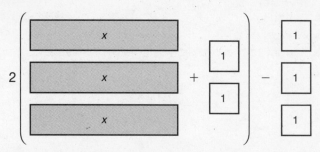

a. Use the distributive property to rewrite the expression without parentheses.

$2(3x + 2) - 3 =$ _____

b. Model your new expression using algebra tiles and operations symbols.

c. Rearrange the tiles to reduce the number of terms to the fewest possible terms. Then, write the algebraic expression that is represented.

9. Now, you will create your own expression and model.

   a. Write your own algebraic expression that has 4 terms with 2 pairs of like terms.

   b. Model your expression using algebra tiles and operations symbols.

   c. Rearrange the tiles to reduce the number of terms to the fewest possible.

What is the same about everyone's expression in the end?

   d. Write the algebraic expression that is represented.

   e. Could you rearrange the tiles so there are fewer terms? Explain your reasoning.

Problem 2   What about the Expressions?

1. Represent $4x + 2x$ using algebra tiles and the operations symbols.

   a. Sketch the model of the expression.

   b. Write an equivalent algebraic expression with one term.

   c. Represent the algebraic expression from part (b) using algebra tiles and operators.

   d. What property tells you that $4x + 2x = (4 + 2)x$?

2. Represent $2x + 5 + 3x$ using algebra tiles and the operations symbols.

   a. Sketch the model of the expression.

   b. Write an equivalent algebraic expression by combining like terms.

   c. Represent the algebraic expression from part (b) using algebra tiles and operations symbols.

   d. What property tells you that $2x + 5 + 3x = 2x + 3x + 5$?

   e. What property tells you that $2x + 3x + 5 = (2 + 3)x + 5$?

3. Represent $7x + 2x^2 - 3x - x^2$ using algebra tiles and operations symbols.

  a. Sketch the model of the expression.

  b. Write an equivalent algebraic expression by combining like terms.

  c. Represent the algebraic expression from part (b) using algebra tiles and operations symbols.

The tiles really help me see what is like and unlike!

Problem 3   Without the Tiles

So, to combine like terms I will look for the same variable with the same exponent.

Simplify each algebraic expression by combining like terms.

1. $3x + 5y - 3x + 2y =$

2. $4x^2 + 4y + 3x + 2y^2 =$

3. $7x + 5 - 6x + 2 =$

4. $x^2 + 5y + 4x^2 - 3y =$

5. $4x^3 - 5y + 3x^2 + 2x^2 =$

6. $x + 5y + 6x - 2y - 3x + 2y^2 =$

Simplify each algebraic expression using the distributive properties first, and then combining like terms.

7. $4(x + 5y) - 3x =$

8. $2(2x + 5y) + 3(x + 3y) =$

9. $3x + 5(2x + 7) =$

10. $\dfrac{4x + 6y}{2} - 3y =$

11. $3(x + 2y) + \dfrac{3x - 9y}{3}$
$=$

12. $2(x + 3y) + 4(x + 5y) - 3x$
$=$

Be prepared to share your solutions and methods.

8.6

DVDS AND SONGS: FUN WITH EXPRESSIONS

Using Algebraic Expressions to Analyze and Solve Problems

8

Learning Goals

In this lesson, you will:

▶ Represent problem situations with algebraic expressions.

▶ Analyze and solve problems with algebraic expressions.

People just love collecting souvenirs. From theaters to zoos, from amusement parks to concert halls, souvenirs are a staple of most public events and locations.

Film souvenirs are very popular among movie fans. Collectors will try to get their hands on souvenirs from a film.

One of the most popular things movie fans collect are the movie posters—the ones like you see at the movie theater. Collectors will often get a copy and frame it—and sometimes try to get the autographs of the director, crew, and actors. Another collectible might be a copy of the screenplay—the actual script of a movie—or a director's chair. Do you think music fans or art fans collect souvenirs too?

Problem 1 DVDs

Jack, Jenny, John, and Jeannie each collect DVDs. Jack likes western movies, Jenny likes comedies, John likes action movies, and Jeannie likes sports movies.

Jenny says: "I have twice as many DVDs as Jack."

John says: "I have four more DVDs than Jenny."

Jeannie says: "I have three times as many as John."

1. If Jack has 10 DVDs, determine the number of DVDs for each friend. Explain your reasoning.

   a. Jenny

   b. John

   c. Jeannie

   d. all of the four friends together

2. If Jeannie has 24 DVDs, determine the number of DVDs for each friend. Explain your reasoning.

   a. John

   b. Jenny

   c. Jack

   d. all of the four friends together

3. Let x represent the number of DVDs that Jack has. Write an algebraic expression that represents the number of DVDs for each friend.

    a. Jenny

    b. John

    c. Jeannie

    d. all four friends together

    e. Simplify the expression you wrote in part (d).

4. Use your expression from part (e) to determine the number of DVDs they have altogether if Jack has:

    a. 10 DVDs.   **b.** 2 DVDs.

    c. 25 DVDs.   **d.** 101 DVDs.

5. Write an algebraic expression to represent the number of DVDs for:

    a. the males.   **b.** the females.

6. Let *y* represent the number of DVDs Jeannie has. Write an algebraic expression that represents the number of DVDs for each friend.

  a. John

  b. Jenny

  c. Jack

  d. all four friends together

> The number of DVDs that John has is less than Jeannie. So, the expression I write in part (a) has to be less than y.

  e. Simplify the expression you wrote in part (d).

7. Use your expression from part (e) to determine how many DVDs they have altogether if Jeannie has:

  a. 72 DVDs.   **b.** 24 DVDs.

  c. 36 DVDs.   **d.** 660 DVDs.

8. Write an algebraic expression to represent the number of DVDs for:

  a. the males.   **b.** the females.

9. Let *z* represent the number of DVDs Jenny has. Write an algebraic expression that represents the number of DVDs for each friend.

   a. Jack

   b. John

   c. Jeannie

   d. all four friends together

   e. Simplify the expression you wrote in part (d).

10. Use your expression from part (e) to determine the number of DVDs they have altogether if Jenny has:

   a. 20 DVDs.   **b.** 24 DVDs.

   c. 50 DVDs.   **d.** 34 DVDs.

11. Write an algebraic expression to represent the number of DVDs for:

   a. the males.   **b.** the females.

12. Let *j* represent the number of DVDs John has. Write an algebraic expression that represents the number of DVDs for each friend.

    a. Jenny

    b. Jack

    c. Jeannie

    d. all four friends together

    e. Simplify the expression you wrote in part (d).

13. Use your expression from part (e) to determine the number of DVDs they have altogether if John has:

    a. 24 DVDs.   **b.** 8 DVDs.

    c. 20 DVDs.   **d.** 60 DVDs.

14. Write an algebraic expression to represent the number of DVDs for:

    a. the males.   **b.** the females.

Problem 2   Songs on an MP3 Player

Five friends have their own MP3 players.

- Marvin has 5 more songs on his MP3 than Melvin has on his.
- Marilyn has half as many songs on her MP3 as Marvin has on his.
- Maryanne has 3 more than twice the number of songs on her MP3 as Melvin has on his.
- Marty has 3 times as many songs on his MP3 as Marilyn has on hers.

1. Let x represent the number of songs on Melvin's MP3 player. Write an algebraic expression that represents the number of songs on each friend's MP3 player.

   a. Marvin

   b. Marilyn

   c. Maryanne

   d. Marty

   e. all five friends together

   f. Simplify the expression you wrote in part (e).

2. Use your expression from part (f) to calculate the number of songs they have altogether if Melvin has:

   a. 15 songs.

   b. 47 songs.

3. Write an algebraic expression to represent the number of songs for:

   a. the males.

   b. the females.

4. Let *y* represent the number of songs on Marilyn's MP3 player. Write an algebraic expression that represents the number of songs on each friend's MP3 player.

    a. Marvin

    b. Melvin

    c. Maryanne

    d. Marty

    e. all five friends together

    f. Simplify the expression you wrote in part (e).

5. Use your expression from part (f) to calculate the number of songs they have altogether if Marilyn has:

    a. 15 songs.   **b.** 20 songs.

6. Write an algebraic expression to represent the number of songs for:

    a. the males.   **b.** the females.

 Be prepared to share your solutions and methods.

Chapter 8 Summary

Key Terms

- ▶ sequence (8.1)
- ▶ term (8.1)
- ▶ simplify (8.2)
- ▶ like terms (8.2)
- ▶ equivalent expressions (8.4)

Properties

- ▶ Commutative Property of Addition (8.2)
- ▶ Commutative Property of Multiplication (8.2)
- ▶ Associative Property of Addition (8.2)
- ▶ Associative Property of Multiplication (8.2)
- ▶ Distributive Property of Multiplication over Addition (8.3)
- ▶ Distributive Property of Multiplication over Subtraction (8.3)
- ▶ Distributive Property of Division over Addition (8.3)
- ▶ Distributive Property of Division over Subtraction (8.3)

8.1 Predicting the Next Term in a Sequence

A sequence is a pattern involving an ordered arrangement of numbers, geometric figures, letters, or other objects. A term is a number, variable, or product of numbers and variables. The first term is the first object or number in the sequence, the second term is the second object or number in the sequence, and so on. Look at the relationship between adjacent known terms and apply that same relationship to determine the next terms.

Did you know your brain contains synapses that transfer, store and process information like a computer? Only your brain contains hundreds of trillions of these little computers which is more than all the computers on Earth!

Example

Write the missing terms in the sequence.

Number of ants: 1, 2, 3, 4, 5, 6

Number of legs: 6, 12, 18, ____, ____, ____

Each ant has 6 legs. So, each time an ant is added, add 6 to the number of legs.
The missing terms of the sequence are: 24, 30, 36.

8.1 Writing an Algebraic Expression to Represent a Sequence or Situation

Whenever you perform the same mathematical process over and over, you can write a mathematical phrase, called an algebraic expression, to represent the situation. An algebraic expression is a mathematical phrase involving at least one variable and sometimes numbers and operation symbols.

Examples

The algebraic expression $100 + 3n$, where n is the term number, represents the sequence shown.

103, 106, 109, 112,…

The algebraic expression $2.49p$ represents the cost of p pounds of apples.
One pound of apples costs $2.49.

8.2 Using the Associative and Commutative Properties of Addition and Multiplication to Simplify Expressions

The Commutative Properties of Addition and Multiplication state that the order in which you add or multiply two or more numbers does not affect the sum or the product. The Associative Properties of Addition and Multiplication state that changing the grouping of the terms in an addition or multiplication problem does not change the sum or the product. Use these rules to group addends or factors into expressions that are easy to compute in your head.

Example

$$7 + 9 + 23 + 11 = (7 + 23) + (9 + 11)$$
$$= 30 + 20$$
$$= 50$$

8.2 Using Algebra Tiles to Simplify Algebraic Expressions

To simplify an expression is to use the rules of arithmetic and algebra to rewrite the expression as simply as possible. An expression is in simplest form if all like terms have been combined. Like terms in an algebraic expression are two or more terms that have the same variable raised to the same power. Only the numerical coefficients of like terms are different. In an algebraic expression, a numerical coefficient is the number multiplied by a variable.

8

Example

You can use algebra tiles to represent each term in the algebraic expression. Combine like tiles and describe the result.

$(3x + 2) + (5y + 3) + (x + 2y)$

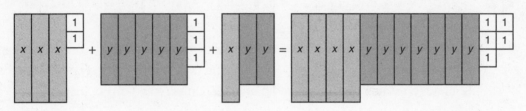

$4x + 7y + 5$

8.3 Modeling the Distributive Property Using Algebra Tiles

The Distributive Property of Multiplication can be modeled by placing the tiles that match the first factor along the left side of a grid and the tiles that match the second factor along the top of a grid. The Distributive Property of Division can be modeled by separating a model of an expression into parts with an equal number of each type of tile.

Examples

a. $3(2x + 1) = 6x + 3$

b. $6y + 12 = 3(2y + 4)$

8.3 Simplifying Algebraic Expressions Using the Distributive Property of Multiplication

The Distributive Property of Multiplication over Addition states that for any numbers a, b, and c, $a \times (b + c) = a \times b + a \times c$. The Distributive Property of Multiplication over Subtraction states that if a, b, and c are real numbers, then $a \times (b - c) = a \times b - a \times c$.

Examples

$9(4x + 2)$
$36x + 18$

$4(2x - 6)$
$8x - 24$

8.3 Simplifying Algebraic Expressions Using the Distributive Property of Division

The Distributive Property of Division over Addition states that if a, b, and c are real numbers and $c \neq 0$, then $\frac{a + b}{c} = \frac{a}{c} + \frac{b}{c}$. The Distributive Property of Division over Subtraction states that if a, b, and c are real numbers and $c \neq 0$, then $\frac{a - b}{c} = \frac{a}{c} - \frac{b}{c}$.

Examples

$$\frac{2x + 8}{2} = \frac{2x}{2} + \frac{8}{2}$$
$$= x + 4$$

$$\frac{3x - 7}{3} = \frac{3x}{3} - \frac{7}{3}$$
$$= x - \frac{7}{3}$$

8.4 Determining If Two Expressions Are Equivalent Using a Table or a Graph

You can determine if two expressions are equivalent in one of two ways:
(1) by calculating values for each or (2) by graphing each. If the output values of each expression are the same for each input, then the expressions are equivalent. If the graph of each expression is the same, then the expressions are equivalent.

Example

The table shows that the expression $(x + 12) + (4x - 9)$ and the expression $5x + 3$ are equivalent.

x	$(x + 12) + (4x - 9)$	$5x + 3$
0	3	3
1	8	8
2	13	13

The outputs for each expression are the same, so $(x + 12) + (4x - 9) = 5x + 3$.

The graph shows that the expression $3(x + 3) - x$ and the expression $3x + 3$ are not equivalent.

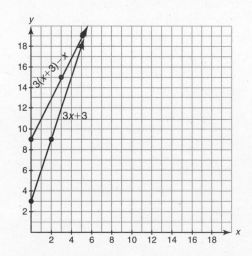

The graphs shown are not the same line, so $3(x + 3) - x \neq 3x + 3$.

8.4 Writing and Solving an Expression Using the Distributive Property

You can use the Distributive Property to solve a problem for any input.

Example

Two friends split the cost of a rental car for three days. Each day the car costs $26 for insurance and fees plus 18¢ per mile driven. If the two friends plan to drive the same number of miles each day, how much will each one pay?
Let m represent the number of miles driven each day.

$$\frac{3(26 + 0.18m)}{2} = \frac{78 + 0.54m}{2}$$
$$= \frac{78}{2} + \frac{0.54m}{2}$$
$$= 39 + 0.27m$$

If each friend drives 250 miles each day, how much will each friend pay?
$39 + 0.27(250) = 106.5$, so each friend will pay $106.50.

8.5 Combining Like Terms Using Algebra Tiles

Algebra tiles can be used to model algebraic expressions. The tiles can then be rearranged so that multiple terms with identical tiles, called like terms, can be combined into one term. After all of the like terms are combined, the original algebraic expression can be rewritten with the fewest possible terms.

Example

Represent the algebraic expression $3x + 5 + x - 1$ using algebra tiles and the operation symbols. Sketch your model.

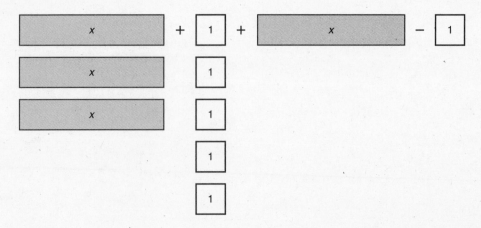

Rearrange the tiles to combine like terms and to reduce the number of terms to the fewest possible terms.

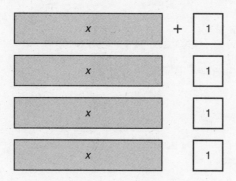

Write the algebraic expression represented by the model.

$4x + 4$

8.6 Using Algebraic Expressions to Analyze and Solve Problems

Many real-life situations can be represented using algebraic expressions. The algebraic expressions can then be used to answer questions about the situation.

Example

Sophia, Hector, Gavin and Jenna are comparing their video game collection. Sophia has 5 more games than Hector. Gavin has twice as many games as Sophia. Jenna has 12 fewer games than Gavin.

a. Let x represent the number of video games that Hector has. Write an algebraic expression that represents the number of video games that each person has.

Hector: x

Sophia: $x + 5$

Gavin: $2(x + 5)$

Jenna: $2(x + 5) - 12$

All 4 friends together: $x + x + 5 + 2(x + 5) + 2(x + 5) - 12$

$$= 6x + 13$$

b. Use your expression to determine the number of video games they have altogether if Hector has:

18 video games

$6(18) + 13$

$= 121$

They have 121 video games.

46 video games

$6(46) + 13$

$= 289$

They have 289 video games.

GLOSSARY

absolute deviation

The absolute value of each deviation is called the absolute deviation.

Example

$$11 - 12 = -1$$
$$\uparrow \qquad \uparrow \qquad \uparrow$$
$$\text{Data} \quad \text{mean} \quad \text{deviation}$$
$$|-1| = 1$$
$$\uparrow \qquad \uparrow$$
$$\text{deviation} \quad \text{absolute}$$
$$\text{deviation}$$

absolute value

The absolute value of a number is its distance from zero on a number line.

Example

The absolute value of -3 is the same as the absolute value of 3 because they are both a distance of 3 from zero on the number line.

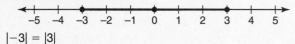

$$|-3| = |3|$$

acute triangle

An acute triangle is a triangle with three acute interior angles.

Example

Angles A, B, and C are acute angles, so triangle ABC is an acute triangle.

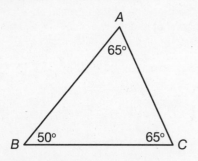

algebraic expression

An algebraic expression is a mathematical phrase involving at least one variable and sometimes numbers and operation symbols.

Examples

$$a \quad 2a + b \quad xy \quad \frac{4}{p} \quad z^2 \quad \sqrt{(4y + 4)^2} \quad 2.5 \times 10^y$$

altitude of a parallelogram

An altitude of a parallelogram is a line segment drawn from a vertex, perpendicular to the line containing the opposite side.

Example

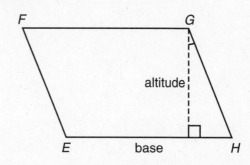

altitude of a trapezoid

An altitude of a trapezoid is a line segment drawn from a vertex perpendicular to a line containing the opposite side.

Examples

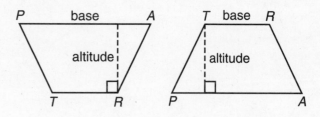

Glossary

altitude of a triangle

An altitude of a triangle is a line segment drawn from a vertex perpendicular to a line containing the opposite side.

Examples

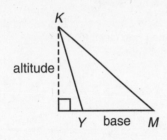

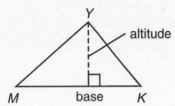

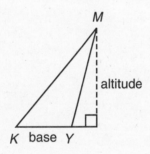

apothem

The apothem of a regular polygon is the perpendicular distance from the center of the regular polygon to a side of the regular polygon.

Examples

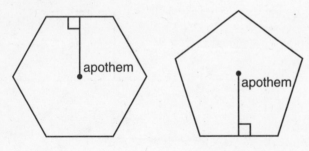

area model

An area model for multiplication is a pictorial way of representing multiplication. In an area model, the rectangle's length and width represent factors, while the rectangle's area represents the product.

Example

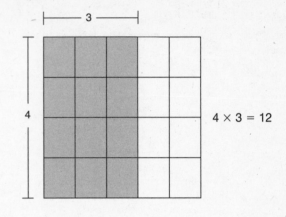

$4 \times 3 = 12$

array

An array is a rectangular arrangement that has an equal number of objects in each row and an equal number of objects in each column.

Example

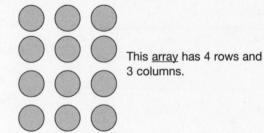

This <u>array</u> has 4 rows and 3 columns.

Associative Property of Addition

The Associative Property of Addition states that changing the grouping of the terms in an addition problem does not change the sum. For any numbers a, b, and c, $(a + b) + c = a + (b + c)$.

Example

$$(9 + 4) + 3 = 9 + (4 + 3)$$
$$\downarrow \qquad\qquad \downarrow$$
$$13 + 3 \qquad\qquad 9 + 7$$
$$\downarrow \qquad\qquad \downarrow$$
$$16 \quad = \quad 16$$

Glossary

Associative Property of Multiplication

The Associative Property of Multiplication states that changing the grouping of the factors in a multiplication statement does not change the product. For any numbers a, b, and c, $(a \times b) \times c = a \times (b \times c)$.

Examples

$$4 \times (3 \times 2) = (4 \times 3) \times 2$$

$$4 \times 6 = 12 \times 2$$

$$24 = 24$$

$$(2 \times 5) \times 5 = 2 \times (5 \times 5)$$

$$10 \times 5 = 2 \times 25$$

$$50 = 50$$

—— **B** ——

balance point

When you look at a number line of a set of data, the mean can be thought of as the point at which the number line would balance. This is called the balance point.

Example

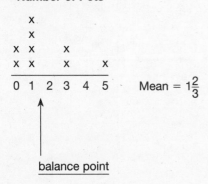

bar graph

A bar graph is a way of displaying categorical data by using either horizontal or vertical bars so that the height or length of the bars indicates the value for that category.

Example

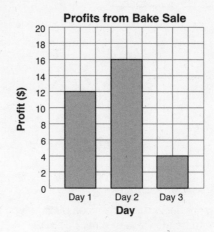

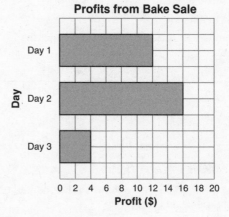

base

In an exponent expression, the base is the factor that is repeatedly multiplied.

Examples

$$2^3 = 2 \times 2 \times 2 = 8 \qquad 8^0 = 1$$

base base

bases of a prism

The two parallel and congruent faces of a prism are known as the bases of a prism.

bases of a trapezoid

The parallel sides of a trapezoid are called the bases of the trapezoid.

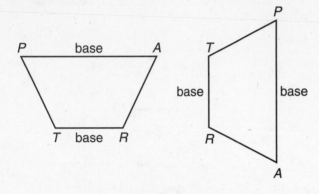

benchmark decimal

A benchmark decimal is a common decimal you can use to estimate the value of other decimals.

Example

The numbers 0, 0.5, and 1 are some benchmark decimals.

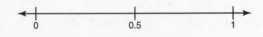

benchmark fractions

Benchmark fractions are common fractions you use to estimate the value of fractions.

Example

The numbers 0, $\frac{1}{2}$, and 1 are some benchmark fractions.

benchmark percents

A benchmark percent is a percent that is commonly used, such as 1%, 5%, 10%, 25%, 50%, and 100%.

box-and-whisker plot

A box-and-whisker plot is a graph that summarizes data using the median, the upper and lower quartiles (Q1 and Q3), and the minimum and maximum values.

Example

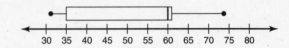

Data: 32, 35, 35, 53, 55, 60, 60, 61, 61, 74, 74

Minimum = 32
Q1 = 35
Median = 60
Q3 = 61
Maximum = 74

— C —

Cartesian coordinate plane

The Cartesian coordinate plane, often referred to as a coordinate plane, is a two-dimensional region determined by a pair of axes. It uses numerical values measured in the same unit of length to represent the location of an object.

Example

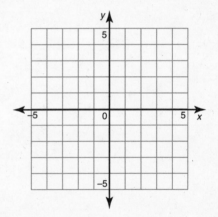

categorical data

Categorical data are data for which each piece of data fits into exactly one of several different groups or categories. Categorical data are also called "qualitative" data.

Examples

Animals: lions, tigers, bears, etc.
U.S. Cities: Los Angeles, Atlanta, New York City, Dodge City, etc.

Glossary

circle graph

A circle graph shows how parts of the whole relate to the whole and to each other.

Example

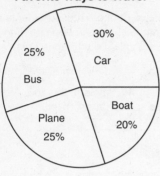

Favorite Ways to Travel

clusters

Clusters are area of the graph where data are grouped close together.

commission

Sales commission is an amount or percent of an item that is paid to employees or companies that sell merchandise in stores, or by calling customers.

Example

5% commission on $350
.05 × 350 = $17.50 ←commission

common denominator

A common denominator is a whole number that is a common multiple of the denominators of two or more fractions.

Example

$$\frac{2}{3} = \frac{4}{6}$$
$$+\frac{1}{2} = \frac{3}{6}$$
$$\frac{7}{6} = 1\frac{1}{6}$$

common denominator

common factor

A common factor is a number that is a factor of two or more numbers.

Example

factors of 60: **1**, **2**, **3**, **4**, 5, **6**, 10, **12**, 15, 20, 30, 60
factors of 24: **1**, **2**, **3**, **4**, **6**, 8, **12**, 24
common factors of 60 and 24: 1, 2, 3, 4, 6, and 12

common multiple

A common multiple is a number that is a multiple of two or more numbers.

Example

multiples of 60: 60, **120**, 180, **240**, 300, 360, 420, 480 . . .
multiples of 24: 24, 48, 72, 96, **120**, 144, 168, 192, 216, **240** . . .
some common multiples of 60 and 24: 120, 240 . . .

Commutative Property of Addition

The Commutative Property of Addition states that changing the order of two or more terms in an addition problem does not change the sum. For any numbers a and b, $a + b = b + a$.

Example

$$8 + 7 = 7 + 8$$
$$\downarrow \qquad \downarrow$$
$$15 \; = \; 15$$

Commutative Property of Multiplication

The Commutative Property of Multiplication states that changing the order of two or more factors in a multiplication sentence does not change the product. For any numbers a and b, $a \times b = b \times a$.

Examples

$$\begin{array}{r} 29 \\ \times\ 3 \\ \hline 87 \end{array} = \begin{array}{r} 3 \\ \times\ 29 \\ \hline 27 \\ +\ 60 \\ \hline 87 \end{array}$$

$$\frac{1}{5} \times \frac{2}{3} = \frac{2}{3} \times \frac{1}{5}$$
$$\frac{2}{15} \qquad\quad \frac{2}{15}$$

compass

A compass is a tool that is used to create arcs and circles.

composite numbers

Composite numbers are numbers that have more than two distinct factors.

Examples

$9 = 3 \times 3, 1 \times 9$
$15 = 1 \times 15, 3 \times 5$
The numbers 9 and 15 are <u>composite numbers.</u>

congruent

Congruent means having the same size, shape, and measure.

congruent polygons

When two polygons are exactly the same size and exactly the same shape, the polygons are said to be congruent polygons.

Example

Triangle *ABC* and triangle *DEF* are congruent triangles.

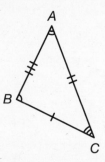 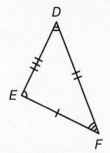

consecutive sides

Consecutive sides are sides that do share a common endpoint.

constant

A number or quantity that does not change its value is called a constant.

Examples

$$0, \pi, 4.5, \frac{1}{2}$$

construct

When you construct a geometric figure, you create it using only a compass and a straightedge.

continuous data

When quantitative data are measurements and can have values that fall between two counting numbers, then the data are called continuous data.

Example

Heights of different animals at the zoo. Area covered by different U.S. cities in square miles.

convention

A convention in mathematics is a way mathematicians have agreed to write and format math statements.

Example

The Order of Operation Rules are a convention so you are sure to get the same answer every time an expression is evaluated.

convert

To convert a measurement means to change it to an equivalent measurement in different units.

Example

To <u>convert</u> 36 inches to feet, you can multiply:

$$36 \text{ in.} \left(\frac{1 \text{ ft}}{12 \text{ in.}} \right) = \frac{36 \text{ ft}}{12}$$
$$= 3 \text{ ft}$$

cube

A cube is a regular polyhedron whose six faces are congruent squares.

cube of a number

To calculate the cube of a number you multiply the number by itself 3 times.

Example

$$5 \times 5 \times 5 = 125 \leftarrow \text{cube of a number}$$

Glossary

cube root

A cube root is one of 3 equal factors of a number.

Example

$$\sqrt[3]{8} = 2 \leftarrow \text{cube root}$$

———————— **D** ————————

data

Data are the facts or numbers that describe the results of an experiment.

Examples

Heights of different animals at the zoo, area covered by different U.S. cities in square miles.

data analysis

Data analysis is the process of asking questions and collecting, organizing, and analyzing data to answer those questions.

Example

When you study the results of a survey to see which choice was the most popular, you are doing data analysis.

decagon

A decagon is a ten-sided polygon.

Example

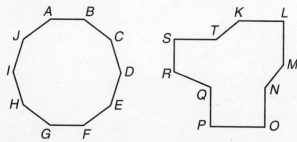

The polygons ABCDEFGHIJ and KLMNOPQRST are both decagons.

decimals

A decimal is a number that is written in a system based on multiples of 10.

Examples

0.11 1.75213 10,446.0 0.0001 ◄——— decimals

denominator

The denominator is the number below the fraction bar. The denominator indicates how many parts make up the whole.

Examples

$$\frac{7}{12} \qquad \frac{a}{b}$$

denominators

density property

The Density Property states that between any two rational numbers there is another rational number.

dependent quantity

The dependent quantity is the quantity that depends on another in a problem situation.

Example

Max just got a new hybrid car that averages 51 miles to the gallon. How far does the car travel on 15 gallons of fuel?

number of gallons · miles per gallon = miles traveled

The dependent quantity is the total miles traveled. The miles traveled depend on the gallons of fuel.

dependent variable

The variable that represents the dependent quantity is called the dependent variable.

Example

Max just got a new hybrid car that averages 51 miles to the gallon. How far does the car travel on 15 gallons of fuel?

number of gallons · miles per gallons = miles traveled
$$g \cdot m = t$$

The dependent quantity is the total miles traveled. Since t represents total miles traveled in the equation, t is the dependent variable.

deviation

The deviation of a data value indicates how far the data value is from the mean.

Example

$$\text{deviation} = \text{data value} - \text{mean}$$

diameter

The diameter is the distance across a circle through its center.

Example

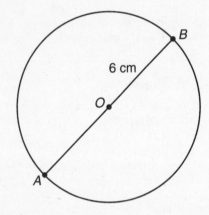

discrete data

When quantitative data are counts of how many, the data can be described as discrete data. Discrete data can only have values that are counting numbers (0, 1, 2, 3, . . .).

Examples

The zoo has 4 lions, 3 tigers, and 6 bears.

In 2006, Los Angeles had a population of about 3,849,378. In the same year, Atlanta had a population of about 429,500.

distinct factors

Distinct factors are factors that appear only once in a list.

Example

$9 = 1 \times 9$ and 3×3

To write the <u>distinct factors</u> of 9, you write each factor only once. So, the <u>distinct factors</u> of 9 are 1, 3, and 9.

distribution

The overall shape of a graph is called the distribution of data. A distribution is the way in which the data are distributed.

Distributive Property of Division over Addition

The Distributive Property of Division over Addition states that if a, b, and c are real numbers and $c \neq 0$, then $\frac{a+b}{c} = \frac{a}{c} + \frac{b}{c}$

Example

$$\begin{aligned} \frac{8+6}{2} &= \frac{8}{2} + \frac{6}{2} \\ &= 4 + 3 \\ &= 7 \end{aligned}$$

Distributive Property of Division over Subtraction

The Distributive Property of Division over Addition states that if a, b, and c are real numbers and $c \neq 0$, then $\frac{a-b}{c} = \frac{a}{c} - \frac{b}{c}$

Example

$$\begin{aligned} \frac{12-9}{3} &= \frac{12}{3} - \frac{9}{3} \\ &= 4 - 3 \\ &= 1 \end{aligned}$$

Distributive Property of Multiplication over Addition

The Distributive Property of Multiplication over Addition states that for any real numbers a, b, and c, $a \cdot (b + c) = a \cdot b + a \cdot c$

Example

$$\begin{aligned} 11(8 \times 4) &= (11 \times 8) + (11 \times 4) \\ &= 88 + 44 \\ &= 132 \end{aligned}$$

Distributive Property of Multiplication over Subtraction

The Distributive Property of Multiplication over Subtraction states that for any real numbers a, b, and c,
$a \cdot (b - c) = a \cdot b - a \cdot c$

Example

$$7(4 - 2) = (7 \times 4) - (7 \times 2)$$
$$= 28 - 14$$
$$= 14$$

dividend

The dividend is the number or decimal that is being divided into equal groups.

Examples

dividend
$3.5 \overline{)18.9}$ dividend

$\dfrac{5}{12} \div \dfrac{1}{2}$ $\dfrac{49}{7}$ ← dividend

divisibility rules

Divisibility rules are tests for determining whether one positive whole number is divisible by another.

Examples

A number is divisible by 2 when its ones digit is 0, 2, 4, 6, or 8.
A number is divisible by 3 when the sum of its digits is divisible by 3.
A number is divisible by 4 when the number formed by its last two digits is divisible by 4.
A number is divisible by 5 when its ones digit is 0 or 5.
A number is divisible by 6 when it is divisible by both 2 and 3.
A number is divisible by 9 when the sum of its digits is divisible by 9.

divisible

One number is divisible by the second number when the second number divides "evenly" into the first number with no remainder.

Example

$\dfrac{90}{3 \overline{)270}}$ 270 is divisible by 3.

divisor

The divisor is the number or decimal that divides the dividend.

Example

divisor
$3.5 \overline{)18.9}$ $\dfrac{5}{12} \div \dfrac{1}{2}$ $\dfrac{49}{7}$ ← divisor
divisor

dot plot (line plot)

A dot plot (sometimes called a line plot) is a graph that shows how the discrete data is graphed using a number line. Dot plots help organize and display a small number of data points.

Example

Number of Pets

```
x
x     x              ← dot plot
x     x
x  x     x     x
0  1  2  3  4  5
```

double bar graph

A double bar graph is used when each category contains two different data sets. The bars may be vertical or horizontal.

Example

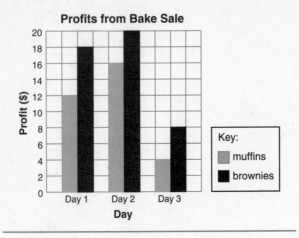

double number line

A double number line is a model that is made up of two number lines used to represent the equivalence of two related numbers. Each interval on the number line has two sets of numbers and maintains the same ratio.

Example

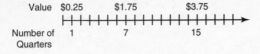

draw

When you draw a geometric figure, you create it using tools such as a ruler, a straightedge, a compass, or a protractor.

—————— **E** ——————

edge

An edge is the intersection of two or more faces of a three-dimensional figure.

ellipses

The three periods before and after the number set are called ellipses and they are used to represent infinity in a number set.

Example

$$\{..., -2, -1, 0, 1, 2, ...\}$$

ellipses   ellipses

equation

An equation is a mathematical sentence that contains an equal sign.

Examples

$$y = 2x + 4$$
$$6 = 3 + 3$$
$$2(8) = 26 - 10$$
$$\frac{1}{4} \cdot 4 = \frac{8}{4} - \frac{4}{4}$$

equiangular triangle

An equiangular triangle is a triangle with all angles congruent.

Examples

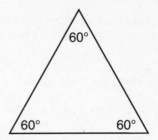

equilateral triangle

An equilateral triangle is a triangle that has all three sides equal. The measure of each interior angle of an equilateral triangle is 60 degrees.

Example

Triangle *ABC* is an equilateral triangle, so the measure of angle 1 is 60 degrees, the measure of angle 2 is 60 degrees, and the measure of angle 3 is 60 degrees. $m \angle 1 = 60°$, $m \angle 2 = 60°$, and $m \angle 3 = 60°$

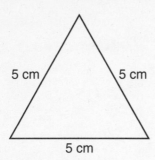

5 cm 5 cm

5 cm

equivalent expressions

Two algebraic expressions are equivalent expressions if, when any values are substituted for variables, the results are equal.

Example

$$(x + 10) + (6x - 5) = 7x + 5$$
$$12 + 7 = 14 + 5$$
$$19 = 19$$

equivalent fractions

Fractions that represent the same part-to-whole relationship are equivalent fractions.

Example

| $\frac{1}{2}$ | | $\frac{1}{2}$ | |
| $\frac{1}{4}$ | $\frac{1}{4}$ | $\frac{1}{4}$ | $\frac{1}{4}$ |

$\frac{1}{2} = \frac{2}{4}$ $\frac{2}{2} = \frac{4}{4}$

equivalent fractions

evaluate

To evaluate an expression means to calculate an expression to get a single value.

Example

$$19 - 4 \times 3$$
$$19 - 12$$
$$7$$

evaluate an algebraic expression

To evaluate an algebraic expression means to determine that expression's value.

Example

Evaluate the expression $\dfrac{4x + (2^3 - y)}{p}$ for $x = 2.5$, $y = 8$, and $p = 2$.

- First replace the variables with numbers: $\dfrac{4(2.5) + (2^3 - 8)}{2}$.
- Then calculate the value of the expression: $\dfrac{10 + 0}{2} = \dfrac{10}{2} = 5$.

experiment

An experiment is an investigation conducted to answer a question by performing a test for which you decide the conditions. Experiments test something to determine a specific result.

Example

Do students get higher grades on a quiz if they study while listening to music or if they study without music? To help answer this question, you can conduct an experiment. You can divide your class randomly into two groups. You can ask one group to study while listening to music and the other group to study while not listening to music.

exponent

The exponent of a power is the number of times the base is used as a factor of repeated multiplication.

Examples

$2^3 = 2 \times 2 \times 2 = 8$ $8^4 = 8 \times 8 \times 8 \times 8 = 4096$

exponent   exponent

_____ **F** _____

face

A face is one of the polygons that makes up a polyhedron.

Example

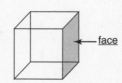
face

factor

A factor occurs when two or more numbers are multiplied. Each number is a factor of the product.

Examples

$$4 \times 3 = 12$$

The factors are 4 and 3.

$$\frac{1}{2} \times \frac{8}{9} = \frac{8}{18} = \frac{4}{9}$$

The factors are $\frac{1}{2}$ and $\frac{8}{9}$.

---

factor pair

A factor pair is two natural numbers other than zero that are multiplied together to produce another number.

Example

Multiplication		Factor Pairs
$1 \times 16 =$		1 and 16
$2 \times 8 =$	16	2 and 8
$4 \times 4 =$		4 and 4

The table shows the <u>factor pairs</u> of 16.

---

factor tree

A factor tree is a way to organize and help you determine the prime factorization of a number. Factor trees use branches to show how a number is broken down into prime numbers.

Examples

This is a <u>factor tree</u> for 16.

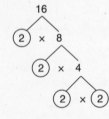

This is a <u>factor tree</u> for 12.

---

five number summary

The five number summary consists of (1) the minimum value in the data set, (2) the first quartile, (3) the median, (4) the third quartile, and (5) the maximum value in the data set. (See *box-and-whisker plot*.)

Example

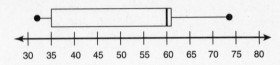

Five number summary:
<u>minimum</u> = 32,
<u>first quartile</u> = 35,
<u>median</u> = 60,
<u>third quartile</u> = 61,
<u>maximum</u> = 74.

---

fraction

A fraction represents a part of a whole object, set, or unit. A fraction is written using two whole numbers separated by a bar.

Examples

Each of the models below represents the <u>fraction</u> $\frac{3}{5}$.

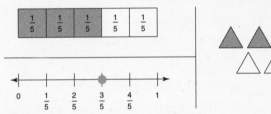

---

fractional numbers

The set of fractional numbers which is the set of all numbers that can be written as $\frac{a}{b}$, where a and b are whole numbers and $b \neq 0$.

Example

4, $\frac{1}{2}$, 7.25, $10\frac{5}{6}$ are all examples of fractional numbers

frequency

Frequency is the number of times an item, number, or event occurs in a data set.

Example

Number Rolled	Tally	Frequency
2	JHI II	7

The number 2 was rolled 7 times, so its <u>frequency</u> was 7.

frequency table

A frequency table is a table used to organize data according to how many times a data value occurs.

Example

Number Rolled	Tally	Frequency
1	III	3
2	JHI II	7
3	I	1
4	II	2
5	IIII	4
6	III	3

Fundamental Theorem of Arithmetic

The Fundamental Theorem of Arithmetic states that every natural number is either prime or can be written as a unique product of primes.

Examples

$$90 = 2 \times 3^2 \times 5$$
$$91 \text{ is prime}$$
$$92 = 2^2 \times 23$$
$$93 = 3 \times 31$$

gaps

Gaps are areas of the graph where there are no data.

geometric solids

Geometric solids are all bounded three-dimensional geometric figures. Their dimensions are length, width, and height.

Examples

Spheres, cylinders, cubes, and cones are examples of <u>geometric solids</u>.

gram (g)

The standard unit of mass in the metric system is the gram (g). Grams are used to measure the amount of matter in an object.

graph of an inequality

The graph of an inequality in one variable is the set of all points on a number line that make the inequality true.

Example

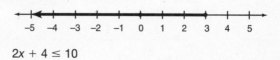

$$2x + 4 \le 10$$

gratuity

Gratuity, also known as a tip, is generally a percent of the total amount of the bill given to show appreciation for a good service.

Example

15% tip on a bill of $45

$0.15 \times 45 = \$6.75 \leftarrow$ gratuity

greatest common factor (GCF)

The greatest common factor, or GCF, is the largest factor two or more numbers have in common.

Example

factors of 16: **1**, **2**, **4**, 8, 16

factors of 12: **1**, **2**, 3, **4**, 6, 12

common factors: 1, 2, 4

greatest common factor: 4

Glossary

height of a parallelogram

In a parallelogram, the height is the perpendicular distance between the two bases.

Example

In parallelogram PRLM, the height is the length of segment AG.

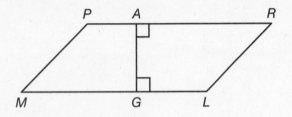

height of a prism

The height of a prism is the length of a line segment that is drawn from one base to the other base. This line segment must be perpendicular to the other base.

height of a pyramid

The height of a pyramid is the length of a line segment drawn from the vertex of the pyramid to the base. This line segment is perpendicular to the base.

height of a trapezoid

In a trapezoid, the height is the perpendicular distance between the two bases.

Example

In trapezoid TRAP, the height is the length of segment HG.

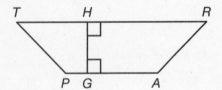

height of a triangle

In a triangle, the height is the perpendicular distance from a vertex to the side opposite the vertex.

Example

In triangle MAH, the height is the length of segment AT.

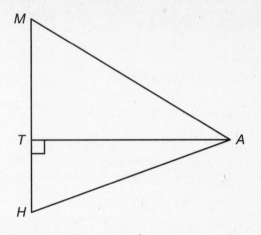

heptagon

A heptagon is a seven-sided polygon.

Examples

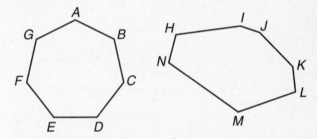

The polygons ABCDEFG and HIJKLMN are both heptagons.

hexagon

A hexagon is a polygon with six sides.

Examples

The polygon POINTS and the polygon BISECT are both hexagons.

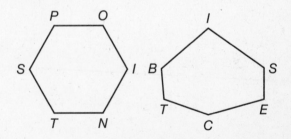

Glossary

histogram

A histogram is a way of displaying quantitative data using vertical or horizontal bars so that the height or the length of the bars indicates the frequency.

Example

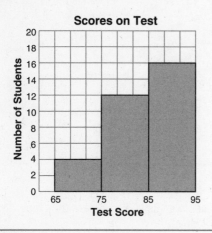

homonyms

Homonyms are words that have the same spelling and the same pronunciation, but have different meanings.

Example

right- direction, "Go to the right,"
right- correct, "You got the right answer!"

---

improper fraction

An improper fraction is a fraction in which the numerator is greater than or equal to the denominator.

Examples

$$\frac{17}{7} \quad \frac{2+5}{4} \quad \frac{4}{4} \quad \longleftarrow \text{ improper fractions}$$

independent quantity

The independent quantity is the quantity the dependent quantity depends on.

Example

Max just got a new hybrid car that averages 51 miles to the gallon. How far does the car travel on 15 gallons of fuel?

  number of gallons · miles per gallon = miles traveled

The independent quantity is the number of gallons. The other quantity (miles traveled) is dependent upon this quantity.

independent variable

The variable that represents the independent quantity is called the dependent variable.

Example

Max just got a new hybrid car that averages 51 miles to the gallon. How far does the car travel on 15 gallons of fuel?

  number of gallons · miles per gallon = miles traveled
  $$g \cdot m = t$$

The independent quantity is the number of gallons. Since g represents the number of gallons in the equation, g is the independent variable.

index

The index is the number placed above and to the left of the radical to indicate what root is being calculated.

Examples

$$\overset{\text{index}}{\underset{\downarrow}{}}$$
$$\sqrt[3]{512} = 8$$

inequality

An inequality is any mathematical sentence that has an inequality symbol.

Examples

  $8 > 2 \quad a \le b \quad 6.051 > 6.009 \quad 2x + 4 \ge 16$

infinity

Infinity means a quantity without bound or end. The symbol ∞ means infinity.

Examples

Negative infinity   Positive infinity

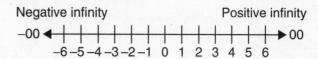

integers

The integers are the set of whole numbers with their opposites.

Example

The set of integers can be represented as {... −3, −2, −1, 0, 1, 2, 3, ...}.

interquartile range (IQR)

The interquartile range, or IQR, is the difference between the third quartile, Q3, and the first quartile, Q1. The IQR indicates the range of the middle 50 percent of the data.

Example

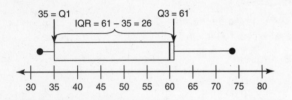

inverse operations

Inverse operations are operations that undo each other.

Examples

Addition and subtraction are inverse operations: $351 + 25 − 25 = 351$.

Multiplication and division are inverse operations: $351 \times 25 \div 25 = 351$.

irregular polygon

An irregular polygon is a polygon whose sides are not the same length and whose angles are not the same measure.

Example

The sides of this polygon are not the same length, and the angles of this polygon are not the same measure.

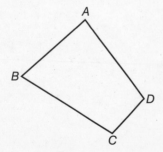

isosceles trapezoid

A trapezoid with congruent non-parallel sides is an isosceles trapezoid.

Example

Sides *AD* and *BC* are congruent, so trapezoid *ABCD* is an isosceles trapezoid.

isosceles triangle

An isosceles triangle is a triangle with at least two congruent sides.

Example

Triangle *ABC* is an isosceles triangle.

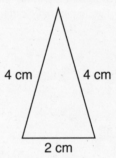

K

key

A key explains how each data set is represented by a color or a pattern in the graph.

Example

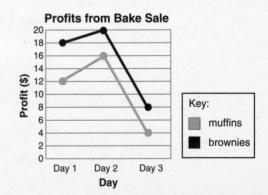

kite

A kite is a quadrilateral with two pairs of consecutive congruent sides with opposite sides that are not congruent.

Example

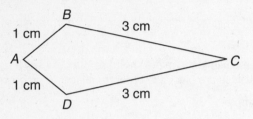

---

lateral faces

The faces of a prism that are not bases are called lateral faces.

---

least common denominator (LCD)

The least common denominator, or LCD, is the least common multiple of the denominators of two or more fractions.

Example

The <u>least common denominator</u> of

$\frac{7}{60}$ and $\frac{9}{24}$ is 120: $\frac{7}{60} = \frac{14}{120}$ and $\frac{9}{24} = \frac{45}{120}$.

---

least common multiple (LCM)

The least common multiple, or LCM, is the smallest multiple (other than zero) that two or more numbers have in common.

Example

multiples of 60: 60, **120**, 180, **240**, 300, 360, 420, 480 . . .

multiples of 24: 24, 48, 72, 96, **120**, 144, 168, 192, 216, **240** . . .

some common multiples of 60 and 24: 120, 240 . . .

<u>least common multiple</u> of 60 and 24: 120

---

legs of a trapezoid

The non-parallel sides are called the legs of the trapezoid.

Example

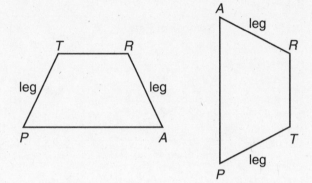

---

like terms

In an algebraic expression, like terms are two or more terms that have the same variable raised to the same power.

Examples

like terms

$4x + 3p + x + 2 = 5x + 3p + 2$

like terms

$24a^2 + 2a - 9a^2 = 13a^2 + 2a$

no like terms
$m + m^2 - x + x^3$

---

line segment

A line segment is a portion of a line that includes two points and all the points between those two points.

---

liter (L)

The standard unit of capacity in the metric system is the liter (L). Liters are used to measure volume.

mean

The mean is the arithmetic average of the numbers in a data set.

Example

Number of Pets

```
        x
        x
x   x       x
x   x       x       x
0   1   2   3   4   5
```

$$\text{Mean} = \frac{0 + 0 + 1 + 1 + 1 + 1 + 3 + 3 + 5}{9}$$

$$= \frac{15}{9} = 1\frac{2}{3} \text{ pets}$$

mean absolute deviation

The mean absolute deviation is the average or mean of the absolute deviations.

measure of center

A measure of center tells you how data are clustered, or where the "center" of the data is.

Examples

Mean, median, and mode are each a <u>measure of center</u> for data.

measurement

A measurement has two parts: a number and a unit of measure.

Examples

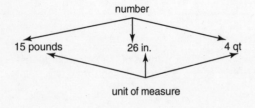

15 pounds   26 in.   4 qt

number

unit of measure

measures of variation or variability

The measure of variation describes how spread out or clustered the data are in a data set.

Example

Range is a <u>measure of variation</u> for data.

median

The median is the middle number in a data set when the values are placed in order from least to greatest.

Example

Number of Pets

```
        x
        x
x   x       x
x   x       x       x
0   1   2   3   4   5
```

0, 0, 1, 1, 1, 1, 3, 3, 5

↑

<u>median</u>

meter (m)

The standard unit of length in the metric system is the meter (m). Meters are used to measure distance.

mixed number

A mixed number has a whole number part and a fraction part.

Examples

$1\frac{1}{8}$ $2\frac{3}{4}$ $3\frac{7}{7}$ ⟵   mixed numbers

mode

The mode is the data value or values that occur most frequently in a data set.

Example

Number of Pets

```
        x
        x
x   x       x
x   x       x       x
0   1   2   3   4   5
```

0, 0, 1, 1, 1, 1, 3, 3, 5

The <u>mode</u> of the data is 1.

Glossary

multiple

A multiple is the product of a given whole number and another whole number.

Example

multiples of 10:

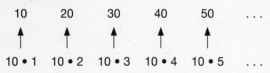

10	20	30	40	50	. . .
↑	↑	↑	↑	↑	
10 • 1	10 • 2	10 • 3	10 • 4	10 • 5	. . .

multiple representations

Problem situations can be represented in several ways including a diagram of figures, a table of values, a verbal description, an algebraic expression, and a graph.

multiplicative identity

The multiplicative identity is the number 1. When it is multiplied by a second number, the product is the second number.

Examples

$6 \times 1 = 6$ $\qquad \frac{1}{2} \times 1 = \frac{1}{2}$

Multiplicative Identity Property

The Multiplicative Identity Property states that $a \times 1 = a$, where a, is a nonzero number.

Examples

$6 \times 1 = 6$ $\qquad \frac{3}{4} \times \frac{4}{4} = \frac{12}{16}$

multiplicative inverse

The multiplicative inverse of a number $\frac{a}{b}$ is the number $\frac{b}{a}$, where a and b are nonzero numbers. The product of any nonzero number and its multiplicative inverse is 1.

Examples

The multiplicative inverse of $\frac{3}{7}$ is $\frac{7}{3}$:

$\frac{3}{7} \times \frac{7}{3} = \frac{21}{21} = 1$

The multiplicative inverse of 5 is $\frac{1}{5}$:

$\frac{5}{1} \times \frac{1}{5} = \frac{5}{5} = 1$

Multiplicative Inverse Property

The Multiplicative Inverse Property states:

$\frac{a}{b} \times \frac{b}{a} = 1$, where a and b are nonzero numbers.

Examples

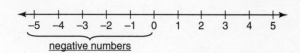

$\frac{3}{7} \times \frac{7}{3} = \frac{21}{21} = 1$ $\qquad \frac{5}{1} \times \frac{1}{5} = \frac{5}{5} = 1$

---N---

negative numbers

Numbers to the left of zero on the number line are called negative numbers.

Example

```
  ←——+——+——+——+——+——+——+——+——+——+——+——→
    -5  -4  -3  -2  -1   0   1   2   3   4   5
    ⌣_____⌣
        negative numbers
```

negative sign

Attaching a negative sign to a number means reflecting that number across zero on the number line.

Example

-20
↑
negative sign

net

A net is a two-dimensional representation of a three-dimensional geometric figure. A net is cut out, folded, and glued or taped to create a model of a geometric solid.

nonagon

A nonagon is a nine-sided polygon.

Examples

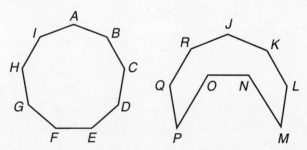

The polygons *ABCDEFGHI* and *JKLMNOPQR* are both nonagons.

numerator

The number above the fraction bar is the numerator. The numerator indicates how many parts in the whole are counted.

Examples

numerators

$$\frac{7}{12} \qquad \frac{a}{b}$$

numerical coefficient

A number or quantity that is multiplied by a variable in an algebraic expression is called the numerical coefficient.

Examples

$$14x \qquad \frac{1}{3}(g) \qquad \pi d \qquad w + 2.5$$

numerical coefficient   The numerical coefficient is 1, even though it is not shown.

numerical expression

A numerical expression is a mathematical phase containing numbers.

Example

$5 \times 4 - 9$

—————— O ——————

obtuse triangle

An obtuse triangle is a triangle with one obtuse angle.

Example

Angle *B* is an obtuse angle, so triangle *ABC* is an obtuse triangle.

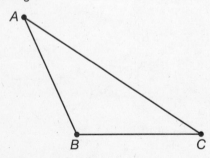

<B = 125, <A = 25, <C = 35

octagon

An octagon is a polygon with eight sides.

Examples

The polygon *ABCDEFGH* and the polygon *STUVWXYZ* are both octagons.

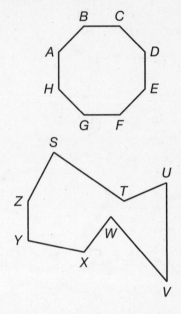

one-step equation

An equation that requires only one operation to solve it is called a one-step equation.

operations

The operations in an expression are addition, subtraction, multiplication, and division.

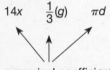

opposite sides

Opposite sides are sides that do not share a common endpoint.

Order of Operations

The Order of Operations is a set of rules that ensures the same result every time an expression is evaluated.

Example

$44 + (6 - 5) - 2 \times 75 \div 5^1$ Parentheses

    ↓

$44 + 1 - 2 \times 75 \div 5^1$ Exponents

      ↓

$44 + 1 - 2 \times 75 \div 5$ Multiplication and Division

      ↓

$44 + 1 - 150 \div 5$ (from left to right)

    ↓

$44 + 1 - 30$ Addition and Subtraction

    ↓

$45 - 30$ (from left to right)

    ↓

15

ordered pair

An ordered pair is a pair of numbers which can be represented as (x, y) that indicate the position of a point on the coordinate plane.

Example

$(8, 5)$

origin

The origin is the point of intersection of the y-axis and the x-axis of a coordinate plane.

Example

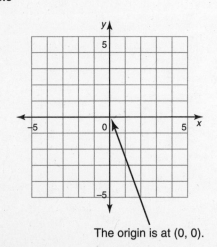

The origin is at (0, 0).

outlier

An outlier is a number in a data set that is significantly lesser or greater than the other numbers.

Example

Number of Pets

```
    x
    x
x   x       x
x   x       x   x           x  ←—The value 7 is an outlier.
0   1   2   3   4   5   6   7
```

— P —

parallelogram

A parallelogram is a quadrilateral in which both pairs of opposite sides are parallel.

Examples

In parallelogram $ABCD$, opposite sides AB and CD are parallel; opposite sides AD and BC are parallel.

In parallelogram $EFGH$, opposite sides EF and GH are parallel; opposite sides FG and EH are parallel.

In parallelogram $IJKL$, opposite sides LK and IJ are parallel; opposite sides JK and IL are parallel.

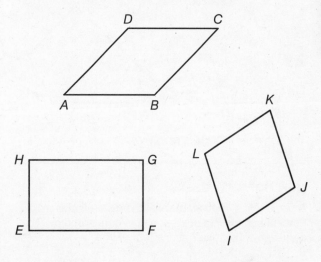

parameter

When data are gathered from a population, the characteristic used to describe the population is called a parameter.

Example

If you wanted to find out the average height of the students at your school, and you measured every student at the school, the characteristic "average height" would be a parameter.

parentheses

Parentheses are symbols used to group numbers and operations, and are used to change the normal order in which you perform operations.

Example

$$(5 + 3) \times 10$$
$$8 \times 10$$
$$80$$

pentagon

A pentagon is a five-sided polygon.

Examples

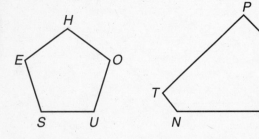

The polygons *HOUSE* and *POINT* are both pentagons.

percent

A percent is a fraction in which the denominator is 100. Percent can also be another name for hundredths. The percent symbol, "%," means "out of 100."

perfect cube

A perfect cube is the cube of a whole number.

Example

$$4 \times 4 \times 4 = 64 \leftarrow \text{perfect cube}$$

perfect square

A number that is the product of a distinct factor multiplied by itself is called a perfect square.

Examples

9 is a perfect square: $3 \times 3 = 9$.

25 is a perfect square: $5 \times 5 = 25$.

point

A point is a location in space. A point has no size or shape, but it is often represented by using a dot and is named by a capital letter.

poll

A poll is a specific survey that may be used to gain the opinions of voters during an election process.

polygon

A polygon is a closed figure that is formed by joining three or more line segments and their endpoints.

Examples

A trapezoid is a polygon.

A pentagon is a polygon.

A circle is NOT a polygon.

polyhedron

A polyhedron is a three-dimensional figure that has polygons as faces.

Example

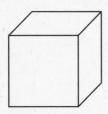

A cube is a <u>polyhedron</u>. It has six square faces.

population

The population is the entire set of items from which data can be selected. When you decide what you want to study, the population is the set of all elements in which you are interested. The elements of that population can be people or objects.

Example

If you wanted to find out the average height of the students at your school, the number of students at the school would be the <u>population</u>.

positive sign

A positive sign is a plus sign attached to a number to show that it is a positive number.

power

A power consists of two elements: the base and the exponent.

Example

base ⟶ 6^2 ⟵ exponent

<u>power</u>

prefix

A prefix is a letter or letters that is attached to the beginning of a word that changes the meaning of the word.

prime factorization

Prime factorization is the long string of factors that is made up of all prime numbers.

Examples

$$225 = \mathbf{3^2 \times 5^2} \qquad 360 = \mathbf{2^3 \times 3^2 \times 5} \qquad 81 = \mathbf{3^4}$$

prime factorization

prime numbers

Prime numbers are numbers greater than 1 with exactly two distance factors, 1 and the number itself.

Examples

The first twenty prime numbers are 2, 3, 5, 7, 11, 13, 17, 19, 23, 29, 31, 37, 41, 43, 47, 53, 59, 61, 67, and 71.

prism

A prism is a polyhedron with two parallel and congruent faces and all other faces parallelograms.

Example

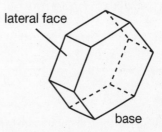

lateral face

base

A prism is named for the shape of its bases. The prism shown is a hexagonal prism.

Properties of Equality

The Properties of Equality allow you to balance and solve equations involving any number.

Examples

- Addition Property of Equality
  If $a = b$, then $a + c = b + c$.
- Subtraction Property of Equality
  If $a = b$, then $a - c = b - c$.
- Multiplication Property of Equality
  If $a = b$, then $ac = bc$.
- Division Property of Equality
  If $a = b$, and $c \neq 0$, then $\frac{a}{c} = \frac{b}{c}$.

prototype

A prototype is a working model of a possible new product.

protractor

A protractor is a tool that can be used to approximate the measure of an angle.

pyramid

A pyramid is a polyhedron with one base and the same number of triangular faces as there are sides of the base.

Example

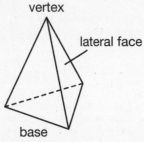

A pyramid is named according to the shape of its base. The pyramid below is a triangular pyramid.

——— Q ———

quadrant

The *x*- and *y*-axes divide the coordinate plane into four regions called quadrants. These quadrants are numbered with Roman numerals from one to four, starting in the upper right-hand quadrant and moving counterclockwise.

Example

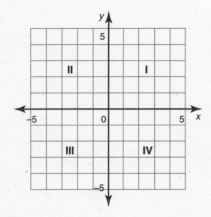

quadrilateral

A quadrilateral is a polygon that has four sides.

Examples

Figure *ABCD*, figure *FGHI*, and figure *JKLM* are quadrilaterals.

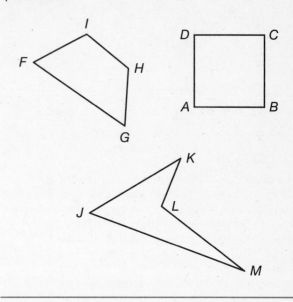

quantitative data

Quantitative data are data for which each piece of data can be placed on a numerical scale. Quantitative data are also called "numerical" data.

Examples

The zoo has 4 lions, 3 tigers, and 6 bears.

In 2006, Los Angeles had a population of about 3,849,378. In the same year, Atlanta had a population of about 429,500.

quartiles (Q)

When data in a set are arranged in order, quartiles are the numbers that split the data into quarters (or fourths).

Example

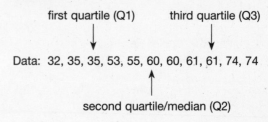

first quartile (Q1)   third quartile (Q3)

Data: 32, 35, 35, 53, 55, 60, 60, 61, 61, 74, 74

second quartile/median (Q2)

Glossary

quotient

The quotient is the result of the division sentence. Quotients can be whole numbers, decimals, or fractions.

Examples

quotient ⟶ **5.4**
$3.5)\overline{18.9}$

quotient
↓

$$\frac{5}{12} \div \frac{1}{2} = \frac{5}{6}$$

$\frac{49}{7} = 7$ ◂— quotient

—————— R ——————

radical

The symbol $\sqrt{\ }$ is called a radical, and it is used to indicate square roots.

Example

┌— radical

$\sqrt{256} = 16$

---

radicand

The radicand is the quantity under a radical sign.

Example

$\sqrt{1024} = 32$
↑
└— radicand

---

range

The range is the difference between the maximum and minimum values in a data set.

Example

Number of Pets

```
    x
    x
x   x       x
x   x       x       x
0   1   2   3   4   5
```

0, 0, 1, 1, 1, 1, 3, 3, 5

$5 - 0 = 5$

The range of the data is 5.

---

rate

A rate is a ratio that compares two quantities that are measured in different units.

Example

The speed of 60 miles in two hours is a rate:

$$\frac{60 \text{ mi}}{2 \text{ h}} = \frac{30 \text{ mi}}{1 \text{ h}}.$$

---

ratio

A ratio is a comparison of two quantities that uses division.

Examples

☆ ☆ ☆

The ratio of stars to circles is $\frac{3}{2}$, or 3:2, or 3 to 2.

○ ○

The ratio of circles to stars is $\frac{2}{3}$, or 2:3, or 2 to 3.

---

rational numbers

Rational numbers are numbers that can be written as $\frac{a}{b}$, where a and b are integers, but b is not equal to 0.

Examples

$4, \frac{1}{2}, \frac{2}{3}, 0.67,$ and $\frac{22}{7}$ are examples of rational numbers.

---

ray

A ray begins at a starting point and goes on forever in one direction.

Examples

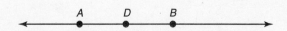

There are five rays labeled: ray *DA*, ray *BA*, ray *BD*, ray *DB*, and ray *AB*.

---

reciprocal

The reciprocal of a number is also known as the multiplicative inverse of the number. (See *multiplicative inverse*.)

Examples

The reciprocal of $\frac{3}{7}$ is $\frac{7}{3}$: $\frac{3}{7} \times \frac{7}{3} = \frac{21}{21} = 1$

The reciprocal of 5 is $\frac{1}{5}$: $\frac{5}{1} \times \frac{1}{5} = \frac{5}{5} = 1$

rectangle

A rectangle is a quadrilateral with opposites congruent and all angles congruent.

Examples

Figure *ABCD*, figure *FGHI*, and figure *JKML* are rectangles.

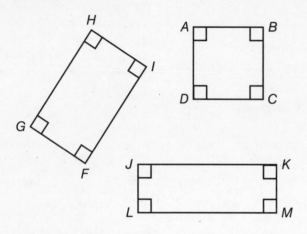

rectangular prism

A rectangular prism is a prism that has a rectangle as its base.

regular polygon

A regular polygon is a polygon with all sides congruent and all angles congruent.

Examples

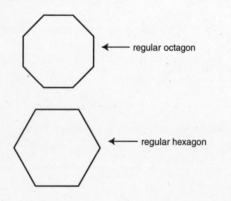

← regular octagon

← regular hexagon

regular polyhedron

A regular polyhedron is a three-dimensional solid that has congruent regular polygons as faces and has congruent angles between all faces.

Example

A cube is an example of a regular polyhedron.

relatively prime numbers

Two numbers that do not have any common factors other than 1 are called relatively prime numbers.

Examples

Positive whole number pairs that have a difference of 1 (4 and 5, 10 and 11, 15 and 16) are always relatively prime numbers.

repeating decimal

A repeating decimal is a decimal with one or more digits that repeat infinitely. A repeating decimal can be represented by placing a bar over the repeating digits.

Example

The decimal 0.14141414... is a repeating decimal that can be written as $0.\overline{14}$. In the decimal, the digits 1 and 4 repeat in a pattern infinitely.

rhombus

A rhombus is a quadrilateral with all sides congruent. The plural form of "rhombus" is "rhombi"

Examples

Figure *JKLM* is a rhombus. Figure *ABCD* is a rhombus.

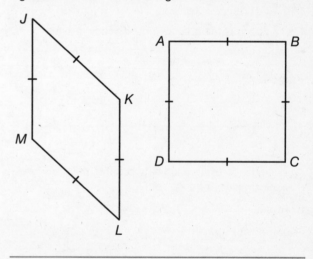

right prism

A right prism is a prism that has bases aligned one directly above the other and has lateral faces that are rectangles.

right triangle

A right triangle is a triangle that has one angle that measures exactly 90°

Examples

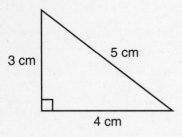

round

One way to round a number to a given place value is to look at the digit to the right of the place to which you want to round. If the digit to the right is 4 or less, round down. If the digit to the right is 5 or greater, round up.

Examples

The number 23 rounded to the nearest ten is 20.

The number 2466 rounded to the nearest hundred is 2500.

The number 6.5 rounded to the nearest whole is 7.

— **S** —

sample

Where data are collected from a selection of the population, the data are called a sample.

Example

If you wanted to find out the average height of the students in your school, you could choose just a certain number of students and measure their heights. The heights of the students in this group would be your sample.

scalene triangle

A scalene triangle is a triangle with no sides of equal length.

Examples

None of the side lengths of triangle *ABC* are the same. So, triangle *ABC* is a scalene triangle. None of the side lengths of triangle *DEF* are the same. So, triangle *DEF* is a scalene triangle.

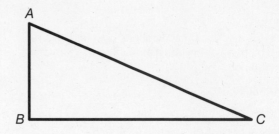

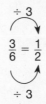

scaling down

Scaling down means you divide the numerator and denominator by the same factor.

Example

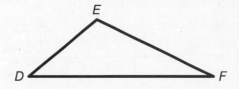

scaling up

Scaling up means you multiply the numerator and denominator by the same factor.

Example

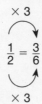

sequence

A sequence is a patterns involving an ordered arrangement of numbers, geometry figures, letters, or other objects.

Example

The numbers 1, 2, 4, 8, 16 . . . form a <u>sequence.</u> Each number is multiplied by 2 to get the next number.

set

A set is a collection of numbers, geometric figures, letters, or other objects that have some characteristic in common.

Examples

The set of counting numbers is {1, 2, 3, 4 . . .}.
The set of even numbers is {2, 4, 6, 8 . . .}.

side-by-side stem-and-leaf plot

A side-by-side stem-and-leaf plot is a stem-and-leaf plot that allows a comparison of two data sets.

Example

Books Read in Two Classes

Ms. Miller		Mr. Brown
2, 1	0	3, 6
4, 4, 2	1	0, 1, 5
7, 1, 1, 1	2	
	3	9, 9
0	4	0, 0, 0

Key: 2 | 1 | 0 = 12 and 10.

simplest form

Simplest form is a way of writing a fraction so that the numerator and denominator have no common factors other then 1.

Example

$\frac{100}{200} = \frac{1}{2}$

The fraction $\frac{1}{2}$ is in <u>simplest form.</u>

simplify

To simplify an expression is to use the rules of arithmetic and algebra to rewrite that expression with fewer terms.

Examples

Expression	Simplified
$2 + 2$	4
$23x - 19 + x + 22$	$24x - 19 + 22$
$a + a + a$	$3a$
$\frac{1}{3} \cdot \frac{1}{3} \cdot \frac{1}{3}$	$\left(\frac{1}{3}\right)^3$

sketch

When you sketch a geometric figure, you create it without the use of tools.

skewed left distribution

In a skewed left distribution of data the peak of the data is to the right side of the graph. There are only a few data points to the left side of the graph.

Example

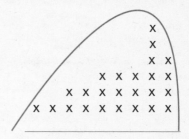

skewed right distribution

In a skewed right distribution of data the peak of the data is to the left side of the graph. There are only a few data points to the right side of the graph.

Example

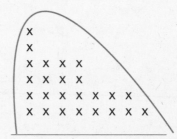

slant height of a pyramid

The slant height of a pyramid is the distance measured along a lateral face from the base to the vertex of the pyramid along the center of the face.

Example

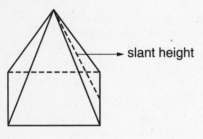

→ slant height

solution

A solution to an equation is any value for a variable that makes the equation true.

Example

The <u>solution</u> to the equation $2x + 4 = 8$ is $x = 2$.

solution set of an inequality

The set of all points that make an inequality true is the solution set of the inequality.

Example

$X \geq 7$
The solution set for $X \geq 7$ is all the numbers greater than or equal to 7.

square

A square is a quadrilateral with all sides congruent and all angles congruent.

Examples

Figure *FGHI* and figure *ABCD* are squares.

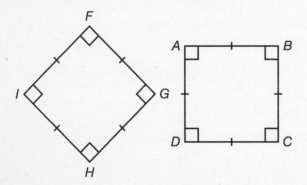

square of a number

To calculate the square of a number you multiply the number by itself 2 times.

Examples

$6 \times 6 = 36$ ← square of a number

square root

A square root is one of two equal factors of a non-negative number. Every positive number has two square roots: a positive square root and a negative square root.

Examples

$\sqrt{49} = 7$ and -7 $\sqrt{81} = 9$ and -9

stacked bar graph

A stacked bar graph is a graph that stacks the frequencies of two different groups for a given category on top of one another so that you can compare the parts to the whole. Each bar represents a total for the whole category, but still shows how many data pieces make up each group within the entire category.

Example

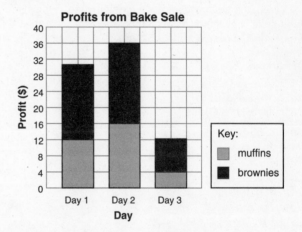

standard units of measure

Standard units of measure are units that are used by everyone in a certain area, and they do not change from person to person.

Example

Inch, foot, yard, and mile are some standard units of length in the United States.

statistical question

A statistical question is a question about a *population* or a *sample*.

Example

"What sport is the most popular in your school?" is a statistical question because you do not know the answer and it can be asked from a population or a sample.

statistic

When data are gathered from a sample, the characteristic used to describe the sample is called a statistic.

Example

If you wanted to find out the average height of the students in your school, and you chose just a certain number of students randomly and measured their heights, the characteristic "average height" would be called a statistic.

stem-and-leaf plot

A stem-and-leaf plot is a graphical method used to represent ordered numerical data. Once the data are ordered, the stem and leaves are determined. Typically, the stem is all the digits in a number except the right-most digit, which is the leaf.

Example

Books Read in Mr. Brown's Class

```
0 | 3, 6
1 | 0, 1, 5
2 |
3 | 9, 9
4 | 0, 0, 0
```
Key: 1 | 0 = 10.

straightedge

A straightedge is a ruler with no numbers.

surface area

Surface area is the total area of the two-dimensional surfaces (faces and bases) that make up a three-dimensional object.

survey

A survey is one method of collecting information about a certain group of people. It involves asking a question or set of questions of those people.

Example

A restaurant may ask its customers to complete a survey with the following questions:

- On a scale of 1–10, with 1 meaning "poor" and 10 meaning "excellent," how would you rate the food you ate?

  ☐ 1 ☐ 2 ☐ 3 ☐ 4 ☐ 5 ☐ 6 ☐ 7 ☐ 8 ☐ 9 ☐ 10

- On a scale of 1–10, with 1 meaning "poor" and 10 meaning "excellent," how would you rate the friendliness of your server?

  ☐ 1 ☐ 2 ☐ 3 ☐ 4 ☐ 5 ☐ 6 ☐ 7 ☐ 8 ☐ 9 ☐ 10

symmetric distribution

In a symmetric distribution of data the left and right halves of the graph are mirror images of each other. There is often a "peak" in the middle of the graph.

Example

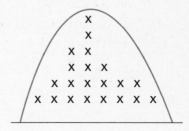

── T ──

term

Each object or number in a sequence is a term in the sequence. (See *sequence*.)

terminating decimal

A terminating decimal is a decimal quotient with a remainder of 0.

Example

$$\begin{array}{r} 0.9 \\ 3)\overline{2.7} \end{array}$$ ◄─── terminating decimal

trapezoid

A trapezoid is a quadrilateral with exactly one pair of parallel sides.

Example

Quadrilateral *ABCD* is a trapezoid.

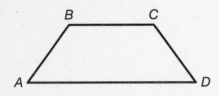

triangle

A triangle is the simplest closed three-sided geometric figure.

Example

In triangle *ABC* below, vertices *A*, *B*, and *C* are joined by segments *BA*, *AC*, and *CB*.

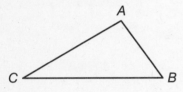

─── U ───

unit cube

A unit cube is a cube that is one unit in length, one unit in width, and one unit in height.

unit fraction

A unit fraction is a fraction that has a numerator of 1 and a denominator that is a positive integer greater than 1.

Examples

$\frac{1}{9}$ $\frac{1}{12}$ $\frac{1}{23}$ $\frac{1}{4}$ $\frac{1}{1249}$

unit rate

A unit rate is a comparison of two measurements in which the denominator has a value of one unit.

Example

The speed 60 miles in 2 hours can be written as a unit rate: $\frac{60 \text{ mi}}{2 \text{ h}} = \frac{30 \text{ mi}}{1 \text{ h}}$.

The unit rate is $\frac{30 \text{ mi}}{1 \text{ h}}$, or 30 miles per hour.

─── V ───

variable

A variable is a letter or symbol that is used to represent a number.

Examples

$x \bullet \square = 81$ $\frac{4}{p}$ z^2

variables

When measuring distance driven over time, both time and distance driven can be called variables.

Venn diagram

A Venn diagram is a picture that illustrates the relationships between two or more sets.

Example

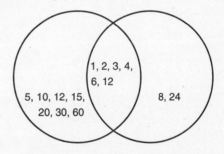

Factors of 60   Factors of 24

vertex

A vertex of a polygon is the common endpoint of two sides of the polygon. A vertex can also be the point where three edges of a polyhedron meet. The plural of *vertex* is *vertices*.

vertex of a pyramid

The vertex of a pyramid is the point at which all lateral faces intersect.

volume

Volume is the amount of space occupied by an object.

— X —

x-axis

The horizontal number line on a Cartesian coordinate plane is called the x-axis.

Example

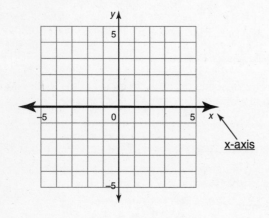

— Y —

y-axis

The vertical number line on the Cartesian coordinate plane is known as the y- axis.

Example

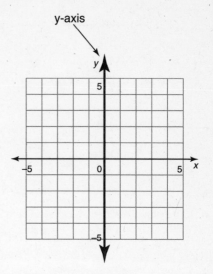

Glossary

INDEX

Index

Bases (*cont.*)
of pentagons, 957–958
of a polyhedron, 935
of powers, 57
of prisms, 947, 948, 949, 950
of pyramids, 964, 966–969, 975, 977
of a regular hexagonal prism, 957
of a regular pentagonal prism, 957
regular polygonal, of a prism, 957
of trapezoids, 867–870
of triangles, 855–859, 886
Benchmark decimals, 247–249
Benchmark fractions
common, 143
definition of, 143
estimating fractions by using,
143–145
estimating sum of expression with,
179
greatest fractional parts determined
with, 149–150
inequalities and, 146–147
multiplying fractions and, 194
Benchmark percents
definition of, 408
in estimating percents, 407–409
Boundary lines, 858–859
Box-and-whisker plots
for analyzing and interpreting data,
1123–1134
box in, description of, 1125
definition of, 1124
distribution of, 1127, 1128
five number summary values
identified with, 1124–1128
graphing calculator used to construct,
1132–1133, 1134
interquartile range identified with,
1126
mean determined with, 1131
median determined with, 1124, 1127,
1131, 1134
minimum and maximum values
represented in, 1125, 1128
quartiles represented in, 1125
range identified with, 1126
of waiting times at two restaurants,
1130–1131
whiskers in, description of, 1125

C

Calculators, negative sign on, 688
Cartesian Coordinate Plane
coordinate geometry analyzed with,
726–727
ordered pairs graphed on
See also Coordinate plane
Categorical data
on bar graphs, 1005, 1018
on circle graphs, 1016, 1018
definition of, 1004
examples of, 1018
identifying, 1005, 1020
Centimeter (cm), 783
Circle graph, 1016–1017
Clusters, 1024

Coefficients
in algebraic expressions, 497–498
of like terms, 545
of variables, 620, 630
Colons, 308–309, 395
Commission, 450
Common denominators
calculating and converting to
equivalent fractions, 279
definition of, 168
like and unlike denominators and,
167–176
in number sentences equaling 1,
168–169
Common factors
definition of, 72
least, 72
relatively prime numbers and, 74
solving problems with, 77–88
Venn diagram used to determine, 82
See also Greatest common factor
(GCF)
Common multiples
definition of, 62
solving problems with, 77–88
See also Least common multiple
(LCM)
Commutative Property
of Addition, 541, 544–547, 572,
584, 656
of Multiplication, 5–6, 53–54, 541,
545–547, 572
in simplifying algebraic expressions,
545–547
variables used to state, 656
Comparing decimals, 238–241
Compass, 820
Composite figures
rectangles and congruent trapezoids,
870–871
rectangles and kites, 881–882
rectangles and regular hexagons, 872
rectangles and triangles, 860–862
two regular hexagons, 892
Composite numbers
definition of, 32
factors in, 32–33
investigating, 31–34
vs. prime numbers, 34
Congruent, 924
Congruent polygon, 886
Congruent sides
of kites, 826, 878
of triangles, 821–822
Consecutive sides, 823, 824
Constants, 497–498
Construct, 820
Continuous data, 1004, 1038,
1047, 1050
Conventions
definition of, 461
for graphing relationships between
variables, 733–734
Conversions
fraction statements in metric,
789–790

from metric to customary units of
measure, 793–800
metric units of measure, 787–792
standard units of measure, 775–780
Coordinate geometry, 726–727
Coordinate plane, 717–765
extending, 720–722
graphing geometric figures on,
725–730
graphing problems with multiple
representations on, 731–738
interpreting graphs on, 739–759
ordered pairs on, 721–724
origin on, 720, 721, 737–738
quadrants on, 721–722
x-axis on, 720, 733, 735, 737, 743
x-coordinate on, 720, 721, 724
y-axis on, 720, 733, 735, 737, 743
y-coordinate on, 720, 721, 724
See also Points on coordinate plane
Counting numbers. *See* Natural numbers
Cube, 921–940
base of, 935–936, 959
characteristics of, 927–928
definition of, 924
diameter of, 925
face of, 927, 932
net for, 929–931
surface area of, 932–940
unit, 479, 924
volume formula of, 935–936
volume of, 933–934
volume of, calculating, 479–480
Cube of a number, 479
Cube roots
definition of, 480
estimating, 481–482
in expressions, 480–482
index of, 480
of perfect cubes, writing, 480
Cubit (early measurement type), 769
Cup (c), 770, 779
Customary units of measure. *See*
Standard units of measure

D

Data, 995–1065
analyzing and interpreting (*See* Data,
analyzing and interpreting)
collecting, displaying, and analyzing,
1003–1018
continuous, 1004, 1038, 1047, 1050
definition of, 998
discrete, 1004, 1038, 1047, 1050
experiments and, 1053–1056
histograms and, 1037–1051
line plots and, 1020–1024
statistical questions in, designing,
997–1002
stem-and-leaf plots and, 1025–1035
See also Categorical data;
Quantitative data
Data, analyzing and interpreting,
1067–1144
box-and-whisker plots used in,
1123–1134

Index

Index

Index

Index